A FIELD GUIDE TO THE CROPS OF BRITAIN AND EUROPE

A FIELD GUIDE TO THE

CROPS

OF BRITAIN AND EUROPE

G. M. de Rougemont

with 42 colour plates by
Elizabeth Rice and Elisabeth Dowle
and 2 plates and 32 figures in line drawings by
Rosemary Wise

COLLINS
8 Grafton Street, London W1

This book is for Maggie Hanbury

William Collins Sons & Co. Ltd
London · Glasgow · Sydney · Auckland
Toronto · Johannesburg

First published 1989
ISBN 0 00 219713 8

Colour reproduction by Bright Arts, Hong Kong
Filmset by Ace Filmsetting Ltd, Frome, Somerset
Printed in Hong Kong by South China Printing Co.

CONTENTS

Preface **7**

Acknowledgements **8**

Introduction **9**
The scope of this book **9**
What information is given about each plant **10**
Layout of the book **10**
Abbreviations **12**
Use of keys **12**

List of plates **13**
Colour plates **13**
Black and white plates **14**

ANNONACEAE Custard Apple Family **15**
LAURACEAE Laurel Family **16**
ROSACEAE Rose Family **18**
LEGUMINOSAE Pea Family **36**
GROSSULARIACEAE Currant Family **60**
CORNACEAE Dogwood Family **62**
CAPRIFOLIACEAE Honeysuckle Family **63**
FAGACEAE Beech Family **64**
CORYLACEAE Hazel Family **66**
JUGLANDACEAE Walnut Family **68**
URTICACEAE Nettle Family **69**
CANNABACEAE Hemp Family **70**
MORACEAE Mulberry Family **72**
CAPPARACEAE Caper Family **75**
PASSIFLORACEAE Passionflower Family **76**
CUCURBITACEAE Marrow Family **77**
CACTACEAE Cactus Family **85**
TILIACEAE Lime Family **86**
MALVACEAE Mallow Family **88**
LINACEAE Flax Family **91**
ACTINIDIACEAE Yang Tao Family **92**
ERICACEAE Heather Family **93**
MYRTACEAE Myrtle Family **97**
PUNICACEAE Pomegranate Family **98**
RHAMNACEAE Buckthorn Family **99**
ELEAGNACEAE Oleaster Family **100**
VITACEAE Grape Family **101**
EBENACEAE Ebony Family **103**
RUTACEAE Rue Family **104**
ANACARDIACEAE Cashew Family **111**
OLEACEAE Olive Family **113**
RUBIACEAE Madder Family **115**
PEDALIACEAE Sesame Family **116**
SCROPHULARIACEAE Figwort Family **117**
VERBANACEAE Vervain Family **118**

RANUNCULACEAE Buttercup Family **120**
PAPAVERACEAE Poppy Family **121**
BRASSICACEAE (CRUCIFERAE) Cabbage Family **122**

Colour plates 128

AIZOACEAE Ice-plant Family **234**
PORTULACCACEAE Purselane Family **235**
POLYGONACEAE Dock Family **236**
PLANTAGINACEAE Plantain Family **240**
CHENOPODIACEAE Goosefoot Family **241**
GENTIANACEAE Gentian Family **247**
ONAGRACEAE Willow-herb Family **248**
APIACEAE (UMBELLIFERAE) Carrot Family **249**
VALERIANACEAE Valerian Family **263**
ASTERACEAE (COMPOSITAE) Daisy Family **264**
SOLANACEAE Nightshade Family **277**
CONVULVULACEAE Bindweed Family **286**
HYDROPHULACEAE Phacelia Family **287**
BORAGINACEAE Borage Family **288**
LAMIACEAE (LABIATAE) Mint Family **289**
MUSACEAE Banana Family **300**
ARACEAE Arum Family **301**
IRIDACEAE Iris Family **303**
LILIACEAE Lily Family **304**
POACEAE (GRAMINAE) Grass Family **313**
CYPERACEAE Sedge Family **330**
PINACEAE Pine Family **332**
CUPRESSACEAE Cypress Family **332**
FUNGI **334**

Glossary 343

Meanings of some Latin specific epithets common in cultivated plants 354

Index of English names 356

Index of scientific names 362

PREFACE

In the last few decades changing social and economic patterns and a great increase of affluence and leisure have modified people's views of nature. As cities sprawl and citizens become increasingly alienated from nature and the sources, natural or cultivated, of the products they consume every day, more and more people have felt the need not just for outdoor recreation but to reestablish contact with nature and the life of the countryside. This interest has been met by the production of illustrated field guides to different groups of animals and plants which aim to enable those without any specialised knowledge of zoology or botany to identify the things they see, whenever possible, from illustrations. As far as Britain and Europe are concerned, the major groups of wild fauna and flora have been covered by these guides, yet the cultivated plants, which are much more in evidence than the wild ones, have not been comprehensively presented to the non-specialist public in this convenient form.

That this book should usefully fill the gap cannot be doubted. Most of us who profess a love of the country are more ignorant than we should like to admit. While it is embarrassing to realise that we cannot tell whether young plants of a grain crop are wheat or barley, or that we are a little hazy about the differences between colza, rape, kales and mustards and their uses, few will go as far as buying textbooks of agricultural botany and learning a whole glossary of botanical terms necessary to understand them just to satisfy an amateur curiosity.

It is hoped, therefore, that this book will provide those who do not grow the crops themselves, and are not expert botanists, with a guide to a very broad area. After all, most of the land that makes up our countryside is covered by crops.

ACKNOWLEDGEMENTS

Colour plates 1, 2, 3, 5, 10, 11, 12, 15, 16, 17, 18, 19, 20, 25, 26, 27, 28, 29, 30, 34, 35, 36, 37, 38, 39, 40, 41, 42 were painted by Elizabeth Rice. Colour plates 4, 6, 7, 8, 9, 13, 14, 21, 22, 23, 24, 31, 32, 33 are the work of Elisabeth Dowle. The black and white line drawings are by Rosemary Wise, except those which appear in the Glossary and on pp. 19, 242, 315, 330 and 335, which are the work of the author.

The author wishes to thank the three artists for their excellent work, and in particular E. Rice, who was left with the inestimably time-consuming task of researching and obtaining plant specimens. In this she was greatly assisted by the following people and institutions: The Royal Botanic Gardens, Kew, in particular Brian Halliwell, Alan Cook, Mark Sparrow, Martin Staniforth and Sue Minter; The Herbarium and Dr. Christopher Gray-Wilson; the Royal Horticultural Society Gardens, Wisley, especially Harry Baker, Haden Williams, Bertie Doe, Sid Love and Mrs Ecklin; Duncan Donald, Curator of the Chelsea Physic Garden; Denis Cousins of Battersea Park Garden; T. J. Wallace for help with fungi; Mr. N. Weston, of Weston and Sons; Pamela Rice, for growing some of the exotic plants, and many personal friends who also provided specimens.

INTRODUCTION

THE SCOPE OF THIS BOOK

The term *crop plant* is used in its broadest sense to cover not only those plants grown by farmers but also all the economic plants of the region, whether grown on a field scale for human or animal food, as a green manure, or for any other use; it is also applied to all those grown in market gardens and by home-gardeners for their own use, and to those gathered in the wild which are to be found in commerce, either on a large scale or only occasionally on country market stalls. This last category includes many important species such as the Mediterranean herbs, some fungi, and various other products. The number of these must perforce be limited in this book, which is not a guide to edible or medicinal wild plants, a subject covered by other books, in which, following a current back-to-nature trend, one is encouraged to make salads from every non-poisonous plant found in our hedgerows. It does not, therefore, include all the products available in health food shops.

Because such a broad definition of the term crop plant has been adopted, certain major categories have had to be excluded in order to keep the book to a manageable size. The book covers all crops grown on a field scale and in the manner defined above, except:

A. Trees grown only for timber

B. Ornamental plants

C. Medicinal plants: A few of these have been included, in particular ones which might be seen growing as field crops in the open, the restrictions having been applied in accordance with the thinking already outlined.

D. Grasses other than those grown for grain: This is an omission more open to challenge, particularly since forage crops belonging to other families such as the *Leguminosae* are included, and because the pasture grasses are of outstanding economic importance. However, to provide a reliable identification guide to the many useful European species would require illustrated keys including hundreds of non-economic ones, an exercise that would expand the book to unmanageable proportions. It is assumed that general interest in the grasses is not such that their absence will seriously vitiate the book; a particular interest in these species may be satisfied by consulting Gill & Vear's *Agricultural Botany*, or one of the field guides devoted exclusively to the subclass *Commelinidae*.

E. Algae: About a dozen species of seaweed are gathered in various parts of Europe as a source of human or animal food, of chemical compounds used in industry, or of manure, and by the definition of a *crop plant* given above, ought to have been included. It was deemed preferable to devote the space necessary to illustrate this marginal group to other terrestrial species.

WHAT INFORMATION IS GIVEN ABOUT EACH PLANT

A field guide should serve principally to identify plants or animals. In those devoted to wild plants, the information about each species can be practically limited to a description of diagnostic features supplemented by indications of habitat, distribution range, and flowering and fruiting periods. Economic species, especially the old established and widely cultivated ones, must be treated differently for the following reasons:

Many of the species have, through selection, hybridisation, methods of propagation and husbandry, developed a bewilderingly wide range of variation, sometimes with hundreds or even thousands of varieties. It is of course beyond the scope of this book to describe the varieties: to give a comprehensive account of all the forms of a single species, for example, the apple, would require more text and illustrations than are contained in this book. Varieties are therefore not listed, except for a few of the better known or more extreme forms. Instead, the concept of species has been retained as the basic unit of classification, as is usually the case in books dealing with wild plants. Thus more emphasis is put on the vegetative characters that distinguish the apple from the pear tree than on the diversity of forms of each.

The most interesting aspects of economic plants, as opposed to wild ones, are not or only indirectly relevant to identification. Uses, culinary value, relative economic importance, history of their spread in cultivation, and their sometimes revolutionary impact on economies are some of the subjects that cannot be ignored, and indeed are given particular attention.

Another subject that does not arise in the case of wild plants is the complex and often highly technical one of husbandry. This has been ignored in this book, except where it is an aid to identification. The fact that a particular crop plant is usually trained to climb on strings or wires, for instance, is relevant in this respect. The book is not conceived as a gardening manual; a wealth of expert literature is available on this popular and specialised subject.

LAYOUT OF THE BOOK

Economic plants are sometimes classified according to their products or uses. This method has been rejected here for two reasons. Firstly such an arrangement separates plants of true and usually obvious affinity: Oil Seed Rape, for instance, is so closely related to mustards and other crucifers cultivated for other purposes that they are easily confused, whereas no one could possibly mistake it for Sesame, Olive, or Maize. Grouping species together in their natural families is therefore necessary in order to make the relevant comparisons necessary for identification. Secondly, many if not most crops are grown for more than one purpose, and often yield several different products; the same species of Rape might be grown for oil, as a leafy forage crop, for the roots (used as human or animal food), or simply as a green manure crop. Any other system would necessitate several entries and many irksome cross references.

Accordingly, the species are grouped in their botanical families, which are arranged in a conventional systematic order. A brief introduction is given to each family mentioning its chief characteristics, relative economic importance, and in some cases, well known ornamentals or important tropical crops which belong to it.

This is followed in some cases by an identification key to the cultivated European members of the family. Other keys in the text are given for a single genus or groups of species or genera within the family.

The information on each species is set out under 5 headings:

1. Description: This consists of a brief botanical description of the species, mentioning the range of variability and principal or extreme varieties. Botanical terms likely to be unfamiliar to most readers have been kept to a minimum, but some are unavoidable if a reasonable degree of accuracy is to be maintained. A glossary of these terms is provided on p. 343 and ff.

2. Names: These include Latin synonyms (preceded by 'syn.' or 'syns.') by which the plant may be named in other books, alternative English names, and the vernacular names in certain other European languages. These are given because, especially in the case of economic plants, where people may be available at market stalls etc. to provide information, the most direct way of checking a plant's identity is often to ask its name of those who are in the best position to know.

In English a single word such as 'apple' applies equally well to the species as to its fruit, but other languages use different words for each. Since space is limited it is not possible to give them both. The choice, for instance, between '*pomme*' and '*pommier*' is arbitrary and has not been made consistently; it has been made according to which word seems likely to be the most useful in each case.

3. Uses

4. Origin, distribution and cultivation: The natural distribution range of a species, or its origin in cultivation, the history of its spread and present distribution in Europe is followed by indications of the extent and scale of cultivation: whether it is grown as a field crop, as a market-garden crop, or only by home-gardeners, or whether it is also or only gathered in the wild. Details of husbandry, such as whether the species is grown under glass or in the open, and periods of flowering and fruiting, are only mentioned where they may aid identification. Maps, which provide a conveniently concise illustration of the distribution of wild species, have not been used, because while the range of cultivated species is often broadly limited by climatic barriers, their actual distribution depends on constantly changing factors such as economic demand.

5. Similar plants: In cases where the species might be confused with others, its salient diagnostic features are given. Several categories of plants are mentioned under this heading: closely related ones, for example, or plants belonging to other groups with which it could be confused (either because of superficial resemblances, or because a common vernacular name is applied to both, eg. 'water chestnut', which may designate either of two quite distinct plants).

ABBREVIATIONS

It is, in the author's experience, tiresome to read text crammed with unfamiliar abbreviations and to refer repeatedly to a different section of the book for explanations of these. Accordingly they have been avoided, with the exception of the usual abbreviations of units of measurements (m: metre, cm: centimetre, mm: millimetre) and of a few other words which recur so often that they are easily memorised:

fl/s: flower/s
frt/s: fruit/s
lf, lvs: leaf, leaves
cv/s: cultivar/s
sp., spp.: species (singular and plural)
ssp., sspp.: subspecies (singular and plural)
var.: variety

Abbreviations of European languages are also used: Fr. (French); It. (Italian); Sp. (Spanish); Ger. (German); Dtch. (Dutch); Dan. (Danish); Gr. (Greek); Russ. (Russian); Yug. (Serbo-Croat).

USE OF KEYS

Dichotomous keys are a useful tool for the identification of plants, because they use only strictly relevant detail. They may be constructed in various ways, but always depend on a series of two alternative choices which lead, if they are interpreted correctly, to the name of the specimen being examined.

The easiest way to understand the method used in this book is by example. Given, for instance, a sprig of Kidney Vetch, and having established or guessed that it belongs to the Pea Family, one should turn to the key on p. 37.

Line 1 'Plant is a tree' is not applicable, so one turns to the alternative line 2 (given in brackets). The specimen being an herb, this line leads to (3). Here the choice is between palamate leaves (incorrect) and (4) trifoliate or pinnate leaves (correct), leading to line (5). Since the leaves are not trifoliate, but pinnate, one proceeds to the alternative to (5), which is (36). The pinnate leaves having a terminal leaflet, (37) leads to (38), where the choice is between 'leaflets 5 in number' (incorrect) and (41) 'leaflets more than 5 in number' (correct). The next line, (42), confirms the identity on the basis of the larger terminal leaflet.

LIST OF PLATES

COLOUR PLATES

1. ROSACEAE: Quince, Medlar, Loquat, Service tree, Azarole, Rose.
2. ROSACEAE: Apples and Pears.
3. ROSACEAE: *Prunus* spp.: Apricot, Peach, Nectarine, Almond, Cherries.
4. ROSACEAE: *Prunus* spp.: Sloe, Damsons, Bullace, Gages, Plums.
5. ROSACEAE: Strawberries and fruits of the bramble group (*Rubus* spp.).
6. LEGUMINOSAE: Lima Bean, Scarlet Runner Bean, Common Bean, Broad Bean.
7. LEGUMINOSAE: Peas, Asparagus Pea, Lentil, Chick Pea, Soya Bean.
8. LEGUMINOSAE: Herbage legumes: Lupins, Sainfoin, Lucerne, Yellow Trefoil, Bokhara Clover, Serradella, Common Vetch.
9. LEGUMINOSAE: Clovers, Liquorice, Fenugreek, Carob, Kidney Vetch.
10. GROSSULARIACEAE, CORNACEAE, CAPRIFOLIACEAE: Gooseberry, Worcesterberry, Currants, Cornelian Cherry, Elder.
11. FAGACEAE, CORYLACEAE, JUGLANDACEAE: Beech, Sweet Chestnut, Oaks, Hazel Nut, Filbert, Walnut, Black Walnut.
12. CANNABACEAE, MORACEAE, CAPPARCEAE: Hops, Hemp, Mulberries, Fig, Caper.
13. PASSIFLORACEAE, CUCURBITACEAE: Passionfruit, Cucumbers, Gherkin, Melons.
14. CUCURBITACEAE: Water Melon, Marrow and Courgette, Pumpkins, Squashes.
15. CACTACEAE, TILIACEAE, MALVACEAE, LINACEAE, ACTINIDIACEAE: Barbary Fig, Okra, Lime, Cotton, Flax.
16. ERICACEAE, VACCINIACEAE: Strawberry Tree, Blueberries, Bilberries, Cranberry, Cowberry.
17. MYRTACEAE, PUNICACEAE, RHAMNACEAE, EBENACEAE, RUTACEAE: Feijoa, Pomegranate, Kaki, Date Plum, Kumquat.
18. VITACEAE: Grapes.
19. RUTACEAE: Oranges, Tangerine.
20. RUTACEAE: Citron, Pomelo, Grapefruit, Lemon.
21. ANACARDIACEAE, LAURACEAE, ANONACEAE: Pistachio, Terebinth, Lentisc, Sweet Bay, Avocado, Cherimoya.
22. BRASSICACEAE: Mustards, Charlock, Rapes, Swede, Turnip, Cabbage and Kales.
23. BRASSICACEAE: Watercress, Garden Cress, Land Cress, Woad, Rocket, Seakale.
24. BRASSICACEAE: Radishes, Horse Radish, Pe Tsai, Pak Choi, Gai Choi.
25. PEDALIACEAE, VERBANACEAE RANUNCULACEAE, PAPAVERACEAE, OLEACEAE: Sesame, Vervain, Black Cumin, Opium Poppy, Olive, Jasmine.
26. AIZOACEAE, PORTULACCACEAE, POLYGONACEAE: New Zealand Spinach, Purselane, Buckwheat, Sorrels, Rhubarb, Fleawort.

27. CHENOPODIACEAE: Beets, Mercury, Orach, Spinach.
28. APIACEAE: Carrot, Parsnip, Parsley, Chervil.
29. APIACEAE: Dill, Fennel, Celery, Celeriac.
30. APIACEAE: Angelica, Caraway, Coriander, Cumin, Anise, Lovage, Sweet Cicely.
31. VALERIANACEAE, ASTERACEAE: Corn Salad, Lettuce, Chicory, Dandelion, Salsify, Scorzonera.
32. ASTERACEAE: Sunflower, Jerusalem Artichoke, Globe Artichoke, Cardoon.
33. ASTERACEAE: Southernwood, Tarragon, Wormwood, Chamomiles, Safflower, Pyrethrum.
34. SOLANACEAE: Deadly Nightshade, Garden Huckleberry, Tomato, Peppers and Chillies.
35. SOLANACEAE, CONVULVULACEAE: Tobacco, Potato, Aubergine, Cape Gooseberry, Sweet Potato.
36. HYDROPHULACEAE, BORAGINACEAE, LILIACEAE: Phacelia, Comfreys, Asparagus, Saffron Crocus.
37. LAMIACEAE: Lavenders, Rosemary, Savorys, Basil, Sage, Clary, Chinese Artichoke.
38. LAMIACEAE: Mints, Marjorams, Thymes, Chinese Artichoke.
39. ALLIACEAE: Leek, Garlic, Welsh Onion, Onion, Shallot, Chinese Chives, Chives.
40. GRAMINAE: Wheats, Rye, Barleys, Oats, Rice, Millet.
41. GRAMINAE: Maize, Sorgum, Bulrush Millet, Italian Millet, Japanese Millet.
42. FUNGI: Cultivated Mushroom, Ceps, Chanterelle, Horn of Plenty, Oyster Mushroom, Shiitake Mushroom, Parasol Mushroom, Morel, Perigord Truffle, Italian White Truffle, Saffron Milk Cap.

BLACK AND WHITE PLATES

1. Forms of Lettuce, Endive and Chicory.
2. Forms of *Brassica oleracea*.

ANNONACEAE

Custard Apple Family

Members of the genus *Annona* are small trees, native to tropical America. Many produce edible fruits, of which at least six species are widely cultivated in the tropics. The English name Custard Apple is sometimes used collectively for all these fruits, but more often designates *A. squamosa*, and in the W. Indies, *A. reticulata*, otherwise known as Bullock's Heart. Two species, and their hybrid are cultivated in Europe, one of them on a commercial scale.

The genus is characterised by the peculiar structure of the flowers and fruits, described below.

Annona cherimolia
CHERIMOYA

(p. 168)

Description: A small tree, to 6 m in height, varying from compact and bushy to tall and straggling. Young shoots covered in velvety yellow-brown hairs. Lvs alternate, ovate-lanceolate, velvety on undersides. Fl with 3 long pale green, slightly spreading and curling bracts; petals minute, scale-like, scarcely longer than the numerous stamens packed together on the bud-like receptacle and surrounding the cluster of scale-like carpels at the centre. Frt is composed of a large number of carpels fused together in a round or slightly elongate, heart-shaped mass, the individual carpels showing on the surface as fingerprint-like depressions, the lower edges of which are often raised in a lip or tubercle; the surface is dull green often flushed with dark pink or maroon. Frts vary in size from about 7–15 cm in diameter; they contain a yellowish white creamy pulp in which are embedded numerous dark brown seeds.

Names: Also known as Custard Apple. Fr.: Anonne cherimolier; It.: Cerimolia; Sp.: Cherimoya; Ger.: Cherimoya, Zuckerapfel; Dtch.: Cherimoya; Dan.: Cherimoya; Russ.: Anona cherimoya.

Uses: The fruit, which is said to be the best of the Custard Apples, has a rich fruity, slightly acid taste reminiscent of Pineapple. It is eaten raw, or used to flavour ice-creams or drinks. Like the other species, the frts are soft and perishable, and therefore difficult to export.

Origin, distribution and cultivation: A native of the mountain valleys of Peru and Equador, and cultivated elsewhere in tropical highlands and in the subtropics. It is grown commercially in orchards in southern Spain; whence frts are exported in small quantities.

Similar plants: The yellowish-brown velvety tomentum on the undersides of lvs distinguish Cherimoya from all the other cultivated *Annona* spp.

A. squamosa L., Custard Apple, Sugar Apple or Sweetsop is also cultivated to a small extent in southern Spain and perhaps elsewhere in the Mediterranean, although it requires generally warmer conditions than *A. cherimolia*. The tree is similar but with quite different lvs; these are narrowly lanceolate, 3 or 4 times longer than broad, and lack the velvety tomentum on their undersides. The frt is round, conical or heart-shaped, but smaller, 5–8 cm in diameter, pale grey-green with a bloom, never flushed with red; the carpel segments are entirely raised in convex bumps, not depressed, and separate easily so that the fruit can be pulled apart with the fingers.

More difficult to identify may be the Atemoya, a hybrid of these two species with characters of both parents. It is cultivated in

Israel where one form is called Kaller, and may be adopted in some of the hotter parts of south Europe.

Another species of Custard Apple, *A. reticulata*, is sometimes available from luxury grocers in Europe, but is not cultivated here. The frt is yellow flushed with red on one side, the surface smooth and covered with a network of fine lines indicating the division of the carpels. It may be marketed under either of two names, Custard Apple or Bullock's Heart.

LAURACEAE

Laurel Family

A family of mainly tropical trees and shrubs which only includes a few commercial species: besides the two described below, Cinnamon and the Camphor Tree are the most important.

Lvs simple, alternate, evergreen, leathery, with aromatic oil glands. Fls without petals, with 4–6 sepals in 1–2 whorls, or 12 stamens arranged in 4 whorls; ovary superior, with 1 carpel. Frt a 1-seeded berry.

Laurus nobilis
LAUREL or **SWEET BAY**

(p. 168)

Description: A dense evergreen shrub or tree to 20 m, but kept short by pruning in cultivation. Lvs dark green, very aromatic, 4–10 cms long, with margins often wavy, and translucent, as can clearly be seen by holding it against the light. Fls unisexual, on different plants, in small axillary clusters; whorl of 4 sepals; male with 10–14 stamens; female with 4 staminodes. Frt black when ripe, slightly elongate, resembling a small olive.

Names: Fr.: Laurier; It.: Alloro, Lauro; Sp.: Laurel; Ger.: Lorbeer; Dtch.: Laurier; Dan.: Laurbaer; Gr.: Dáphni, Vaïa; Russ.: Lavr; Yug.: Lovor.

Uses: Bay is primarily cultivated for its leaves, widely used either fresh or dried, although they may be unpleasantly bitter when fresh, as a flavouring in most European, but especially Mediterranean, cooking. When dried leaves are too old, such as those often sold, they lose their essential oil (cineole) and are useless. The oil, known as oil of bay, was formerly used medicinally and in veterinary surgery. The berries are distilled or pressed in a minor industry to flavour certain liqueurs.

The leaves were a symbol of victory and wisdom to the Romans who used them to crown distinguished men – hence such titles as Poet Laureate. Those who had matriculated for university were formerly called bachelors, from the Latin *baccalaureus* (laurel berry), and were forbidden to marry during the course of their studies. In English the word has been extended to all unmarried men.

Origin, distribution and cultivation: A native of Asia Minor and the Mediterranean, where it has been cultivated since antiquity. Being hardy, it is now grown in much of western Europe outside its natural range, although it will not stand severe frost; it is particularly suited to coastal areas. Cultivation is rarely on a crop scale, most commercial growers cropping only a few trees. It is widely grown individually in gardens or in tubs for domestic use.

Similar plants: Bay is not to be confused with the many plants bearing the name 'laurel' but which belong to other families, such as Cherry Laurel (Rosaceae) or Japanese Laurel (*Aucuba*, of the Cornaceae family), both grown for ornament. The former has much larger lvs without wavy margins, tall upright flower clusters and round scarlet fruit. The only other true laurel, the Canary Island Laurel *L. azorica* is rarely cultivated; it can be distinguished by its larger (7–12 cms long) leaves and downy twigs. Bay leaves are most easily distinguished from all these by the strong aromatic smell when crushed, and by their translucent margins.

Persea americana
AVOCADO

(p. 168)

Description: An evergreen tree to 20 m, but budded plants in cultivation usually much smaller, 3–5 m. Lvs entire, the underside glaucous, variable in shape and size from 3 x 12 cm to 5 x 30 cm. Fls in axillary clusters at ends of branches, small, with brown hairy bracts, the calyx yellowish, hairy, 1–1.5 cm in diameter consisting of 6 sepals in 2 whorls, without petals. Frt familiar, a large more or less pear-shaped berry 6–25 cm long, dark green, sometimes flushed with red or purple, containing a single large round pale seed surrounded by pale green flesh.

Three principal races are recognised: Mexican, W. Indian and Guatemalan. Hundreds of cvs have been developed from these. Those grown in Europe are the small-fruited hardier vars derived from the Mexican highland stock; the skin of these frts is smooth, unlike the warty types of some other cvs, and the large seed is often loose in the cavity.

Names: Fr.: Avocatier; It.: Avocado; Sp.: Abuacado; Ger.: Avocatbirne; Dtch.: Advocaat; Dan.: Advocatpaere; Gr.: Avokato; Russ.: Avokado.

Uses: The high protein and fat content makes Avocado the most nutritious of all frts, and it is therefore an important food crop in its native countries. The distinctively flavoured flesh is eaten raw; it is best served simply as half frts with lemon juice and salt, but is often dressed more elaborately, or diced and mixed in salads. The mashed pulp may also serve as a base for an excellent cold soup, or in milkshakes.

Origin, distribution and cultivation: Avocado is a native of South and Central America, where it was in cultivation in precolumbian times. The Spaniards introduced it to southern Spain in 1601 and it was spread to many countries of the Old World tropics and to the USA in the 19th century, but it is only since air transport enabled rapid delivery of this soft perishable frt that it has gained popularity in Europe. Although Avocado remains a mainly tropical crop it is grown commercially in a few of the hotter parts of Europe, especially Cyprus. Israel is now the main source of imported frts.

Similar plants: Bearing in mind the characteristics of the family: none. Those who have germinated the seed for amusement may have noted the similarity to Bay.

ROSACEAE

Rose Family

A very large and varied family of trees, shrubs and herbs, worldwide in distribution but particularly plentiful in northern and temperate regions. Lvs simple or compound, with stipules. Fls with petals and sepals usually in fives, the stamens more numerous, usually 10, 15 or 20. Throughout the great range of different forms, from small grassland herbs to the familiar fruit trees a general similarity in the structure of fls is readily discernible, but the frts are of several distinct types – berries, pomes, achenes and drupes – so different in appearance that their affinity is far from obvious. Drawings A to F below illustrating the fls and frts of the main types in vertical section show how these types have evolved.

The family includes many ornamentals, of which the roses are the most important. Although it is represented in the tropics, those regions have not contributed any economic species.

Rosa canina agg. and others
DOG ROSE and **Other Wild Roses**

Description: Shrubs with long, erect or arching prickly stems. Prickles, recurved or straight, vary in shape according to spp. Lvs pinnate, with stipules, can be hairy or downy. Fls solitary or in clusters, with 5 pink or white petals and many stamens. There are also many styles and carpels enclosed in a deep receptacle cup. This ripens to a bright orange or red (most spp.) or blackish hip, which often retains dried sepals and styles, in which case the disc is flat or it is joined into a column that remains on the ripe frt. The frt-stalk may be smooth or hairy.

Dog Rose *Rosa canina* has arching prickly stems, with recurved prickles. Lvs are hairless or sometimes hairy beneath. Fls in clusters, with pink or white petals (as above). Hips are bright red, with flat discs. Frt-stalk is smooth.

Names: Fr.: Eglantier; It.: Rosa de macchia; Sp.: Escaramujo; Ger.: Dornrose; Dtch.: Hondroos; Dan.: Hunderose; Russ.: Dikaya rose; Yug.: Divlja ruza.

Uses: The fine-flavoured hips of Dog Rose and of other wild spp. are made into jams and a syrup which has a very high vitamin C content. The seeds within the hip are surrounded by sharp irritating hairs (frequently used as 'itching powder' by children) which must be removed from the cooked pulp by straining through a cloth.

Origin, distribution and cultivation: *Rosa canina* and many other spp. are native to Europe where they are not cultivated but rather encouraged to grow in hedgerows in areas where the frt is gathered regularly. Rose hip syrup became an invaluable substitute for other sources of vitamin C in Britain during the Second World War, when large-scale production was encouraged. Today this industry is mainly a home one, but commercially produced syrup is still marketed.

Similar plants: *R. canina* is the most widely used sp. in western Europe, but many other spp. exist. Some of the forms are ancient hybrids and therefore very difficult to identify.

Rosa spp.
(*gallica*, *damascena*, *centifolia*, etc.)
ROSES

(p. 128)

Description: The countless varieties of cultivated roses are too well known as ornamental plants to require a botanical description. Basically they differ from *R. canina* and other wild species by their much larger fls with multiple rows of petals.

Names: Fr.: Rose; It.: Rosa; Sp.: Rosa; Ger.: Rose; Dtch.: Roos; Dan.: Rose; Gr.: Triantafylia; Russ.: Rosa; Yug.: Ruža.

Uses: The vast majority of Roses are cultivated purely for ornament; a few exceptions however merit their inclusion in this book. *R. damascena* and *R. centifolia* are both grown for the production of rose oil, or attar of roses, obtained by distillation of the petals, and used in the perfume industry. In Turkey and the Balkan countries they are used to flavour foods such as jam, *locoum* and other confectioneries. Bulgaria produces a rose liqueur. *Rosa gallica medicinalis*, a cultivated variety of the wild Provence Rose, was formerly much cultivated for the same oil which was used medicinally.

Origin, distribution and cultivation: The origin of cultivated roses is thought to be Persia, which was already exporting rose water and essence in Roman times. Although roses were already common in European gardens in the Middle Ages, commercial cultivation in Europe dates only from the 17th century. The two major centres of production are Bulgaria (*R. damascena*) and the south of France, particularly the area around Grasse, where a cabbage rose, *R. centifolia* is cultivated on a field scale. Bushes may remain productive for twenty years or more; the flowers are picked by hand and dried before maceration and distillation.

Similar plants: The only cultivated plants which it would be possible to confuse with roses are *Rubus* spp., below.

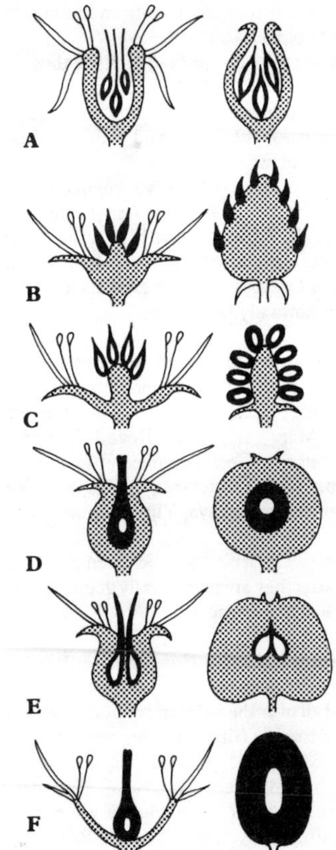

Diagram of vertical sections of flowers and fruit of certain cultivated members of the Rose Family. Receptacle marked by shading; carpels in black.
A: Azarole; **B**: Strawberry **C**: Raspberry **D**: Rose **E**: Apple **F**: Plum
The succulent parts of **A, B, D, E** are formed by the receptacle; those of **C** and **F** by the thickened carpel wall.

Rubus fruticosus agg.
BLACKBERRY, BRAMBLE

(p. 136)

Description: Bramble is an aggregate of some 400 species and subspecies, differing in the disposition and type of spines on the stem, lf shape, fl colour, frt shape, colour and flavour, and hair and gland distribution. Identification is made even more confusing by the numerous hybrids which occur. In general the plant is a scrambling shrub up to 3 m, with arching angled stems bearing hairs, prickles and hooked spines, and leaves with 3–5 (occasionally 7) oblong to oval leaflets. Fls white or pink in panicles on previous year's growth. Frts ripen from red to purple-red or black.

The best wild fruits to pick are those of *R. ulmifolius*, a pink-flowered sp. with long recurved spines only on stem angles, is entirely roughly hairy, and with lvs distinctly felted below.

One of the most easily recognisable of the older cultivated forms is Cut-Leafed Blackberry *R. laciniatus*, with its long coarsely serrate leaflets; a spineless cv of this sp. exists, called Oregon; cvs also exist for other spp., with normally shaped lvs.

Names: In the Latin languages there is much confusion between Blackberry and Mulberry (Lat. *Morus*). Fr.: Mûre (de ronce); It.: Mora selvatica, Rovo; Sp.: Mora, Zarzamora; Ger.: Brombeere; Dtch.: Bram; Dan.: Brombaer; Gr.: Vatomouriá; Russ.: Yeznyevika neskaya; Yug.: Kupina.

Uses: The fruits may be eaten raw or used in tarts; they are particularly good for making jams. They freeze well.

Origin, distribution and cultivation: *Rubus* species belonging to this group occur wild all over the holarctic region; many forms have been in cultivation for centuries, either improved wild species, or cvs obtained by hybridisation. American Blackberries, derived from *R. alleghanensis* are cultivated in Europe, but do not do well in Britain or the colder central and eastern countries.

Blackberries ripen in late summer or early autumn, according to the variety. Because wild fruit are so common, few people in the country buy commercially-produced fruit, so they remain a crop of only secondary importance. Although in the past home-gardeners transplanted rooted canes from hedgerows to their gardens, real cultivation of blackberries only began in the 19th century, mainly in America. Canes are trained along fences or wires, and those that have borne fruit are cut back to ground level and half a dozen or so of the current year's new growth are allowed to remain to fruit in the following year.

Similar plants: Other *Rubus* spp., especially Dewberry, below.

Rubus caesius
DEWBERRY

(p. 136)

Description: Very similar to Blackberry, but the stems are prostrate or at the most low-arched, and are on the whole more slender. Fls are white, and the frt is smaller, with fewer drupelets, has a slight whitish bloom and is not shiny. Many cultivated varieties, however, are hybrids of American species, with larger frts, and are more difficult to tell from Blackberries.

Names: Fr.: Ronce bleue; It.: Mora palustre; Sp.: Zarza de los rastojos; Ger.: Kratzbeere; Dtch.: Drauwbraam; Dan.: Korbaer; Gr.: Drosomouriá.

Uses: As Blackberries.

Origin, distribution and cultivation: *R. caesius* is a native of northern Europe where it grows wild in damp limestone areas, but many of the cvs are derived from American spp, some crossed with *R. alleghanensis* which is considered a Blackberry. The crop is usually lighter than that of Blackberries, but are still cultivated because they fruit earlier.

Similar plants: See description above.

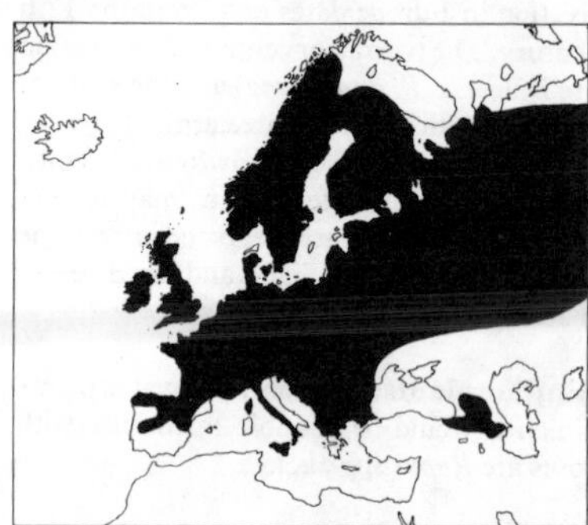

Natural distribution of Raspberry

Rubus idaeus
RASPBERRY

(p. 136)

Description: Basically as Bramble. Stems are erect, rounded, with slender straight prickles. Lvs with 3–7 leaflets, green above, woolly-white below. Fls white, with narrow erect petals; frts ripen to characteristic downy pinkish carmine and have a distinctive flavour; when picked, they 'plug' (when the mass of drupelets detaches easily from the core which remains attached to the plant).

Many different varieties are in cultivation, some of them having been developed at East Malling Research Station and introduced after the Second World War to replace older, degenerate and virus-sensitive strains. The most striking of the varieties is a very old, yellow-fruited, strain, sometimes called 'White Raspberry'. The whole plant looks etiolated in comparison to other Raspberries, as not only the fruits are pale, but the stems and leaves are weaker and pale green. **Black Raspberry** *R. occidentalis* is an American species. A hybrid of this and *R. idaeus*, known as **Black-Red Raspberry** with dark purple, not bicolorous, berries, is spreading in cultivation in Europe.

Names: Fr.: Framboise; It.: Lampone; Sp.: Frambueso; Ger.: Himbeere; Dtch.: Framboos; Dan.: Hindbaer; Gr.: Frampouaz; Russ.: Malina; Yug.: Malina.

Uses: Raspberries are the most important economically of all the cane fruits, the habit of 'plugging' when picked adds to their value, since the fruit core does not have to be removed later. They are consumed in the same way as Blackberries and other *Rubus* spp., but their popularity and distinctive taste have led to a wider range of uses, particularly in flavouring ice-creams, sweets, confectioneries and liqueurs. 'Wine' is sometimes made from Raspberries, as from other *Rubus*. Much of the commercial crop is canned or frozen.

Origin, distribution and cultivation: The wild *R. idaeus* probably originated in Asia, but the species is now naturalised in Europe as an escape from cultivation, through dispersal of seeds by birds and occurs in shady areas and heathland. Some varieties are summer-fruiting, so a selected range of cvs can extend the fruit grower's productive season from July to the end of the autumn. Canes are cut back after fruiting in the same manner as for Blackberries.

Similar plants: Other *Rubus* spp., especially Loganberry, below.

Rubus longanobaccus
LOGANBERRY
(p. 136)

Description: A very vigorous *Rubus* producing stems up to 3 m long, similar to Blackberry in growth, but with larger, softer lvs and shoots less erect, trailing unless supported. Frts dull red, resembling Raspberry, but do not 'plug'. Crops are heavy.

Names: Known universally as Loganberry.

Uses: The particularly juicy frt of this *Rubus* is rather too acid for fresh dessert, but ideal for jams, stewing, freezing, canning and juice and 'wine' making.

Origin, distribution and cultivation: When discovered by Judge Logan in California at the end of the 19th century, this fruit was assumed to be a natural hybrid between Blackberry and Raspberry. It was later given full specific status, but is now generally thought to be a spontaneous hybrid of *R. vitifolius* and another unknown parent. Largest commercial production is in the USA, but it has been in constant production on a limited scale in Britain and other European countries since the turn of the century.

Similar plants: Raspberry, Blackberry.

Rubus phoenicolasius
WINEBERRY
(p. 136)

Description: A very distinctive species: the long calyx lobes envelop the frts until they are nearly ripe, and stems, petioles and calyces are covered in fine red hairs, those on the fls being distinctly club-shaped. Plant forms a clump with long arching canes, with or without prickles, which must be trained on wires or trellises in the same way as Loganberry. Open fls distinctive, with small narrow white petals, and very long pointed sepals. Frts ripen unevenly to golden, orange or cherry-red.

Names: Fr.: Ronce du Japon; It.: Mora giaponesa; Sp.: Zarza japonesa; Ger.: Japanische Weinbeere; Dtch.: Wijnbes; Dan.: Vinbrombaer; Russ.: Yeznyevika japonskaya.

Uses: The fruit is sweet and juicy, not too acid, and makes a fine dessert, especially with added sugar and cream. It also makes good jams.

Origin, distribution and cultivation: Wineberry is a native of northern China and Japan. It has been in cultivation in Europe, often for ornamental reasons, since the turn of the century.

Similar plants: None.

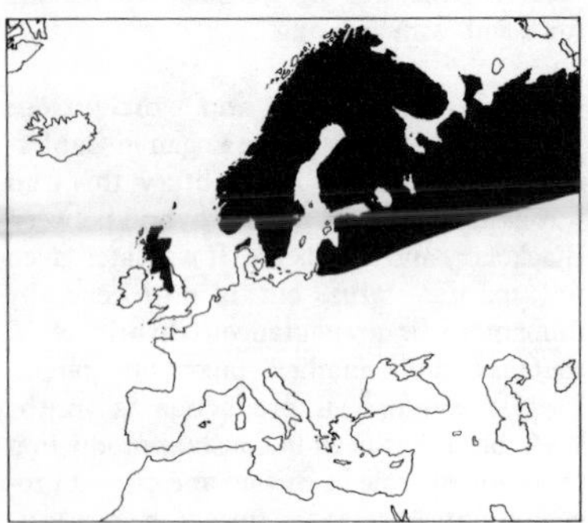

Natural distribution of Cloudberry

Rubus chamaemorus
CLOUDBERRY
(p. 136)

Description: A small low perennial herb, not exceeding 20 cms, with creeping rhizome. Lvs few, simple, not pinnate, shallowly palmate and downy. Fls solitary, borne at the tips of erect shoots, with white petals longer than sepals. Frt small, with few relatively large drupelets, ripening to orange.

Names: Fr.: Mûrier nain; It.: Lampone de Lapponia; Sp.: Mora amarilla; Ger.: Moltebeere; Dtch.: Bergframboos; Dan.: Multebaer; Fr.: Vatomouriá; Russ.: Morshka.

Uses: The fruits may be used in jams, or stewed.

Origin, distribution and cultivation: Cloudberry is a native of the far north of Europe – Scandinavia, Arctic Russia and Siberia, Northern Britain including the Hebrides, and Canada. It is rarely cultivated, but has been a valuable source of rare fruit for the inhabitants of its inhospitable homelands for many centuries.

Similar plants: This species' growth habit and simple lvs distinguish it from all the other economic members of the genus in Europe.

STRAWBERRIES

Strawberries are easily distinguishable as a genus owing to the peculiar structure of the fruit, and enlarged fleshy receptacle coloured red when ripe, bearing numerous small brown achenes on its surface.

Although edible species for native European strawberries have been in cultivation for centuries, they were scarcely improved in size or productiveness. It was not until a hybrid of two American species was produced that the large Garden Strawberry, with hundreds of very similar looking strains, made it an important economic crop.

The main edible species may be identified as shown in the key below:

Fragaria vesca
WILD STRAWBERRY and **ALPINE STRAWBERRY**
(p. 136)

Description: A herb 5–30 cm tall, producing long arching runners bearing small leaf clusters which take root and grow into new plants. Lvs long-stalked, bright glossy green, hairy; leaflets oblong, 1–6 cm long, with acutely toothed margins, the terminal tooth longer than lateral teeth. Fls 12–18 mm in diameter, white, with 5 petals longer than sepals. Frt 1–2 cm long, bright red. Alpine Strawberry, var. *semperflorens*, has rather larger, more elongate frt.

Names: Fr.: Fraise de bois, - de montagne; It.: Fragola selvatica; Sp.: Fresa silvatica; Ger.: Worbel, Gemeine Erdbeere; Dtch.: Wilde aardbei; Dan.: Vilde jordbaer; Gr.: Fráoula; Russ.: Zemlyanika vishnaya; Yug.: Divlja jagoda.

Uses: Eaten as a fresh dessert fruit.

Origin, distribution and cultivation: *F. vesca* occurs wild in woods and shady grasslands all over Europe, where it fruits during the summer months. Much of the fruit consumed is picked from wild plants, for they are superior in flavour, and less acid than Garden Strawberries, but the species, in particular strains of var. *semperflorens* such as 'Baron Solemacher' and 'Alpine Yellow', a yellow-fruited form, are in cultivation.

Similar plants: see key p. 23. Barren Strawberry, a common wild plant of grasslands and open woods, does not belong to the genus *Fragaria*, but is a species of *Potentilla* with trifoliate lvs. It does not produce a fleshy frt, only a small cluster of dry achenes. It may be distinguished from Wild Strawberry before the fruiting stage by the leaflets, of which the terminal tooth is shorter than the lateral teeth.

Fragaria moschata
HAUTBOIS STRAWBERRY

Description: As *F. vesca*, but plant is generally taller, with fewer or no runners; leaflets have longer stalks; fl-stalks with erect hairs. Frts a darker, almost purplish red, with achenes concentrated towards tip, sparse or absent from base.

Names: Fr.: Caperon; It.: Fragola di Germania; Sp.: Fresa moschata; Ger.: Moschuserdbeere; Dtch.: Tuinaardbei; Dan.: Moskusjordbaere; Gr.: Agriofráoula; Russ.: Zemlyanika muskusnaya; Yug.: Nijemica jagoda.

Uses: As Wild Strawberry.

Origin, distribution and cultivation: *F. moschata* has a less extensive natural distribution than *F. vesca*. It probably originated in central Europe and has been introduced as an escape from cultivation elsewhere, as in Britain. It is now rarely cultivated, commercial producers of 'wild strawberries' preferring the Alpine Strawberry.

Similar plants: See key p. 23. Another wild European species, *F. viridis*, is similar to the Hautbois Strawberry, but is smaller, and

KEY TO STRAWBERRIES

1	Fls (2–3.5 cm in diam.) and frts (at least 3 cm) larger; achenes imbedded on frt flesh; leaflets not or scarcely hairy above; terminal leaflets with broadly rounded bases = **Garden Strawberry**	**(2)**
2	Fls (1.2–2 mm) and frts (less than 1.5 cm wide) smaller; achenes protruding above surface of flesh; leaflets hairy above; terminal leaflets narrowed to base = **3**	**(1)**
3	Frt generally smaller (1.2–2 mm) evenly covered in achenes; fl-stalk with adpressed hairs; runners long and numerous = **Wild Strawberry**	**(4)**
4	Frt generally larger (1.5–2.5 mm) with achenes concentrated towards apex, sparse at base; fl-stalk with erect hairs; runners few or absent = **Hautbois Strawberry**	**(3)**

the sepals are adpressed to the fruit which does not detach easily from stalk.

Fragaria x *ananassa*
GARDEN STRAWBERRY
(p. 136)

Description: Basically as *F. vesca*, but all parts of plant are larger. Fls 20–35 mm in diameter. Ripe frts at least 3 cms wide, round, oblong, more or less pointed or misshapen according to cv; terminal leaflets with rounded bases, and all leaflets more or less hairy above; long runners are freely produced in most varieties.

Many varieties, not differing greatly in appearance, exist, and are continually being developed. They are chosen for their resistance to virus disease, suitability to local climates, and fruiting habits; some varieties are able to bear a second crop.

Names: Fr.: Fraise; It.: Fragola; Sp.: Freson; Ger.: Erdbeere; Dtch.: Aarbei; Dan.: Jordbaer; Gr.: Germanikí fráoula; Russ.: Zemlyanika sadvaya; Yug.: Jagoda.

Uses: As a fresh dessert, with added sugar and cream, or with wine or spirits, and for making jams. Strawberry is also one of the main fruit flavours used in ice-creams, sweets, confectioneries, liqueurs and many processed dessert foods.

Origin, distribution and cultivation: The many varieties of Garden Strawberry ultimately derive from two American species, *F. virginiana* which occurs wild on the East coast, and *F. chiloensis*, from the Pacific seaboard from California to Chile. The first was introduced into Europe in the early 17th century, *F. chiloensis* in the 18th century. The two hybridised freely in cultivation in Europe, giving forms which were selected and re-crossed many times to produce the modern commercial varieties.

Strawberries are cultivated in all European countries, on home-garden to extensive market-garden scale. The name refers to the traditional practice of laying straw under the fruiting stems in order to protect the fruit from damp and dirt. Unlike Wild Strawberries which unaccountably offer little temptation to little birds, Garden Strawberries are heavily threatened and must be protected by nets if grown in the open.

Similar plants: See key p. 23.

Crataegus azarolus
AZAROLE
(p. 128)

Description: A shrub or small tree, 4–6 m, but occasionally to 10 m, with few spines. Young twigs, lvs and fl-stalks with dense woolly adpressed hairs. Lf-stalks short, 1 cm or less; lvs grey-green underneath with 3–5 blunt lobes which are untoothed or with 1–3 teeth at apex. Fls (April–May) in clusters, white, 1.5–2 cm across. Frt ca. 2 cm in diameter, round, yellow to orange-red; styles and frt nutlets number 1–3.

Names: Fr.: Azarole; It.: Azzeruolo; Sp.: Acerolo; Ger.: Azaro-Hagedorn; Gr.: Azaróli; Russ.: Boyarishnik paniski.

Uses: The fruit may be eaten fresh, but are more often used for making jellies or fermented to produce 'wine' and spirit.

Origin, distribution and cultivation: Azarole is a native of Crete, but is widely cultivated on a small scale in southern France, Italy, Yugoslavia and Greece. The ripe fruit is harvested in early autumn, mostly for home use, but is sometimes offered for sale in country markets.

Similar plants: The genus *Crataegus* (Hawthorns) has hundreds of species throughout the temperate holarctic region, being most numerous in North America. Azarole, the only species cultivated for its fruit in Europe, may be distinguished from Common and Midland Hawthorn by its densely hairy twigs and leaves, the latter and especially the fruit being much larger. *C. laciniata*, a common shrub of S. Europe, has frt almost as large and of the same colour, but lf lobes (3–7) are acutely toothed at apices.

In North China another *Crataegus* is widely cultivated in orchards. Its caramelised fruits, like tiny sugared apples, are sold spitted on little bamboo slivers from street stalls throughout the winter months.

Mespilus germanica
MEDLAR
(p. 128)

Description: A small spreading deciduous tree to 7 m. Branches often armed with long (2.5 cm) spines. Lvs long, ca. 15 x 5 cm, oval or ovate, hairy, leathery looking, crinkled with sunken veins, nearly stalkless. Fls large, 3–6 cm across, stalkless, solitary, appearing in late spring. Frt light brown, globular, with a hollow apex in which the five seed vessels are visible, surrounded by the long persistent sepals, the size varying greatly (3–8 cm) in proportion to the size of the tree.

Names: Fr.: Nèfle; It.: Nespolo; Sp.: Nispola; Ger.: Mispel, Mehlbeer; Dtch.: Mispel; Dan.: Mispel; Gr.: Mousmouliá; Russ.: Mushmula; Yug.: Mušmula.

Uses: In hotter countries where the fruit ripen thoroughly they may be eaten fresh. Elsewhere they only become palatable after frost has 'bletted' them, breaking up the hard tissue which then partially rots. In this form they are traditionally eaten with wine in winter, but are more often used for making jellies and jams, after the seeds have been removed.

Origin, distribution and cultivation: Medlar is known in the wild from much of S.E. Europe, extending eastward to central Asia. Because it is one of the hardiest of all rosaceous fruits it has long been in cultivation in most of Europe, including Scandinavia and Britain, where it is now rare. Today it is of minor importance, and cultivated only on a small scale for home use or local markets. The plant's bearing and vigour are often improved by grafting on to Quince, Pear or *Crataegus* rootstock.

Similar plants: See Loquat, p. 26.

Cydonia oblonga
QUINCE
(p. 128)

Description: A small, densely-branched deciduous tree to 6 m. Lvs alternate, elliptical to ovate, 6–10 cm long, with entire margins, pale but turning dark green above, white-woolly beneath with glandular hairy stipules. Fls solitary, white or pink, 2–5 cm across, with numerous stamens. Frt 2.5–3.5 cm in the wild, up to 15 cm or more in some cvs, pear-shaped, often irregular, pale yellow sometimes blotched with brown, very fragrant, with up to 20 seeds in each carpel.

Names: Fr.: Coign; It.: Cotogno; Sp.: Marmelo, Membrillo; Ger.: Quitte; Dtch.: Kwee; Dan.: Kvaede; Gr.: Kydoniá; Russ.: Ayva; Yug.: Dunja.

Uses: The raw fruit is hard and quite unpalatable, but when cooked the flesh turns a brownish pink with a fine flavour. In Morocco and to a lesser extent in southern Europe it is cooked as a vegetable in stews or to accompany other meat dishes. The commonest use is in jams and jellies. It is a useful flavouring to add to apple or pear compotes, tarts and pies. In France, and particularly in Spain, quince jelly is made into a candy which has a wide commercial market.

Origin, distribution and cultivation: Quince is probably a native of northern Iran and Turkestan, but is naturalised in parts of the Near East and southern Europe. It is of ancient cultivation in Europe, and was much used by the Romans. It is cultivated on a fairly large scale in Portugal and in Spain, which exports the fruit and its manufactured products. In more northern countries it is of only minor importance, grown mainly by home-gardeners. Perhaps its main economic use today is as a rootstock for pears. The tree grows best in deep loam in sheltered sites: in Spain plantations may often be seen in narrow steam valleys.

Similar plants: Quince is the only member of the genus *Cydonia*. 'Flowering Quinces', wrongly called 'Japonicas' in Britain, belong to the genus *Chaenomeles*; they are natives of China and Japan which are widely grown for ornament in Europe. They are distinguished from Quince by their toothed lvs, red or pink flowers almost always in clusters, and different, smaller fruits. The yellow frt, blotched with red and shaped like an Apple ca. 4 cm across, of *C. japonica*, and the ovoid, greenish frt with white speckles of *C. speciosa* may be used in the same way as Quince.

Quince fruits of any shape or size can immediately be distinguished from Apples or Pears by the large number of seeds in each carpel.

Eriobotrya japonica
LOQUAT
(p. 128)

Description: A distinctive evergreen tree to 10 m. Lvs large, 12–25 cm, dark green, leathery looking and conspicuously veined, the undersides covered, as are the twigs and fl stalks, in dense reddish-brown or greyish felted hairs. Fls, which appear in early winter, are white, ca. 1 cm across, fragrant, and borne in densely branched pyramidal clusters, the young buds partially hidden in the dense brown woolly hairs. Frts ripen in late spring; they are elliptic or pear-shaped, 3–7 cm long, smooth-skinned, yellow to orange, containing a single large smooth stone in each carpel.

Names: Fr.: Bibace, Nèfle du Japon; It.: Nespolo del Giappone; Sp.: Nispola de Japón; Ger.: Wollmispel; Dtch.: Japanse mispel; Dan.: Japansk mispel; Gr.: Mousmouliá, Meskouliá; Russ.: Eriobotria yaponskaya; Yug.: Japanska mušmula.

Uses: The fruits may be eaten fresh; they are sweet and slightly acid, very juicy but somewhat insipid. They are often made into jams or jellies, and in some places are fermented for alcohol.

Origin, distribution and cultivation: Loquat is one of the few subtropical fruits of the rose family. It is a native of China and Japan, which remain the main commercial producers. It is widely cultivated for ornament as well as for the fruit, sometimes in large orchards, in all the countries of southern Europe, where the fruit is offered on local markets from April to June.

Similar plants: The name 'Japanese Medlar' by which it is known in the Latin languages alludes to the similarity in the plants' lvs. Those of Loquat are however much larger, with a distinct although very short stalk, and are not shed in winter. The fls and frt borne in clusters also serve to distinguish it from Medlar. The frt could be mistaken for a Plum were it not for the calyx scars at the apex, and the absence of a groove along one side.

Sorbus domestica
TRUE SERVICE TREE
(p. 128)

Description: A tree up to 22 m in central Europe, rarely more than a shrub in the Mediterranean, with a domed crown of level spreading branches. Bark orange and brown fissured into small rectangles; young shoots with fine silky hairs, later glabrous, a darker green to brown above. Lf buds glabrous, bright green, sticky with resin. Lvs pinnate with 11–21 oblong leaflets 3–6 x 1 cm, sharply toothed in apical 2/3rds, softly hairy beneath. Fls (in April–June) white, ca. 1.5 cm across, borne in domed clusters; sepals triangular. Frt 3 cm long, round or more often pear-shaped, greenish to brown, reddish or blotched with red when ripe, hard and very astringent to taste, but sweet when bletted.

Names: Fr.: Cormier, Sorbier domestique; It.: Sorbo; Sp.: Serbal; Ger.: Elzbeere; Dtch.: Peerlijsterbesse; Dan.: Røn; Russ.: Ryabina domashnyaya.

Uses: The fruit are only edible when bletted or over-ripe, after which they may be used for jams (rarely), or fermented to make alcoholic drinks.

Origin, distribution and cultivation: True Service Tree is a native of South Europe, North Africa and the Near and Middle East. It is rare in northern Europe, including Britain, where it exists only as an ornamental in a few gardens. In central and southern Europe it is often planted both for fruit and for ornament, and the fruit of wild plants are also gathered by home-brewers. This limited use would hardly warrant its inclusion as a crop plant had it not been much more commonly exploited in the past.

Similar plants: Other species of *Sorbus* with pinnate lvs (Japanese *S. commixta*, Kashmir *S. cashmiriana*, Sargent's *S. sargentiana* etc.) planted as ornamentals are all exotic, except Rowan or Mountain Ash *S. aucuparia*, which is much commoner than True Service Tree, and a native of the whole of Europe, even to high altitudes. It has a paler bark than *S. domestica*, the branches are more ascending, and the buds have dark purple outer scales with long grey hairs, and densely hairy inner scales. The frts are quite different, round, under 1 cm, yellow ripening suddenly to scarlet in mid-summer. They are edible in a variety called *edulis*, and occasionally used for making jams and alcohol.

Wild Service Tree *S. torminalis* bears no resemblance, having large lvs like a maple.

Malus pumila
APPLES
(p. 130)

Description: The Edible or Cultivated Apple's natural bearing is an upright tree with spreading branches, of extremely variable size. Bark dark brownish-grey, irregularly fissured and scaly. Lvs simple, ovate to oval with more or less broadly rounded or narrowed bases, coarsely toothed margins, generally slightly hairy above and densely so below. Fls in clusters, the petals rounded or ovate, abruptly narrowed to a 'stalk' at base, white almost always flushed with various shades of pink, and with styles fused at base. Frt a large round pome, variously green to yellow and red.

Names: Syns: *M. domestica, M. communis, M. sylvestris* ssp. *domestica, Pyrus malus*. Fr.: Pomme; It.: Mele; Sp.: Manzana; Ger.: Apfel; Dtch.: Appel; Dan.: Aeble; Gr.: Milo; Russ.: Yabloko; Yug.: Jabuka.

Uses: Apples may be classified into four main economic groups: ornamental (which does not concern us here), dessert, cooking, and cider apples. Dessert apples, by far the most important category economically, are medium-sized fruits with a high sugar content subtly balanced with acidity and variously aromatic. Cooking apples are usually larger fruits, mainly green, with a higher acid content, requiring the addition of sugar when they are cooked to make compotes, sauces, and fillings for pies. Cider apples, usually small fruits, are classed as sweet, sharp, bitter-sweet or bitter-sharp according to their flavour; these different types are usually blended to determine the type and quality of cider required. In Normandy and Brittany cider is distilled to produce an outstanding spirit, Calvados.

Other products include unfermented apple juice which is canned or bottled for commerce, liqueurs, vinegar from cider, and pectin.

Origin, distribution and cultivation: With more than 23 million tons produced annually throughout the world, the Apple has become one of the most economically important of all fruits.

The Edible Apple is thought to have originated by chance cross-pollination between wild species in western Asia; some of the resulting forms were later carried westward where they further hybridised with other species. Although selection of seedlings must have long been used to improve varieties, controlled cross-pollination, constantly used to create new cvs, only began in the 18th century. Despite the sophistication of modern techniques of crossing and selection, including the use of irradiation to induce rapid mutation, no new forms have been produced that can rival in popularity such classics as 'Golden Delicious', 'Cox's Orange Pippin', 'Granny Smith', or 'Bramley's Seedling', which all resulted from chance hybridisation. The main wild species which contributed to the range of *M. pumila* have been *M. sylvestris* (N., C. and E. Europe), *M. orientalis* (Caucasus) and *M. sieversii* (C. Asia) as the basic stock, enriched by *M. baccata* (N.E. Asia) and *M. prunifolia* (N. China), with later injections of *M. floribunda* and other Japanese and Far Eastern strains.

The natural range of *Malus* species covers all of Europe except Scandinavia and North Russia, eastwards to China and Japan, and in the New World, the East and West Coasts of the United States joined by a narrower band across the continent. The range of Apples in cultivation has been extended both in the northern hemisphere, and to South Africa and the temperate parts of South America and Australia, and apples are also grown in small areas of highlands in the tropics. They require a climate where the temperature changes from winter to spring will break bud dormancy, but they will not tolerate extremely cold winters such as those that prevail in N. Russia or Siberia.

Most cvs are partially self-sterile, pollinated by insects, and require the presence of other flowering trees in the vicinity to fruit. Other species of *Malus* (see Crab Apples, below) may be planted for this purpose in commercial orchards.

Nearly all dessert apple, and most cooking apple, cvs are grown commercially on dwarf rootstock and trained in various ways (such as cordons and espaliers). Cider apples are still mostly grown on trees with a natural bearing, usually in permanent pastures on mixed farms where cattle do the job of clearing the ground vegetation, and may benefit from fallen fruit.

Similar plants: Although expert apple growers may be able to identify different cvs by bearing, leaf and flower size and shape, the great variability of this complex does not allow *M. pumila* to be distinguished with certainty from many other *Malus* species by any single criterion except the large frt. For other species, see Crab Apples, below. Pear: see p. 28.

Malus sylvestris
EUROPEAN CRAB APPLE

Description: Basically as *M. pumila*, but usually spiny and more intricately branched. Mature lvs differ by being hairless or nearly so. Fls white or pink. Frt 2.5–3.5 cm, green to yellow, very sour.

Names: Fr.: Pomme sauvage; It.: Mela selvatica; Sp.: Manzana silvestre; Ger.: Holzapfel; Dtch.: Wild appel; Dan.: Skovaeble; Gr.: Agriomilo; Russ.: Yabloko vishnaya; Yug.: Divlja jabuka.

Uses: European Crab Apple, although sometimes used to make an excellent jelly, is hardly edible in any other form, and scarcely qualifies as a crop plant. Its chief importance is that it is the native European parent, together with Asiatic species, of cultivated apples, and that it is commonly used as rootstock for cultivated cvs.

Origin, distribution and cultivation: *M. sylvestris* occurs in northern and central Europe. It is replaced in S. and S.E. Europe by another form, perhaps a distinct species, which is less spiny, with lvs hairy underneath, and sweeter, coloured frt, thus more similar to *M. pumila.*

Similar plants: The principal differences with *M. pumila* are given above. Difficulty in identification is compounded by the many feral forms of *M. pumila* which have reverted to a wild habit with small sour frt.

Other *Malus* species, of foreign origin, many grown as ornamentals or used as rootstock, are also called 'crab', one of the most distinctive being Siberian Crab *M. baccata*, with long-stalked frt the size and colour of ripe cherries. Another edible species with similar small round frt but coloured yellow, 'Golden Hornet' should properly be included in *M. pumila*, as should some other 'Crabs' such as 'John Downie' and 'Tanscendant'.

Two other wild *Malus* species of S.E. Europe, *M. trilobata* and *M. florentina*, are immediately recognisable by their lobed lvs recalling hawthorns or maples. Their frts are not eaten.

Pyrus communis
PEARS
(p. 130)

Description: In its natural bearing, the mature pear tree is a taller, more columnar or conical tree than apple, standing up to 20 m in height. Bark dark brown or blackish, finely and deeply fissured into very small squares. Shoots sometimes thorny, often slightly hairy. Lvs rounded-ovate to elliptic, 4–10 cm long, typically with fine rounded teeth, but sometimes entire, glossy yellowish to dark green, usually hairless when mature. Fls 2–4 cm across, with conspicuous dark red to purple anthers, borne in domed clusters and opening in mid spring before lvs are fully formed. Frt variable, typically pear-shaped, but may be globose or turnip-shaped, yellow to green, flushed with brown or red, entirely brown or red in some cvs, sweet when ripe, the flesh characteristically gritty due to the presence of stone cells. Frts ripen in September–October in central and southern Europe, later further north. More than 1000 cvs are known.

Names: Fr.: Poirier; It.: Pero; Sp.: Perál; Ger.: Birne; Dtch.: Peer; Dan.: Paere; Gr.: Ahlati; Russ.: Grisha; Yug.: Kruška.

Uses: The many cultivars of Pear can be grouped into categories according to their uses. The most valuable are the best dessert pears, which should be eaten fresh at optimum ripeness. Others may be canned. Stewing pears are ones which are not acid, but hard and lacking in flavour; many of these are also canned after cooking, and they make good compotes and jams. Perry, a fermented juice comparable to cider, but less common because it does not keep well and is less digestible, is made from certain Perry cultivars, mostly in the same areas as cider (S.W. England, Normandy, Brittany) but also in eastern France, Belgium, Germany, etc. A better use is made of pear juice, especially in France, by distillation, to produce many excellent 'poire' brandies.

Origin, distribution and cultivation: *P. communis* is not a true natural sp., but the result of ancient chance and selected hybridisations between wild spp., which probably include *P. pyraster, P. salvifolia, P. nivalis, P. syriaca* and *P. cordata.* The primary centre of origin is central Asia. From here, one group of spp. and aggregates developed in China, and another, the ancestors of European pears, developed from a secondary centre in Asia Minor. Homer records their cultivation in Greece about 1000 BC, and they have been grown in European gardens ever since. Serious scientific selection of varieties began in the early 17th century, particularly in France, Belgium and western Germany, where, thanks to an ideal climate, the best pears have been produced. Further improvements in America in the 19th century concentrated on hardiness and resistance to disease, contributing to the development of many of the present major economic cultivars. Pears are cultivated in most of central Europe, from England eastwards to Russia, but do not do well in northern regions, nor in the Mediterranean, for they require fairly moist conditions as well as warmer summers than most apples. Like the latter, the trees in commercial orchards are trained in a number of different ways.

Similar plants: Apples *Malus* spp.

In older trees the bark of apples is typically fissured more irregularly, and is more flaking; in pears the bark is fissured in smaller, more regular squares which are adherent. The lvs offer no absolute distinguishing characters; but fls differ notably in the structure of the styles, free in pears, fused at base in apples, and usually in the colour of anthers, red to purple in pears, yellow in apples.

Many other wild pears, all with smaller, sometimes tiny frts, which are harder and more acid, occur in Europe. It may be difficult to distinguish feral Common Pear and Wild Pear *P. pyraster*, which typically is a spinier tree with small hard frts. *P. cordata* is another wild sp. of western Europe which is smaller and spinier, often no more than a bushy shrub. Its tiny frts are recognisable because the calyx is deciduous (retained in Common and Wild Pear). Southern European spp., which are sometimes grown for ornament further north, are distinguished by their much narrower lvs, more than 1.5 times as long as broad. These include Almond-leaved Pear *P. amygdaliformis* which lives in dry parts of the Mediterranean, and has hairless mature leaves; *P. nivalis* from southern and central Europe and *P. eleagrifolia*, from the Balkans, have similar narrow lvs but which are more or less hairy, as are the styles; *P. salvifolia* has even narrower, willow-like lvs almost hairless above and woolly-grey beneath, and the styles are more or less hairless. This sp. occurs naturally throughout continental Europe northwards to Belgium and Germany, and is sometimes cultivated for its frts in Greece and Yugoslavia.

KEY TO THE COMMERCIAL *PRUNUS* SPP.

1	Lvs at least twice as long as broad=**2**	**(6)**
2	Lvs usually broadest before middle, more finely toothed; frt smaller, leathery, ovoid, flattened, yellowish-green; stone smooth=**Almond**	**(3)**
3	Lvs usually broadest at or beyond middle, less finely toothed; frt larger, very fleshy, round; stone prickly=**4**	**(2)**
4	Frt skin velvety=**Peach**	**(5)**
5	Frt skin smooth, shiny=**Nectarine**	**(4)**
6	Lvs broadly ovate or rounded=**7**	**(1)**
7	Lvs very broad, thin, shiny, with finer veins; frt velvety, as Peach=**Apricot**	**(8)**
8	Lvs broad or narrower, thicker, with more prominent veins; frt smooth-skinned (fls solitary or fewer than 10 in small clusters or umbels)=**9**	**(7)**
9	Frt stalk long, at least twice as long as ripe frt=**10**	**(12)**
10	Trees; young lvs hanging limply; scales at base of inflorescence mostly papery, brown; petals broader towards apices=**Wild Cherry (Gean) and Cultivated Cherries**	**(10)**
11	Usually a bush, rarely a real tree; young lvs spreading; scales at base of inflorescence mostly leaf-like, green; petals rounded=**Morello Cherry**	**(10)**
12	Frt stalk short, at most a little longer than ripe frt=**13**	**(9)**
13	Lvs small, 2–4 cm; frt small 1.5–2 cm, round, blue; plant a very thorny intricately-branched shrub=**Sloe**	**(14)**
14	Lvs larger, more than 4 cm; frt larger, at least 2 cm; plant a tree or shrub, not spiny or much less spiny=**15**	**(13)**
15	Young twigs glossy, hairless; frt small, 2–3 cm, cherry-like, yellow to red=**Cherry Plum**	**(16)**
16	Young twigs dull, sometimes hairy; frts larger, or if less than 3.5 cm, dark blue (Bullace)=**Bullace, Damsons, Gages, Plums**	**(15)**

Prunus armeniaca

APRICOT

(p. 132)

Description: A tree, sturdier than most *Prunus*, up to 10 m, with dense upwardly spreading branches. Young twigs and young lvs reddish. Lvs broadly ovate to almost round, thin, smooth, on long stalks. Fls borne on year-old shoots after 3 years, white or very pale pink. Frt smaller than peach, velvety, orange-yellow when ripe, with drier flesh which detaches easily from stone.

Names: Fr.: Abricot; It.: Albicocca; Sp.: Albaricoque; Ger.: Aprikose; Dtch.: Abrikoos; Dan.: Abrikos; Gr.: Verikoko; Russ.: Abrikos; Yug.: Marelica, Kajsija.

Uses: The fruits are eaten fresh, but most of the commercial crop is canned, in which form it loses relatively less of its quality than, for instance, peach. In either form apricots make an excellent filling for tarts and pies. In central Asia, where Apricots have been cultivated since time immemorial, the greatest part of the crop is dried in the manner of Raisins and Prunes, after which they can be kept indefinitely, to provide a valuable food during the harsh continental winter. Part of the produce of southern Europe is marketed in this form. It may later be used in the same way as fresh fruit, after it has been softened in water, for tarts, syrup, etc. The strong aromatic quality of apricot has led to it being widely used for flavouring soufflés, ice-cream, confectioneries, dessert creams or yoghurt and processed baby food. The latter is appropriate, for Apricot has a higher nutritional value than most fruits, being especially rich in Vitamin A, proteins and carbohydrates.

Origin, distribution and cultivation: Apricot is believed to have originated in Chinese Turkestan, whence it reached Italy via the silk road in Roman times; it is recorded in Britain as early as the 13th century. Commercial production requires a warm temperate climate with a hot summer, but it will stand hard winter frosts. Hungary, Spain, France and Italy lead the European producers, surpassed only by the USA. It is grown in orchards in these countries, and on a small scale in gardens further north. Most varieties are self-fertile, and propagation is by budding onto apricot and peach seedling stocks.

Similar plants: The very broad, thin smooth lvs should be sufficient to distinguish Apricot trees from other cultivated *Prunus*. See key opposite.

Prunus persica

PEACH and NECTARINE

(pp. 132, 221)

Description: A small tree to 6–7 m. Lvs narrow, lanceolate, thinner than those of Almond, usually broadest at or beyond middle, finely toothed, almost hairless. Fls solitary, small and rose-pink, or larger, to 3.5 cm and paler pink, rarely white. Frt globose, 5–12 cm, with a velvety skin pale to golden yellow flushed with deep red on exposed side, sometimes entirely red; the flesh may be greenish white or golden yellow.

Nectarine (var. *nectarina*) is usually a richer colour and has skin smooth like that of a plum; despite its quite different appearance, it is merely a variety of peach and may even occur as a bud sport on peach trees.

Names: Fr.: Pêche, Nectarine; It.: Pesca, Pesca noce; Sp.: Melocoton, Nectarina; Ger.: Pfirisch, Nektarine; Dtch.: Perzik; Nectorine; Dan.: Fersken; Gr.: Rothákino; Russ.: Persik, Gladki persik; Yug.: Breskva.

Uses: Peaches are the most delicious of all *Prunus*, and are consequently valued as a dessert fruit. For economic purposes they may be grouped into two main types: 'free-stones' which are mostly sold fresh, and 'clingstones' used mainly for canning. Peaches do not store for more than a few weeks, so a large proportion of the world's crop is processed. Fresh or canned Peaches are consumed on their own, in composite desserts, or in tarts. They are used to a much lesser extent for flavouring ice-creams and confectioneries.

Origin, distribution and cultivation: The Peach's specific name is a misnomer, for although it may have reached Europe via Persia, it originated in China, where it has been in cultivation for at least 2500 years. It is recorded from Greece in the 4th century BC, and was grown by the Romans from the 1st century AD. Today it is cultivated in the warm-temperate areas of all continents; in Europe it is extensively grown in orchards in the Mediterranean, north to the Loire, S. Germany, etc., and in gardens in sheltered situations further north.

Peach varieties are normally self-pollinating. Most rootstocks are grown from seed; some of those used belong to other *Prunus* spp., eg. *P. tomentosus* for dwarfing, or a Peach x Almond hybrid adapted to poor limestone soils in France.

The white-fleshed, usually smaller varieties are hardier, and are often considered superior in flavour, but this view may in part reflect northern European prejudice. The delicate frts of all kinds destined to be sold fresh must be hand picked and packed *in situ*.

Similar plants: Almond (p. 32).

Many varieties of *P. persica*, the so-called flowering peaches, are grown purely for ornament.

Prunus communis ALMOND

(p. 132)

Description: A small tree, 4–6 m, up to 12 m in cultivation, with a flattened globose crown. Bark nearly black, deeply fissured into small squares; twigs and branches not spiny. Lvs ovate-lanceolate, 7–12 cm, finely toothed, often folded at base with a V-shaped midrib, and much subject to the fungal disease 'peach-leaf curl' in which they become contorted and pink. Fls open before lvs in February–March, large, 3–5 cm in diameter, singly or in 2s or 3s. Frt resembles a small ovoid flattened peach, yellowish-green turning dark brown with age, covered in short dense felted hairs, often persistent on tree after lvs.

There are two main cultivated varieties: **Bitter Almond** (var. *amara*) and **Sweet Almond** (var. *dulcis*), the latter divided into many cvs which differ in size, habit, suitability to different climates, and quality of nut.

Names: Synonyms: *P. dulcis, P. amygdalus* Fr.: Amande; It.: Mandorlo; Sp.: Almendro; Ger.: Mandel; Dtch.: Amandel; Dan.: Mandel; Gr.: Amygdaliá; Russ.: Mindalaya; Yug.: Mandula.

Uses: var. *amara* is cultivated for oil of bitter almonds, used for flavouring sweet dishes, biscuits, some meat dishes and ratafias. Two substances, benzaldehyde and hydrocyanic acid are formed when the nut is mixed with water and produce the characteristic bitter taste. The latter is a violent poison, but volatile, and is eliminated by heating. Oil of bitter almonds is also produced by the kernels and the leaves of related species such as plums, peaches, cherries and cherry laurel, and is used in many parts of the world for the same purpose. 'Noyau', French for the stone of these fruits, is a liqueur made from almond and other stones of these plants.

Although Almonds are cultivated in a limited geographic range, the sweet cultivars have the largest share of world trade of any of the nuts. Almond is a flavouring of the most original and refined sort; it is to be regretted that where it was once widely used in European cooking, few dishes make use of it today, romesco sauce in Spain being one of the exceptions. In Europe Almonds are eaten as dessert nuts, but their principal use, flaked, powdered or in a paste, is made by bakers and in confections such as nougat and 'calissons' (lozenge-shaped sweets made of ground almonds). In the Near and Middle East, however, their value as a flavouring with meat is still recognised, and they are a main ingredient in the chicken and rice dishes of the Levant to the mild creamy curries of N.W. India. The whole immature fruits, inedible when they are ripe, are eaten as a local delicacy, with apéritifs in the Mediterranean.

The kernels are marketed whole, or flaked, or ground. The latter is best avoided, for it is often adulterated with inferior nut flower or with Bitter Almond.

Origin, distribution and cultivation: Almond is a native of N. Africa and western Asia, where it has been in cultivation for many centuries. It has been introduced as a commercial crop to other countries with a 'Mediterranean' climate such as South Africa, California and Australia. It is grown as an ornamental in central and northern

Europe, and as a commercial crop in most of the Mediterranean countries, led by Spain and Italy. The cost of labour to harvest the fruit has reduced the extent of cultivation in the more prosperous traditional areas of production such as Provence. Trees are not grafted on dwarf rootstock like other crop *Prunus*, nor are the trees usually protected in fenced-in orchards. Plantations will be seen in open grazed pastures or hillsides on poor land. Young unripe frts for eating whole are picked in early summer. The ripe frts are harvested for their kernels in late autumn.

Similar plants: The early pink fls and narrow lvs resemble those of Peach, but the fls tend to be larger, and lvs are broadest before the middle and more finely toothed than those of Peach, which are broadest at or beyond the middle.

The 'almonds' called for in S.E. Asian recipes are the nuts or kernels of other, quite unrelated, tropical plants such as Badam *Terminalia catalpa*, for which true Almonds may be substituted with advantage.

Prunus avium
GEAN and SWEET CHERRIES
(p. 132)

Description: Wild Cherry, Gean, or Mazzard is a very large *Prunus* tree standing up to 25 m. The bark is dark pinkish grey in young trees, darker, purplish later, rather shiny with many short transverse fissures; crown typically conical in young trees becoming rounder later. Lvs oblong-ovate to obovate, ca. 10 cm long, with sharp forward-pointing teeth on margins, on grooved yellow/red stalks; young lvs drooping. Fls white, 2.5–3.5 cm across, in clusters of 2–5, opening just before lvs in spring; sepals reflexed. Frt globose to ovoid, 2.5–3.5 cm across, glossy yellow ripening to bright red, later turning blackish-red; the flesh acid but not sour.

Cultivated or **Sweet Cherries** which belong to the same sp. vary in tree size; this is usually smaller, and plants may be grafted on other rootstocks and trained by pruning.

Cvs were formerly grouped into two categories according to type of flesh: Bigarreau, with firm crisp flesh, or Gean (Fr. *Guignes*) with soft juicy flesh, but this distinction takes no account of the numerous intermediary forms. Cvs are also classed according to fruiting times (early, mid-season or late) and as being either 'white' (yellow flushed with red, or bright red) or 'black' (dark red to blackish). Most Sweet Cherry cvs are larger than Geans, and vary in flavour according to cv.

Names: Fr.: Cerisier; It.: Ciliego; Sp.: Cerezo; Ger.: Kirsche; Dtch.: Kers; Dan.: Kirsebaer; Gr.: Kerasiá; Russ.: Cherioshnia; Yug.: Trešnja.

Uses: Wild Cherry frts are used for cooking, making jams, etc. Sweet Cherries are principally a dessert frt, but are also used for jams and in the food industry for flavouring various confectioneries. Many Cherries, especially the more acid Geans and Morello (below) are used to make liqueurs and spirits, the best known of which are the *Kirschs* of Alsace, Germany and Switzerland.

Origin, distribution and cultivation: Wild Cherry is a native of Europe, North Africa and Western Asia. Some forms of it are cultivated as well as the improved Sweet Cherries, and some of the latter were developed very early, indeed remain practically unchanged since classical times while others were developed more recently, particularly since the 17th century. Much recent improvement has centred on resistance to diseases, to which *P. avium* is particularly susceptible. Sweet Cherries are also fastidious about climate and situation, and good producing areas are localised. France, Germany and parts of south-central Europe enjoy the most favourable conditions for commercial cultivation.

Similar plants: See Morello Cherry, below, and key p. 34.

Other cherry spp. occur in Europe. They may be roughly divided into two groups: the first, which includes *P. avium* and *P. cerasus*, have fls and frts solitary or in clusters or umbels of fewer than 10, while the second comprises spp. in which the clusters are domed or spike-like, and of many (10–100) fls.

In addition to *P. avium* and *P. cerasus*, the first group includes Ground Cherry *P. fruticosa*, easily recognised because it is a dwarf spreading shrub under 1 m. The small (under 1 cm) dark frts are of little value, but the plant has long been cultivated in Europe, mainly for ornament. Most conspicuous of all the cherries are the many ornamental Chinese and Japanese *Prunus*, mostly forms belonging to *P. speciosa* and *P. serrulata* which differ from those of the *cerasus-avium* group in that the sepals are upright or spreading, not reflexed.

The second group includes such plants as Cherry Laurel *P. laurocerasus* and Portugal Laurel *P. lusitanicus*, with shiny laurel-like evergreen lvs and inedible frt, and also Bird Cherry *P. padus*, a widespread European sp. and Black Cherry *P. serotina*, an American sp. planted for timber in central Europe.

St. Lucie's Cherry *P. mahaleb* falls between the two groups because although the fls are arranged in domed clusters they are fewer, only 3–12 in number. The small black frts are of no use, but the wood of this sp., which is aromatic, is that used for making cherrywood pipe bowls, and the plant is sometimes used as rootstock for grafting *P. avium* cvs.

Prunus cerasus
MORELLO CHERRY

(p. 132)

Description: Similar to Gean and Sweet Cherry, but rarely a real tree, rather a bushy shrub, with dark green, glossier lvs, the young lvs spreading, not drooping. The scales at base of inflorescence are mostly lf-like, less papery or not at all. Petals more rounded, less obovate. Frt usually bright red, similar to Gean, acid and sour.

Names: Fr.: Griotte; It.: Marasco; Sp.: Guindo; Ger.: Saure Kirsche, Morelle; Dtch.: Zure kers, Morel; Dan.: Surkirsebaer, Morel; Russ.: Cherioshnia vishnaya; Yug.: Divlja tresnja; Gr.: Kerasiá morello.

Uses: The sourness gives Morello Cherries a more suitable flavour for making jams and jellies, and for flavouring liqueurs and spirits than Geans or Sweet Cherries. *C. cerasus* is much more resistant to diseases and therefore widely used as rootstock for grafting varieties of Sweet Cherry.

Origin, distribution and cultivation: *C. cerasus* is a native of S.E. Europe and S.W. Asia which moved westwards in cultivation and has become established in most of Europe over the last 2000 years.

Similar plants: See *P. avium*, above, and key p. 30. Hybrids of these two spp., some of which are cultivated, defy naming. See also plants similar to *P. avium*.

Prunus cerasifera
MYROBALAN or CHERRY-PLUM, and MIRABELLE

(p. 134)

Description: Sometimes named Cherry-Plum on account of the small cherry-like frts, but these, unlike cherries, are short-stalked and the plant is in every way typical of plums. It is a shrub or tree up to 10 m, often spiny. Lvs ovate, only hairy on stalks and lower midribs. Fls solitary white, like Sloe but larger, 2.5 cm across, appearing before other plums, with or before lvs. Frt globose, red, sometimes yellow or bronze, 2–3 cm in diameter.

Mirabelle Plum, often confused with gages, is a hybrid between this sp. and *P. domestica*, and often referred to as *P.* x *syriaca*. The frts are larger and sweeter than those of Myrobalan.

Names: Fr.: Prunier Myrobalan; It.: Mirabolano; Sp.: Ciruela mirabolano; Ger.: Kirschpflaume; Dtch.: Kerspruim; Dan.: Kirsebaerblomme; Gr.: Kerasiá-Damaskiniá; Russ.: Mirabolan.

Uses: Myrobalan is planted primarily as a hedge or windbreak, and the frts which are used locally for cooking or making jams do not normally enter commerce. The tree has greater economic importance as a rootstock for other plum spp.

Mirabelle is less hardy than gages and similar forms of *P. domestica* and are rarely seen in Britain, but in France and in central and southern Europe it is preferred to gages for the sharper flavour, which makes one of the finest plum jams, reminiscent of apricot.

Origin: distribution and cultivation: *P. cerasifera* originated in western Asia and in eastern Europe. It has long been in cultivation, and occurs as an old escape in the whole of Europe, except northern Scandinavia, in hedges and old wasteland.

Similar plants: The short fl- and frt-stalks distinguish this sp. from cherries, and the glossy young twigs from other plums, except Alpine Plum *P. brigantina*, which is localised in the S.W. Alps. This sp. has sour yellow frts ca. 2.5 cm in diameter and irregularly cut lvs with downy veins on the underside. *P. cocomilla* is a similar sp. with hairless lvs, and is confined to S.E. Europe.

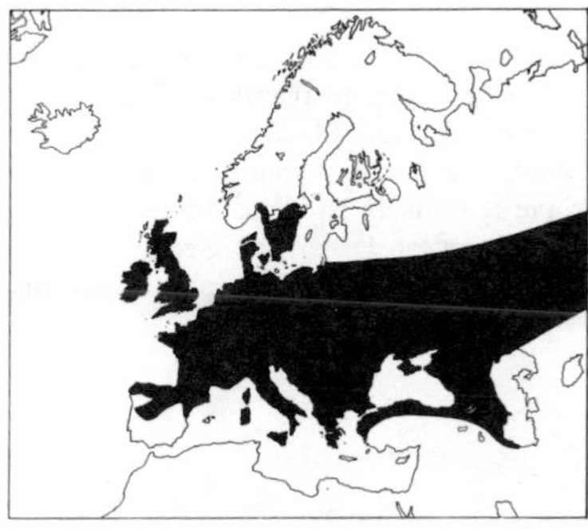

Natural distribution of Sloe

Prunus spinosa
BLACKTHORN or SLOE
(p. 134)

Description: An intricately branched, very thorny shrub forming thickets up to 4 m. Young twigs downy with numerous side shoots that become long straight thorns. Lvs elliptical-lanceolate, dull, toothed. White fls 1–1.5 cm in diameter, appear in spring before lvs. Frt 1–2 cm in diameter, globose, blue-black with a strong bloom, very astringent.

Names: Fr.: Prunelle; It.: Prugnolo; Sp.: Endrino; Ger.: Schlehe, Schwarzdorn; Dtch.: Slee, Sleepruim; Dan.: Slåen; Gr.: Agriokaromiliá; Yug.: Glog.

Uses: Sloes are so sour that they have no value as a fresh or preserved fruit. They are nevertheless used extensively in Britain and other northern European countries for making Sloe wine and Sloe gin.

Origin, distribution and cultivation: Sloe grows wild, in hedges and thickets, all over Europe except the far North. It is not cultivated, but the fruits are harvested in late autumn in many areas both by home-brewers and by industrial distillers.

Similar plants: Bullace, which is larger and less spiny (p. 35).

Prunus domestica agg.
PLUMS, BULLACES, DAMSONS, GAGES
(pp. 134, 221)

Description: This is a very complex aggregate which probably began with hybridisation between Sloe and Myrobalan. The general characters of the plant are those of *P. cerasifera*, but size, habit, lf shape, etc., are very variable. The frts have an external longitudinal groove along one side (shallow and incomplete in cherries), and usually a bloom, particularly noticeable on the blue-skinned varieties.

The great number of varieties fall into 3 main groups, treated here as subspecies, but given full (albeit ill-defined) specific rank by others:

1. ssp. *domestica*:

Plums The plants are trees up to 10–12 m, without spines, have nearly hairless young twigs. Fls are greenish-white, in pairs, ca. 2 cm across. Frts are usually oval, rarely globose, mostly blue-black, also purple or red, less often greenish or yellow (such as 'Pershore', 'Coe's Golden Drop' and 'Jefferson', illustrated (p. 135)). The large cvs dried for prunes such as the *Prune d'Agen* and 'Fellemberg' also belong to this sspp.

2. ssp. *insititia*:

Bullace, Damsons, St. Julien These are smaller shrubs or trees, up to 6 m, often spiny, with young twigs hairy. Fls white, often larger (ca. 2.5 cm across). Frts generally smaller, 2–5 cm, more often globose. Damsons are often attributed to a distinct sp. or ssp., *P. damascena*, thought to have originated in Syria. The differences with *P.*

insititia are usually listed thus: Bullace: frts blue-black, round, sweet; Damsons: frts green, oval, astringent. Some forms, however, such as Shepherd's Bullace, are yellowish-green, while many 'Damsons' such as 'Farleigh', 'Prune Damsons', etc., are blue-black and sometimes oval.

3. ssp. *italica*:

Gages, Reine-Claude This is a hybrid of the two other ssp., *domestica* and *insititia*. Plants have the characteristics of *insititia*, but the frts are distinctive, more or less globose, greenish or yellow, sweet, with a characteristic flavour.

Names: Fr.: Prunier; It.: Susino, Prugno; Sp.: Ciruelo; Ger.: Pflaume; Dtch.: Pruim; Dan.: Blomme; Gr.: Thamáskino; Russ.: Sliva; Yug.: Šljiva.

Uses: As a general rule, sweet varieties are grown as dessert frts or to be used in certain sweet dishes, and some, always large oval black-skinned varieties, for drying as prunes; the more acid or astringent forms are used for cooking, making jams, etc. Many excellent liqueurs and spirits are made from plums all over Europe, the best known being the quetsche brandies of Alsace, Germany and Switzerland, and the *slivovitchs* and *slivovas* of the Balkans.

Origin, distribution and cultivation: Plums of various kinds have been gathered in the wild since prehistoric times. The first hybridisation of Sloe and Cherry-Plum probably occurred in the Caucasus at a remote date. Many of the derived forms have been cultivated in Europe at least since classical times, and many new varieties have been created, especially in the 19th century. Valuable cultivars are grown on a large commercial scale in orchards in nearly the whole of Europe. Prunes are produced in the hotter areas, the best in the South of France. They may be dried on the trees, or artificially. Other, less valuable forms of the species are gathered from trees planted mainly for ornament, or from hedgerows.

Similar plants: Although within the *P. domestica* aggregate plants exhibit a great range of variation, which makes the identification of cultivars difficult, the group as a whole is unlikely to be confused with any other European *Prunus* spp. See Sloe (p. 35) and Cherry-Plum (p. 34); also Mirabelle, listed under the latter.

LEGUMINOSAE

Pea Family

One of the largest families of plants, with some 18,000 species of trees, shrubs, climbers and herbs divided by many authors into three distinct families, Caesalpiniaceae, Mimosaceae and Papilionaceae. The first two are composed largely of tropical trees and shrubs, including a few economic species, such as Cassia, Tamarind and Acacias, and many ornamentals like the Flamboyant, *Bauhinia* spp., *Amherstia*, and mimosas (regarded by most botanists as congeneric with *Acacia*). The last family, the Papilionaceae, besides the plants described below, includes other genera and species of pulses not grown in Europe. These include Yam Bean *Pachyrrhizus erosus*, grown in America for its edible tubers, Sunn Hemp

Crotalaria juncea, the Indian fibre crop used for making rope and sacking and *Derris*, the source of rotenone, used as an insecticide and for poisoning fish.

The family is of outstanding agricultural importance, not only for the principal product, the pulses, which have been staple human and animal foods, but because of their specialised form of nutrition which enables its members to fix nitrogen, vital to nearly all other plants, by means of their root nodules. For this reason they are particularly valuable for crop rotation, indeed essential where synthetic nitrate fertilisers are not used, and even crops usually grown for their edible produce are sometimes sown only to be ploughed in as green manure.

The general characteristics of the family include usually compound lvs, often trifoliate, rarely simple, usually with stipules. Many are climbers with some lvs or parts of lvs modified as tendrils. Fls have petals and sepals usually in 5s, often butterfly-like. Frts are single-celled, many-seeded pods of 2 valves.

KEY TO THE ECONOMIC LEGUMINOUS PLANTS

1	Plant is a tree=**Carob**	(2)
2	Plant is a herb (some may be woody at base)=**3**	(1)
3	Lvs palmate, with 6 or more leaflets=**Lupins**	(4)
4	Lvs trifoliate or pinnate=**5**	(3)
5	Lvs trifoliate (N.B. Asparagus Pea and Bird's Foot Trefoil are apparently trifoliate, but have 2 large lvs resembling stipules at base of lf-stalk in addition to narrow true stipules.)=**6**	(36)
6	Leaflets large, at least 4 cm wide=**7**	(13)
7	Lvs and stems hairy; stems not twining=**Soy Bean**	(8)
8	Lvs and stems glabrous; stems twining=**9**	(7)
9	Fls usually scarlet, sometimes white, or red and white, or pink; mature pods very large, 20 to 60 cm, with diagonal striation on surface=**Scarlet Runner Bean**	(10)
10	Fls usually white, pink or mauve; mature pods smaller, not striate=**11**	(9)
11	Fls white; pods relatively shorter and broader, green ripening to pale brown, not more than 5 times as long as broad; beans larger, white=**Lima Bean**	(12)
12	Fls variable; pods relatively longer, often very long; beans smaller; pods and beans variously coloured=**Common Bean**	(11)

KEY TO THE ECONOMIC LEGUMINOUS PLANTS		
13	Leaflets small, under 4 cm wide=**14**	(6)
14	Fls in 1s or 2s, at bases of upper lvs, yellowish-white=**Fenugreek**	(15)
15	Fls many, in loose racemes, or heads=**16**	(14)
16	Fls in heads (Clovers)=**17**	(29)
17	Fls yellow (see also Black Medick, which has clover-like heads)=**Yellow Sucking Clover**	(18)
18	Fls white, pink, red or purple=**19**	(17)
19	Plant a creeping perennial with rooting runners=**20**	(22)
20	Fls pink, strawberry-like, the calices bladder-like and hairy=**Strawberry Clover**	(21)
21	Fls white or pink, the fls normal, like other clovers, calices not bladder-like=**White Clover**	(20)
22	Plant may be prostrate, but not creeping, without rooting runners=**23**	(19)
23	Fls few, 6 or less, white, in a loose head; stems prostrate; stems and lvs hairy=**Subterranean Clover**	(24)
24	Fls many, in dense heads=**25**	(23)
25	Fl heads cylindrical, 8–10 mm long, white to pinkish, at ends of stems and some at least in lf axils=**Alsike Clover**	(26)
26	Fls red, rarely pinkish-white, at ends of stems only=**27**	(25)
27	Fls in elongate heads; leaflets very broad, not narrowed to apices, usually without dark mark; calyx with long silky adpressed brown hairs=**Crimson Clover**	(28)
28	Fls in ovoid heads; leaflets round or narrowed to apices, usually with a pale crescent-shaped mark; calyx with shorter hairs=**Red Clover**	(27)
29	Fls in looser elongate racemes (Black Medick with small, more compact heads)=**30**	(16)
30	Pods spirally coiled; fls yellow or purple=**31**	(35)

KEY TO THE ECONOMIC LEGUMINOUS PLANTS		
31	Low sprawling plants, less than 20 cm tall; fl heads less than 1 cm long, yellow; leaflets broader, clover-like = **Black Medick**	(32)
32	Erect plants, 30–40 cm tall; fl heads larger, 2–4 cm long; leaflets more elongate = **33**	(31)
33	Fls mauve to purple; fl-stalks shorter than calyx; pod spirals 2 or 3 turns = **Lucerne**	(34)
34	Fls yellow; fl-stalks longer than calyx; pod sickle-shaped, less than 1 complete turn = **Sickle Medick** (Plants with intermediary characters and fls +− variegated purple and yellow are hybrids of these two)	(33)
35	Pods straight; fls white = **White Melilot**	(30)
36	Lvs pinnate = **37**	(5)
37	Lvs with a terminal leaflet = **38**	(50)
38	Leaflets 5 in number, the lower pair stipule-like (ie. lf trifoliate in appearance: *Lotus*) = **39**	(41)
39	Fls dark red; pods large, 5–8 cm long, with 4 prominent ribs = **Asparagus Pea**	(40)
40	Fls orange or yellow; pods smaller, 2.5–5 cm long, slender, spreading stiffly like the toes of a bird from its leg = **Bird's Foot Trefoil**	(39)
41	Leaflets more than 5 in number = **42**	(38)
42	Terminal leaflet larger than others; fls yellow, in dense heads = **Kidney Vetch**	(43)
43	All leaflets similar = **44**	(42)
44	Leaflets with saw-toothed borders; fls white, usually solitary, in axils; pods thin-walled, dehiscent, containing 1–2 large seeds = **Chick Pea**	(45)
45	Leaflets not toothed; fls pink or blue to purple; pods otherwise = **46**	(44)
46	Fls pale blue to purple; pods with 3–4 seeds = **Liquorice**	(47)
47	Fls pink; pods otherwise = **48**	(46)

KEY TO THE ECONOMIC LEGUMINOUS PLANTS

48	Stipules large, membranous, reddish; pods 1-seeded, round, the surface with irregular reticulate ridges=**Sainfoin**	**(49)**
49	Stipules minute, green; pods elongate, with ca. 6 seeds=**Serradella**	**(48)**
50	Lvs without a terminal leaflet, the latter represented by a tendril, or bristle, or absent=**51**	**(37)**
51	Frts ripening underground; lf composed of 2 pairs of leaflets; no tendrils=**Peanut**	**(52)**
52	Frts ripening above ground=**53**	**(51)**
53	Wings of corolla free or almost so from keel (*Lathirus* spp.)=**Vetchlings, Grass Pea, Sweet Peas,** etc.	**(54)**
54	Wings of corolla adhering to keel for at least half of their length=**55**	**(53)**
55	Stipules leaf-like, larger than leaflets; tendrils present=**56**	**(58)**
56	Fls usually white, sometimes red-purple; stipules green; seeds green=**Pea**	**(57)**
57	Fls bicolorous, purple and red; stipules coloured purple at base; seeds brownish or mottled=**Field Pea**	**(56)**
58	Stipules smaller than leaflets=**59**	**(55)**
59	Plant large, erect, with large broad leaflets usually in 2 pairs; tendrils absent. Fls white, sometimes mauve, with conspicuous black blotch on wing petals=**Broad Bean, Field Bean**	**(60)**
60	Plant smaller, erect or scrambling, with numerous (ca. 4–8 pairs) of narrow leaflets, and terminal tendrils=**61**	**(59)**
61	Plant erect; fls white, pale blue or pink; calyx lobes long and narrow; stipules linear; pod rounded, with 1–2 seeds=**Lentil**	**(62)**
62	Plant trailing or scrambling; fls blue to dark purple; calyx lobes short and broad; stipules half arrow-shaped, toothed; pods elongate, with 4–12 seeds=**Common and other Vetches**	**(61)**

Lupinus angustifolius
BLUE or ANNUAL LUPIN
(p. 142)

Description: A herb, always annual, ca. 60 cm but up to 1 m tall, branching, with a partly woody stem. Lvs palmate, small, with usually 7 to 11 narrow blunt leaflets which are hairless above, with flattened hairs below; stipules narrow. Fls small, pale blue (occasionally white), in short racemes. Pods ripen to pale brown, with flattened hairs, ca. 5 cm long, containing 4–6 ovoid brown seeds with darker markings, ca. 9 mm in diameter.

Names: Fr.: Lupin bleu; It.: Lupino azzuro; Sp.: Altramuz azul; Ger.: Blaue Lupine; Dtch.: Blauwe Lupine; Dan.: Smallbladet Lupin; Russ.: Lupin uzkolistni; Yug.: Ozkolistna lupina.

Uses: Blue Lupin is used as a fodder and as a green manure. Like most other lupins, it is poisonous, so 'sweet' varieties with a low alkaline content are preferred for fodder.

Origin, distribution and cultivation: Blue Lupin is a circum-Mediterranean native, widely cultivated on a field scale throughout Europe. It may be sown alone or in combination with other plants such as oats, rape, or mixed herbage, for forage.

Similar plants: Bitter Blue Lupin *L. micranthus* which is also cultivated, is a shorter plant covered in erect brown hairs. Garden Lupin *L. polyphyllus* is a larger plant with 10–17 leaflets and longer racemes of blue, but also white, pink or yellow fls. It is cultivated for ornament, and is often seen wild as a garden escape. Wild Lupin *L. nootkatensis* is an American plant also common as an escape in Britain and elsewhere; leaflets are fewer, from 6 to 8, and the fl is generally darker, blue to purple. Pearl Lupin (see below).

Lupinus mutabilis
PEARL LUPIN

Description: Similar to Blue Lupin. The fls are blue or white, turning purple and then brown with age.

Uses: As a green manure, but also as a pulse and oil seed crop, the seeds being much richer in proteins and oil than those of other species.

Origin, distribution and cultivation: Pearl Lupin was introduced from South America. It is spreading erratically in cultivation as 'sweet' varieties are experimented with.

Similar plants: Blue Lupin.

Lupinus luteus
YELLOW LUPIN
(p. 142)

Description: Yellow Lupin grows to 1 m tall, is hairy, but less branched than Blue Lupin, with 7 to 9 leaflets, and with larger, yellow fls in whorls on longer spikes. Pods ca. 5 cm long, but seeds smaller, 7.5 mm, white with black marbling.

Names: Fr.: Lupin jaune; It.: Lupino giallo; Sp.: Altramuz amarillo; Ger.: Gelbe Lupine; Dtch.: Gele Lupine; Dan.: Gul Lupin; Russ.: Lupin zelti; Gr.: Kítrino Lóupino; Yug.: Močvirska lupin.

Uses: Green manure, forage and fodder. 'Sweet' varieties have been developed, as in Blue Lupin.

Origin, distribution and cultivation: Yellow Lupin is cultivated in western Europe, in the same way as Blue Lupin. Like other lupins, it thrives on poor acid land, unlike most legumes, and so provides a useful break crop in certain areas.

Similar plants: Yellow-flowered Garden Lupin (see above). In Britain Tree Lupin *L. arboreus* is found as an escape from gardens. It is much taller (up to 3 m) plant, also with yellow fls, originally from California.

Lupinus albus
WHITE LUPIN

Description: A rather larger plant than Yellow or Blue Lupin, up to 1.5 m, robust, little-branched and with broader lanceolate leaflets, usually 7–9 in number, which have a marginal fringe of long hairs. Fls white, in long racemes. Pods very large, up to 13 cms; seeds large, up to 1.5 cm, flattened, off-white.

Names: Fr.: Lupin blanc; It.: Lupino bianco; Sp.: Altramuz blanco; Ger.: Weisse Lupine; Dtch.: Witte Lupin; Dan.: Hvid Lupin; Gr.: Leukó Loúpino; Russ.: Lupin beli; Yug.: Beli volcji bob, Beli lupin.

Uses: Green manure and a pulse for fodder. The seeds must be cooked to eliminate poisonous alkaloids, after which they provide a flour comparable to bean flour. This flour, or the boiled 'beans', were formerly used as human food in the Mediterranean. Roasted lupin seeds, belonging to this and to other spp. are still occasionally served as a snack in Italy and Greece.

Origin, distribution and cultivation: White Lupin is much more extensively cultivated than Yellow Lupin, particularly in southern and eastern Europe and the Soviet Union.

Similar plants: The combination of size, large pods and seeds, and the fl colour makes this the most easily identified lupin grown on a crop scale.

Ceratonia siliqua
CAROB BEAN
(p. 144)

Description: A densely branching evergreen bush or tree to 10 m. Trunk stout, bark dark greyish-brown, not notably fissured. Lvs compound, with 2–5 pairs of large leathery leaflets, shiny dark green above, paler below, with entire margins and more or less notched at apices. Fls very small, greenish or reddish (male) on short stalked spikes which grow on old wood among the lvs, either entirely male, or mixed. Pods, numerous, large, 10–20 cm, thick and leathery, pale green ripening and drying to dark brown, containing a variable number of hard round black seeds.

Names: Fr.: Caroube; It.: Carrubo; Sp.: Algarrobo; Ger.: Johannisbrot; Dtch.: Johannesbrood; Dan.: Johannesbrød; Russ.: Rozhvoye derevo; Yug.: Rogač.

Uses: The trees are planted as much for the valuable dense shade they cast in hot dry regions as for the pods which are used extensively to feed cattle, and are eaten by the poor and are relished by children. The dry hard pods soften on chewing, and have a pleasant, if rather bland, sweet taste. They are also used for making a refreshing sweet beverage as well as fermented drinks.

Carob is also known as Locust Bean, and was certainly the 'locusts' eaten by John the Baptist. The hard inedible seeds, because they are remarkably uniform in size, were the original 'carat' weights used by jewellers.

Origin, distribution and cultivation: Carob is a native of all the drier regions of the Mediterranean and the Near East. It is widely cultivated, especially in North Africa, Greece and Cyprus, and to a lesser extent in Spain, S. Italy and Yugoslavia, in small stands on bare hillsides or along roads.

Similar plants: Carob may be distinguished from the majority of leguminous trees in Europe by the peculiar fls, with numerous projecting stamens and no petals. It differs at first sight from the other trees with this type of flower (Acacias and *Gleditsia*) by the broad round leaflets. The pods are much too leathery and hard to be mistaken for any of the larger cultivated beans.

Trifolium pratense
RED CLOVER
(p. 144)

Description: A hairy perennial herb, 10–55 cm tall. Leaflets elliptical to ovate, sometimes almost round, often with a crescent-shaped grey-white mark; stipules narrowly triangular, with reddish or purple veins. Fl heads more or less oval, up to 5 cm long, 12–35 cm across, almost stalkless as is seen from the presence of a pair of lvs just below. Fls pink to purple, the calyx tubes hairy.

The cultivated forms, grouped under the name var. *sativa*, are many, the main types distinguished mainly by flowering dates.

Broad Red is early flowering; leaflets are always longer than broad, somewhat constricted before apices;

Single-Cut Red, so named because it does not yield a second crop, is somewhat denser and less erect, flowering 2 weeks later; it is now largely superseded by new persistent cvs of Broad Red.
Late Flowering Red cvs are much longer-lived plants, first flowering in June (in Britain; earlier further South). The first plants produced in spring are small and bunching with almost circular leaflets, but later the stems become elongated and the lvs produced look more like Broad Red.

Names: Fr.: Trèfle violet; It.: Trifoglio violetto; Sp.: Trebol común; Ger.: Rotklee; Dtch.: Rode klaver; Dan.: Rødkløver; Gr.: Trifilli To Limonion; Russ.: Klever krasni; Yug.: Navadna detelja.

Uses: Red Clover is only surpassed in importance as a herbage legume by Lucerne. In Britain and northern Europe it is far more important, accounting for nearly half the seeds sown for this purpose of any leguminous plant. It is used for forage, fresh or dried fodder (in hay), silage or as a green manure.

Origin, distribution and cultivation: The wild form of *T. pratense* occurs in most of Europe. Cultivated forms have existed at least since the Middle Ages; Broad Red was already firmly established in the 17th century. Red Clover is planted on its own, or mixed with other plants in hayfields and leys.

Similar plants: See key p. 40. Size, colour and the near-stalkless fl heads are the main distinguishing characters. Zigzag Clover *T. medium* is not cultivated, but common in many places in meadows, etc. It has more or less zigzagging stems, narrower, darker green, rarely marked leaflets, and almost hairless calyx tubes.

Trifolium hybridum
ALSIKE CLOVER

(p. 144)

Description: In habit like Red Clover, but the plant is nearly hairless. Fls white flushed with pink below, or nearly all pink, the heads on long stalks, up to 15 cm, all in lf axils, none at the ends of stems. Stipules oblong, oval with long points, untoothed; calyx tooth ca. twice the length of tube, broadly triangular.

Names: Fr.: Trèfle bâtard; It.: Trifoglio ibrido; Sp.: Trebol hibrido; Ger.: Alsikeklee; Dtch.: Zweedse klover; Dan.: Alsikeklover; Gr.: Trifilli To Notho; Russ.: Klever gibridni; Yug.: Svedska detelja.

Uses: As Red Clover, but less valuable because it is smaller and less prolific. It is mainly used as a substitute on certain soils because it is more resistant to acidity or waterlogging.

Origin, distribution and cultivation: Despite its name, this is a true natural species. Alsike is a village in Sweden whence *T. hybridum* was introduced for cultivation to Britain in the 19th century. It occurs in the wild in Europe, except in the hotter southern areas. It is cultivated particularly in the colder, more acid soil regions of the North.

Trifolium incarnatum
CRIMSON CLOVER

Description: An annual, 20–50 cm tall, more or less erect, silky-hairy. Leaflets oval. Fl heads all at ends of stems, 1.5–4 cm long, deep crimson, rarely paler, the fls smothered in the long silky brown hairs on calyx tubes.

Names: Fr.: Trèfle incarnat; It.: Trifoglio incarnato; Sp.: Trebol encarnado; Ger.: Blutklee; Dtch.: Incarnaatklaver; Dan.: Blodkløver; Gr.: Trifilli To Sarcochrun; Russ.: Klever inkarnatni; Yug.: Inkarnatka detelja.

Uses: Mainly planted in mixed herbage as a winter annual for forage, particularly for sheep.

Origin, distribution and cultivation: *T. incarnatum* is a native of S. Europe, extending northward along the Atlantic coast to Brittany and Cornwall. It is fairly widely grown in western Europe, but infrequently in Britain, and only in the south.

Similar plants: See key p. 40. The principal distinguishing character is the long silky hairs which fill much of the space on fl heads.

Trifolium repens
WHITE or DUTCH CLOVER
(p. 144)

Description: A hairless creeping perennial producing leafy stolons which root at the nodes. Leaflets ovate to nearly round, with toothed margins and usually with a whitish chevron, on long (5–25 cm) stalks arising from the lf axils of creeping stems. Fls white, occasionally tinged with pink, the calyx narrow, ca. half the length of tube, on globose heads at least 8 mm wide.

Cultivated plants vary enormously in size according to cvs, and also to grazing or cutting to which they tend to respond by producing smaller lvs, from small-leafed forms scarcely differing from wild plants, to the Italian Ladino, or **Giant White** variety.

Names: Fr.: Trèfle blanc; It.: Trifoglio bianco; Sp.: Trebol blanco; Ger.: Kriechklee, Weissklee.

Uses: White Clover is second only to Red Clover in importance among the cultivated Trifoliums. Its creeping perennial habit makes it essentially a grazing crop, but it may also be cut for hay, silage, etc. Giant White is intolerant of hard grazing, and is used mainly for the latter purposes.

Origin, distribution and cultivation: White Clover is native to most of Europe, and has been in cultivation for a very long time. Small- and medium-leafed forms are cultivated everywhere for forage and fodder; the Giant White variety is grown mainly on its own on irrigated land in central and southern Europe.

Similar plants: *T. repens* is easily identified by the combination of white fls and creeping habit.

Fields of tall, white-flowered clover grown on its own in irrigated land in Greece, Cyprus or Turkey may be Berseem or Egyptian Clover, *T. alexandrinum*, an important crop in Egypt and the Middle East.

Medicago sativa
LUCERNE or ALFALFA
(p. 142)

Description: A robust perennial producing annual erect stems up to 1 m. Lvs trifoliate; leaflets equal, narrowly ovate, with toothed margins, not indented at apices; stipules toothed. Fls purple or lilac, in loose oblong racemes up to 5 cm long. Pods smooth, coiled in a spiral; seeds numerous, ca. 2 mm in diameter, angular, greenish brown.

Plants with fls more or less variegated blue and yellow are cvs obtained by hybridisation with another species, *M. falcata*. It is probable that nearly all European strains of Lucerne now have some mixture of this species, although most cvs retain blue fls.

Names: Fr.: Luzerne; It.: Trifoglia, Erba medica; Sp.: Alfalfa; Ger.: Blaue-Luzerne; Russ.: Lucerna posevnaya; Yug.: Lucerna.

Uses: Lucerne is, by virtue of its high nutritive content and large yield, one of the most valuable of all fodder legumes. It is usually cut for feeding fresh or as hay or silage, as it is intolerant of grazing.

Origin, distribution and cultivation: Lucerne does not exist in a truly wild state, but is known to have originated in the area around the Caspian Sea, possibly derived from the local *M. coerulea*.

The cultivation and spread of Lucerne is linked with the early spread of the horse, which was also first domesticated and improved in central Asia. As the horse became indispensable to the warrior tribes and enabled them to build empires, so it became imperative to provide a fast-growing and nutritious fodder, particularly in those areas of sparse and relatively poor pastures. In this way, Lucerne was taken eastwards to China more than 2000 years ago; it was introduced to Greece from Persia in the 5th century BC and from there spread slowly throughout Europe. Emulating the practice of their nomadic central Asian precursors, the Arabs took Lucerne with them in the 8th century on their conquests, to North Africa and Spain, where it is still known by its Arabic name, Alfalfa.

Lucerne is cultivated all over Europe, though less extensively in some northern areas, which are more favourable to clovers. It is intolerant of competition and is therefore usually grown on its own, or sometimes in specially designed mixtures.

Similar plants: Sickle Medick, *M. falcata* is a closely related sp., native to Asia and central Europe, and widely naturalised elsewhere. It has sprawling stems, smaller lvs, yellow fls, and sickle-shaped pods. As Hybrids between these two spp. have back-crossed many times, a whole range of intermediate forms exist in cultivation and as escapes.

Onobrychis sativa
SAINFOIN
(p. 142)

Description: A perennial producing many usually erect leafy stems 20–50 cm long. Lvs pinnate with 6–12 pairs of lanceolate leaflets and equal or smaller terminal leaflet; stipules characteristic, broad, pointed, chaff-like, red, clasping the stem. Fls many in long conical heads on stalks longer than lvs; fls 10–15 mm long, pink with red veins; calyx hairy, teeth longer than tube. Pods 1-seeded, flat on one side, rounded, strongly toothed and netted on the other, 6–9 mm long; seeds ca. 3 x 4 mm, kidney-shaped, dark olive brown.

Many cvs exist, differing in size and flowering season.

Names: Synonym: *O. viciifolia* Scop. Fr.: Sainfoin, Esparcette, Bourgogne; It.: Lupinello, Cedrangolo; Sp.: Esparcete; Ger.: Esparsette, Schildklee; Dtch.: Esparcette; Dan.: Esparcette; Gr.: Onobrikhis; Russ.: Esparset; Yug.: Esparzeta.

Uses: A valuable fodder crop cut for hay, silage, or processed into food supplements. It is used particularly for sheep; as hay it is considered unrivalled for racehorses.

Origin, distribution and cultivation: A native of western Europe where it has been cultivated for centuries, particularly in France. It remains one of the most important herbage legumes after Lucerne and clovers, but is now being replaced in many areas by the former. It is usually sown on its own. In Britain, cultivation is mostly restricted to the southern parts.

Similar plants: The large red stipules provide the best distinguishing character.

Another legume occasionally cultivated on a field scale in central Europe for its roots, used in herbal teas and in pharmaceutics, is Spiny Rest-harrow *Ononis spinosa*. Its pink fls might cause it to be mistaken for Sainfoin from a distance. Closer inspection will show that it is a woody plant with trifoliate lvs, numerous but solitary fls, and long yellow-brown spines on the stems.

Ornithopus sativus
SERRADELLA
(p. 142)

Description: A more or less erect or prostrate annual with stems up to 50 cm long. Lvs pinnate with 6–10 pairs and one terminal narrow lanceolate leaflet. Fls pink, borne in small heads (usually 4) on long axillary stalks. Pods long, curved, beaded and indehiscent, breaking up into one-seeded segments. Pods in small clusters resembling a bird's foot (not horizontally spreading as in Bird's Foot Trefoil), the 'toes' only partly spread.

Names: Fr.: Serradelle, Ornithope; It.: Serradella; Sp.: Serradella; Ger.: Serradella; Dtch.: Serradella; Dan.: Serradel; Gr.: Ornithopus; Russ.: Serradella; Yug.: Seradela.

Uses: A fodder and green manure crop suited to dry, poor soils.

Origin, distribution and cultivation: Serradella is a native of Portugal and parts of Spain. It is cultivated to a small extent as a field crop in the hotter and drier parts of southern, central and western Europe, alone or in mixed herbage.

Similar plants: Bird's foot *O. perpusillus*, a wild European species which occurs in southern England, is of no agricultural importance. It is like Serradella, but smaller, with fls yellow-white veined with red.

Medicago lupulina
BLACK MEDICK, YELLOW TREFOIL or NONSUCH
(p. 142)

Description: A small annual, sometimes biennial, with trailing much-branched stems. Lvs trifoliate, the leaflets small, ovate, much like those of clovers but with a small terminal mucron. Inflorescence an oval raceme born on axillary stalks, the fls small (3–8 mm), yellow, 10–50 per head. Pods short, curved and ridged, black when ripe, containing a single seed, and borne in elongate clusters.

Names: Fr.: Minette, Lupuline; It.: Lupulina; Sp.: Lupulino; Ger.: Gelbklee, Hirsenklee; Dtch.: Hopklaver; Gr.: Kítrino trifilli; Russ.: Lucerna Kumelevinaya; Yug.: Osenica.

Uses: In mixed leys or permanent pastures as a grazing plant.

Origin, distribution and cultivation: Black Medick is a common wild plant of chalk grasslands in most of Europe. Only sown occasionally as a substitute for Red Clover in dry pastures.

Similar plants: This medick is commonly mistaken for a true clover of the genus *Trifolium.* It resembles Yellow Sucking Clover from which it may be distinguished by the broader, greener leaflets which are tipped with a small point, the larger and brighter fl heads, and by the shape of the pods. Hop trefoils (*Trifolium campestre*, *T. aureum* etc.), wild species with yellow fls, may similarly be distinguished from Black Medick by the absence of a terminal point on the leaflets and by the differently shaped pods.

Medicago arabica
SPOTTED MEDICK

Description: A trailing more or less downy annual, similar to *M. lupulina*, but with larger leaflets usually marked with a characteristic black spot on their centre, and racemes bearing only 1–4 orange-yellow fls. Pods characteristic, spirally coiled and very spiny, like a burr; stipules toothed.

Names: Synonym: *M. maculata* Sibth. Spotted Medick is sometimes called Burr Clover or Burr Medick, although the latter term should properly be restricted to *M. minima.* Fr.: Luzerne tâchetée; It.: Medica maculata; Sp.: Carretón; Ger.: Arabischer Schneckenklee; Dtch.: Gevlekte rupsklaver; Dan.: Sneglebaelg; Gr.: Kilidotó galázio trifilli; Russ.: Lucerna arabskaya.

Uses: An unpalatable weed.

Origin, distribution and cultivation: Spotted Medick is a wild plant of most of southern Europe, occurring in more northern areas in dry grasslands. In Britain it is mostly confined to the South West. It is cultivated in America, but not in Europe except in southern parts where better forage legumes cannot be maintained. It is considered a pest in sheep pastures because the spiny pods become entangled in the wool, greatly reducing its value.

Similar plants: Hairy Medick (see below).

Medicago polymorpha
HAIRY or TOOTHED MEDICK

Description: Like Spotted Medick, but the plant is smaller and hairier, with leaflets unspotted and stipules even more deeply toothed. Pods are similarly burr-like, but with fewer coils, shorter, with longer spines.

Names: Synonym: *M. hispida.* Fr.: Luzerne hérissée; It.: Medica ispida; Sp.: Carreton de amores; Ger.: Steifhaariger Schneckenklee; Dtch.: Ruige rupsklaver; Dan.: Krog-sneglebaeg; Gr.: Fyllódes trifilli; Russ.: Lucerna malenkaya.

Uses: As Spotted Medick; a weed sometimes cultivated as a cover crop.

Origin, distribution and cultivation: As Spotted Medick, but less frequent in Britain.

Similar plants: Spotted Medick, and (Lesser) Burr Medick *M. minima*, which is a yet smaller plant with unspotted leaflets, and untoothed stipules.

Melilotus alba
WHITE MELILOT or BOKHARA CLOVER

(p. 142)

Description: A tall (60–150 cm) erect hairless annual or biennial herb with somewhat woody stems. Lvs trifoliate; leaflets elongate, narrow, pointed, 15–20 mm long. Fl heads elliptical, loose, 2–5 cm long; fls 4–5 mm long, white, with wing petals and keels equal. Frts hairless, net-veined, containing one yellow-brown seed resembling those of clovers.

Names: Hubam Clover is an annual cv. of this species. Sweet Clover is another name for this and other melilots, so-called because of the bitter but sweet-smelling substance called coumarin which they contain. Fr.: Mélilot blanc; It.: Meliloto bianco; Sp.: Meliloto blanco; Ger.: Bucharaklee, Weisser Steinklee; Dtch.: Witte honingklaver; Dan.: Hvid stenkløver; Gr.: Melilotos; Russ.: Donnik beli; Yug.: Bela medena.

Uses: Melilots do not stand hard grazing but, being drought-resistant and tolerant of poor conditions, they are useful fodder and green manure crops where clovers do poorly or where time does not allow the cultivation of Lucerne.

Spoiled melilot silage may be poisonous, as the sweet-smelling coumarin can break down into substances allied to the rat poison warfarin, which prevent clotting of the blood.

Apart from their agricultural uses, the fls and lvs of this and other melilots are used on the continent for perfuming linen cupboards, making teas, and in Switzerland for flavouring cheese.

Origin, distribution and cultivation: White Melilot occurs wild in dry areas throughout Europe, in Britain as an established escape from cultivation. It is widely cultivated on a small scale, especially in central and southern Europe, but infrequently in Britain and then only as a green manure.

Similar plants: Other melilots, but white fls are characteristic.

Melilotus officinalis
YELLOW, COMMON or RIBBED MELILOT

Description: Very similar to *M. alba*, but fls yellow, 5–6 mm long, with keel shorter than wing petals and standard. Pods hairless, oval, with transverse ridges, not netted, brown when ripe.

Names: Synonym: *M. arvensis*. Fr.: Mélilot officinal; It.: Meliloto giallo; Sp.: Meliloto amarillo; Ger.: Gelber Steinklee; Dtch.: Akkerhoningklaver; Dan.: Mark-stenkløver; Russ.: Donnik zolti; Yug.: Rumena medena detelja.

Uses: As White Melilot.

Origin, distribution and cultivation: Yellow Melilot is a native of S.E. Europe but occurs wild in most of Europe except the north in dry places. In Britain it is most frequent in the south and east. It is cultivated in the same way and more or less to the same extent as White Melilot.

Similar plants: Small Melilot or Small Flowered Medick *Melilotus indica*, also cultivated in the same way, is a smaller yellow-flowered species; fls only 2 mm long, the wings and keels both shorter than standard, and pods olive-green when ripe, hairless and net-veined. The wild Tall Melilot *M. altissima* is also similar, but fls are a deeper yellow, with standard, wings and keel all equal, and black downy pods.

Lotus corniculatus
COMMON BIRD'S-FOOT TREFOIL

Description: A low more or less prostrate, downy or hairless perennial with solid stems 10–40 cm long. Lvs apparently trifoliate, but are in fact pinnate with 5 leaflets, the basal pair arising from base of stalk, therefore resembling large stipules; leaflets oval, pointed, variable in size. Fls ca. 1.5 cm long, the buds crimson; open fls deep yellow to orange, grouped 2–8 in a one-sided head; calyx teeth erect in bud, the two superior ones separated by an obtuse angle. Pods slender, cylindrical, 2.5–5 cm long, containing numerous seeds and spreading stiffly in a horizontal plane like the toes on a bird's leg; seeds shiny, brown with darker marks, ca. 1.7 mm in diameter.

Names: Fr.: Lotier corniculé; It.: Ginestrino; Sp.: Loto de los Prados; Ger.: Gemeiner Hornklee; Dtch.: Rolklaver; Dan.: Kaellingetand; Gr.: Lotos; Russ.: Ladvenyets rogati; Yug.: Rozickasta nokota.

Uses: A forage and fodder plant.

Origin, distribution and cultivation: A native of dry places except on very acid soils in most of Europe. It is sown (rarely in Britain) in mixed herbage, usually on permanent pastures or long leys, and sometimes on its own, especially in France.

Similar plants: Narrow-Leaved Bird's-foot Trefoil *L. tenuis*, a distinct species with cvs, is a smaller, often more erect plant with much narrower lvs, less than 3 mm wide, and pale yellow fls, not more than 4 in a head. Greater Bird's-foot Trefoil (see below).

Lotus uliginosus
GREATER BIRD'S-FOOT TREFOIL

Description: Close to *L. corniculatus*, but a larger plant, stems up to 60 cm, more or less erect, and very hairy. Stem hollow; leaflets broad oval, less pointed, 1.5–2 cm long. Fls 5–12 per head, bright yellow, without orange or red flush; calyx teeth spread in bud. Pods more slender, and seeds smaller, 1.2 mm in diameter.

Names: Synonym: *L. major*. Fr.: Lotier velu, des marais; It.: Ginestrino palustre; Sp.: Loto de los pantanos; Ger.: Sumpfhornklee; Dtch.: Moerasrolklaver; Dan.: Sumpkaellingetand; Russ.: Ladvenyets bolotni; Yug.: Močvirska nokota.

Uses: A forage and fodder plant. The particular value of this species is that it thrives in marshy, acid soils, being almost the only agricultural legume to do so.

Origin, distribution and cultivation: A native of most of Europe in damp meadows, marshes, fens, even on acid peaty soils. It is rarely cultivated on its own, except as a break crop and green manure crop for the improvement of wet acid soils, for instance upland bogs, but it is often sown in mixed herbage in suitable conditions.

Similar plants: Hairy Bird's-foot Trefoil *L. hispidus* and Slender Bird's-foot Trefoil *L. angustissimus* are smaller plants restricted to dry places, especially near the sea; not cultivated.

Lotus tetragonolobus
ASPARAGUS PEA

(p. 140)

Description: A hairy annual with trailing stems 15–40 cm long. Lvs pinnate with 5 leaflets, apparently trifoliate because basal pair are stipule-like, arising from base of stalk, but much larger and therefore less deceptive than in Bird's-foot Trefoils; leaflets greyish-green, broadly ovate. Fls larger, 3.5–4 cms long, with broader standard, of a beautiful brownish red. Mature pods 5–8 cm long, square in section with prominent wavy ribs on the angles; seeds smooth, brown, ca. 3 cm in diameter.

Names: Fr.: Tetragonolobe; It.: Pisello inglese; Ger.: Flügelerbse.

Uses: The whole pods are picked when immature, about 2.5–3 cm long, as a vegetable; they are usually steamed and served with butter. Asparagus Pea may also be grown on a field scale as a break crop, for forage or green manure. As a vegetable it has little economic importance.

Origin, distribution and cultivation: Asparagus Pea is a native of southern Europe. It is cultivated there and also further north in home-gardens and sometimes by market-gardeners as a vegetable. It may occasionally be seen as a field crop, either in mixed herbage or alone, as a purely agricultural crop.

Similar plants: *Lotus tetragonolobus* should not, but often is confused with Goa

Bean *Psophocarpus tetragonolobus*, sometimes also called Asparagus Pea, a tropical legume cultivated mainly in S.E. Asia for its almost identically-shaped pods. The plants are easy to distinguish, however, for Goa Bean is a larger, hairless twining herb with true trifoliate lvs; the stipules are small, lanceolate, not large and leaf-like, and its fls are white or pale blue. Mature pods are much larger (15–30 cm) and typically have more jagged wings. Because they are picked for eating while immature, very small imported pods may only be identifiable by ascertaining their provenance.

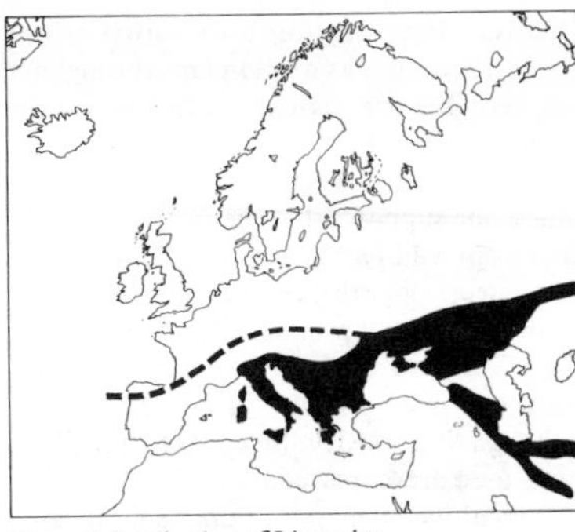

Natural distribution of Liquorice

Anthyllis vulneraria
KIDNEY VETCH
(p. 144)

Description: Prostrate to erect perennial, with silky hairs, up to 50 cm. Lvs pinnate, 3–8 cm long, with 3–5 pairs of lanceolate leaflets, on upper lvs narrow and equal, on lower lvs broader, with terminal leaflet conspicuously larger, elliptic; leaflets silky white below, green above. Fls in rather tight, rounded, more or less paired heads 2–5 cm wide; fls many, with swollen whitish-haired, shortly-toothed calyx tubes; petals usually yellow but may be white to pink, red or purple. Pods in single-seeded, round, flatted, ca. 3 mm long; seeds oval, 2.5 mm in diameter with upper part green, lower part yellow.

Names: Fr.: Anthyllide vulneraire, Trèfle jaune; It.: Antillide; Sp.: Hierba llaguera; Ger.: Gelber Klee; Dtch.: Wondklaver; Dan.: Rundbaelg; Gr.: Mauromático fasóli; Russ.: Yazvenik mnogolistni.

Uses: A forage crop, especially favoured by sheep, and cut for hay or silage. It may be sown as a substitute for Red Clover in dry chalky pastures.

Origin, distribution and cultivation: A native of Europe, very abundant in the wild on calcareous grasslands, especially by the sea. It is rarely sown except to improve sheep pastures or in hay meadows where conditions are too dry for clover, and will only yield one cut per season.

Similar plants: The larger terminal leaflet of lower lvs makes this species unmistakeable.

Glycyrrhiza glabra
LIQUORICE
(p. 144)

Description: A perennial with woody creeping rhizomes and erect branching stems growing to 1.2 m. Lvs pinnate, with 9–17 elliptic to oblong blunt leaflets. Fls numerous, pale blue, narrow, ca. 1–1.5 cm long, borne in long conical heads. Pods reddish-brown, smooth, 1.5–2.5 cm long, each containing 3 or 4 seeds.

Names: Fr.: Réglisse; It.: Liquirizia; Sp.: Regaliz; Ger.: Lakritze, Süssholtz; Russ.: Pakrichik; Yug.: Slatki korijen.

Uses: The roots and underground stolons are used medicinally and as a flavouring.

The whole dried roots are still commonly sold on markets in southern Europe, to be sucked by children. Liquorice sticks are black, hard or soft sticks made from the juice of the root which has been concentrated by boiling, and is then sold as a children's sweet. The extract is also used for flavouring sweets, drinks and pharmaceutical preparations. Liquorice is also a medicine in its own right, with antispasmodic, expectorant and laxative properties which have been made use of since ancient times.

Origin, distribution and cultivation: Liquorice occurs as a wild plant throughout southern Europe, eastwards to Russia, the Caucasus, the Middle East and Afghanistan. Although it has been used since ancient times, one supposes that the roots were gathered from wild plants. It has been in cultivation at least since the Middle Ages. Today the main commercial producers are Spain, Italy, the USSR and Turkey. Pontefract in Yorkshire was once a centre of cultivation, but although the industry still exists there, all the roots used are imported.

It is cultivated in well-drained soils in large plots or on a field scale. The crop is pulled up for harvest after 3 to 5 years' growth.

Similar plants: Wild plants of Liquorice should not be confused with Wild Liquorice *Astragalus glycyphyllos*, a wild species of no economic use occurring in Britain and other parts of Europe. It has similar foliage, but yellowish-white fls.

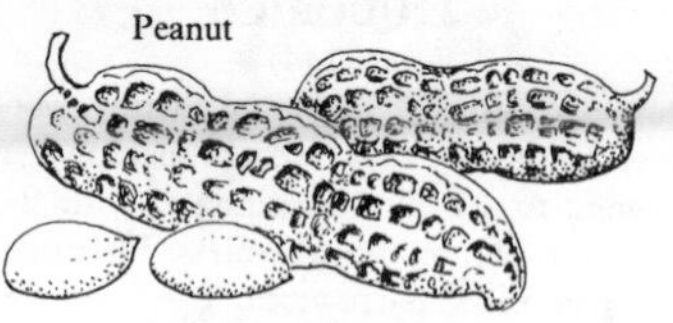

Arachis hypogea
PEANUT

Description: An erect or trailing (depending on cvs) annual herb 15–60 cm high. Stems branching from nodes, the young stems angular and hollow, older stems solid and cylindrical, both sparsely hairy. Lvs spirally arranged, on long (3–7 cm) stalks, pinnate, with 2 opposite pairs of broadly obovate leaflets 3–7 cm long, ending in a point; stipules large (2.5–3.5 cm long), linear and pointed. Fls borne on spikes of 1 or several, mostly on nodes nearest to the ground. Whole fl 5–7 cm long, with very long slender calyx tube; petals yellow, the standard as broad as its length, ca. 1.5 cm. As soon as a fl is fertilised the young frt appears at the end of a pointed 'peg' which elongates and grows downward into the soil to a depth of a few centimetres, after which the fruit grows rapidly. Frts produced more than 15 cm from the ground fail to reach it, and wither and die. Frts 1–5 cm long, irregularly elongate, with a soft 'shell' (pericarp) which hardens with maturity to a light, tough consistency, the surface with 10 longitudinal ridges, and containing 1 to 6 seeds. Mature seeds 1–2.5 cm long, the seed coat varying from white to pink, various shades of brown to purple.

Names: Also known as Groundnut, in some countries as Monkey Nut. Fr.: Arachide, Cacahuète; It.: Arachide; Sp.: Cacahuete; Ger.: Erdnuss; Dtch.: Aardnoot, Grondnoot, Pinda; Dan.: Jordnød; Gr.: Arapico fistiki; Russ.: Arakhis; Yug.: Klokocek, Kikiriki.

Uses: Peanut is highly nutritious, being rich in vitamins B and E and containing about 30% protein and 40–50% oil. It is therefore much used in cooking in most of the tropical countries in which it is grown. A large proportion of the world crop, however, is used for oil, peanut being the second largest source of vegetable oil after soya bean. Oil extraction began in Marseilles in the mid 19th century, and it is the European demand for this product which accounts for much of the world production, particularly in Africa. France alone buys nearly half of the total, and Britain about one sixth.

The oil is non-drying, used mainly for salads and cooking, for packing sardines or other fish, in the manufacture of margarine and soap, and as a lubricant. The residual cake after the expression of oil is the most common oil-cake for feeding livestock.

Peanut butter, an American product which has become popular in Britain in recent years, is obtained by grinding the roasted beans once the seed coat has been removed. Peanuts are of course also consumed whole in Europe, either raw, boiled or roasted.

Origin, distribution and cultivation: Peanut is a South American plant which has been in cultivation there for at least 3000 years. From its origin, in what is today Paraguay and South Brazil, it spread throughout the Continent, reaching Mexico and the West Indies in pre-columbian times. In the 16th century the Portuguese took it to Africa and the Spaniards to the Philippines; whence it soon spread throughout the Asian tropics. Today it is cultivated in all tropical and sub-tropical countries, with India and China leading production. It is also a major crop in the USA. In Europe, its economic importance is based on imports, mainly from Africa, and it is only grown on a small scale, always as a field crop, in some Mediterranean countries, and only for food, since the growers cannot compete with imports for the oil industry.

Similar plants: Peanut is the only leguminous plant cultivated in Europe in which the fruits mature underground. Its uniformly fresh-looking pale green foliage and 4 broad leaflets without terminal leaflets or tendrils make it readily recognisable.

In the tropics another hypogeal species, the Bambara Groundnut *Voandzia subterranea* is cultivated on a much smaller scale; it differs at first sight from Peanut by its trifoliate leaves.

The name Groundnut should not cause confusion with such plants as Earth Almond, Pignut, etc. (pp. 51 and 331) which belong to different families.

Lens culinaris

LENTIL

(p. 140)

Description: An erect much-branched pale green annual with slender softly hairy stems, up to 40cm. Lvs pinnate, usually ending in a tendril or a bristle, with 4–7 pairs of opposite or alternate leaflets, these ca. 1.3 cm long, entire. Fls 1–4 on a stalk, small, under 9 mm long, the petals pale blue, white, or pale pink; calyx with 5 narrow lobes. Pods oblong, broad, somewhat flattened, smooth, less than 1.5 cm long, containing 1 or 2 seeds; seeds lens shaped, bi-convex, of variable size and colour according to cvs.

The cvs can be divided into two main types: large-seeded (6–9 mm in diameter) cvs with larger, more flattened pods and white, rarely blue fls; and small-seeded (3–6 mm in diameter), with smaller, more convex pods and fls pale blue, white or pink.

The two commonest varieties are the large brown 'German' Lentil, and the small pale orange 'Egyptian' Lentil.

Names: Synonym: *L. esculenta*. The Latin name is the eponym of lens: a 'Lentil-shaped' glass. Fr.: Lentille; It.: Lenticchia, Lente; Sp.: Lenteja; Ger.: Linse; Dtch.: Linze; Dan.: Linse; Gr.: Faki; Russ.: Chechevitsa; Yug.: Leča.

Uses: The lentil is a nutritious pulse food. The seeds may be used whole, or split, or ground to a meal which is sometimes mixed with cereal floor in cakes and in infant foods.

The husks, bran and vegetative parts of the plant provide fodder and manure.

The 'German' Lentil, being readily available in Europe, is the one most often used for the many dishes which combine Lentils with salted pork, sausages, etc. The yellow split 'Egyptian' Lentils are only suitable for soups and purées as they disintegrate quickly while cooking. The finest in flavour, and suitable for all dishes, is the French 'Lentille du Puy', which is small and dark green mottled with black.

Origin, distribution and cultivation: Lentils have been an important food crop in the Mediterranean countries and western Asia since the remotest antiquity. They were a staple food in the Fertile Crescent and in ancient Egypt and thence reached India and Ethiopia in classical times. In these countries they remain a staple food, which often provides the only source of protein in poor diets. Lentils are cultivated as a field crop in the whole southern half of Europe, and also do well in the hot summers of eastern Europe.

Similar plants: The Lentil most closely resembles some of the many vetches (*Vicia* spp.). All of these have longer, pea-like pods containing more than two seeds. The flowers may be distinguished from those of the vetches and peas by the calyx lobes which are long and awl-shaped, whereas they are short and broad in vetches, and leaf-like in peas.

Cicer arietinum

CHICK PEA

(p. 140)

Description: An erect or spreading much-branched annual, up to 50 cm tall, entirely covered in small club-shaped glandular hairs. Lvs pinnate with a terminal and 5 to 8 pairs of very small (5–15 mm long) leaflets with coarsely saw-toothed margins; stipules ovate, notched, ca. 8 mm long. Fls usually solitary, on a jointed axillary stalk, the petals greenish, white, pink or blue, pink fls fading to blue with age; calyx with 5 teeth. Pods swollen, oblong, 2–3 cm long, with a small pointed beak and thin walls; seeds 5–10 mm or more in diameter, knobbly, pale brown after testa has been removed, the latter smooth or wrinkled, white, yellow, reddish-brown to nearly black.

Names: Fr.: Pois chiche; It.: Cece; Sp.: Garbanzo; Ger.: Kichererbse; Dtch.: Keker; Dan.: Kikeraert; Gr.: Karos; Russ.: Mielki turetski garoshek; Yug.: Cicerka.

Uses: An important pulse food, blander in taste and somewhat less nutritious than Lentils. It is the most important pulse crop of the Middle East and India, but in Europe is only common in the Mediterranean countries, especially Spain and Greece. In Europe it is usually cooked in meat broth, or used in combination with meat, in stews. 'Hummus', a Levantine dish popular in Greece, is made from mashed boiled Chick Peas, mixed with sesame paste and olive oil and dressed with garlic, salt and lemon juice.

The harvested plants, after threshing, serve as fodder and as a green manure.

The glandular hairs that cover the whole plant exude malic acid, which may be used as vinegar (eg. in India).

Origin, distribution and cultivation: Chick Pea is not known in a truly wild state, but occurs, presumably as an early escape from cultivation, in Iraq and neighbouring countries, where it is thought to have originated. It has been in cultivation for perhaps as long as the Lentil, and followed much the same early migrations eastwards to China and India, to Abyssinia, and into central and western Europe. In Europe it is only grown as a food crop, mainly to the Mediterranean countries; elsewhere it may occasionally be sown as a green manure crop, in both cases always in large plots or on a field scale.

Similar plants: The short ovate and coarsely toothed leaflets make this crop unmistakable; the small size of leaflets give the foliage a characteristic light feathery appearance. The pods, rather like those of Lentils, but hairy and twice the size, are also readily identifiable.

Glycine max
SOYA BEAN or SOYBEAN

(p. 140)

Description: An erect bushy annual, 25–180 cm tall, entirely covered with reddish-grey hairs. Lvs alternate, trifoliate, exceptionally 5-foliate, on long narrow stalks; leaflets ovate to lanceolate, with rounded bases, 4–10 x 2–6 cm, pale green; stipules small, lanceolate. Fls 3–15 per head in axillary racemes, sometimes more numerous in terminal racemes, small, narrow, the petals white or mauve, with standard longer than wings, the latter longer than keel; calyx hairy, persistent, fused for half its length, with 2 upper and 3 lower lobes. Pods in clusters of 3–15, hairy, yellowish-brown, grey or brown to almost black, slightly curved and flattened, 3–7 cm long, containing 1–5 seeds (2 or 3 in most cvs); seeds very variable according to cv, the testa yellow, green, brown or black, or mottled in combinations of these colours; the size and shape equally variable, rounded in most cvs grown for grain, flattened in some others. The whole plant begins to die and turn brown in parts before harvesting, giving it a characteristically 'unhealthy' appearance at this stage, comparable for instance to cotton.

Names: Synonyms: *G. soja, G. hispida, Soja max.* Fr.: Soja; It.: Soia; Sp.: Soja; Ger.: Sojabohne; Dtch.: Soyaboon; Dan.: Sojabønne; Fr.: Glykia; Russ.: Soya; Yug.: Soja.

Uses: Soya Bean has become, on a world basis, the most important source of vegetable oil and protein.

The partly-drying oil is used in cooking, in salads, and for the manufacture of margarine and many industrial products such as paints, soap, printing ink, linoleum; also lecthin, a bi-product used as a wetting and stabilising agent in many industrial processes.

A further industrial use is made of the proteins, in the manufacture of synthetic fibres, fire-fighting foam, adhesives, and other products.

The residual meal after expression of the oil is the basis of a high protein-content cake for feeding livestock, a product which is increasing in importance in relation to oil, especially as an import to Europe.

Crops may also be grown for forage or fodder.

Soya is an important food crop in East Asia, but in Europe its edible products are mostly imported and of minor importance.

Bean sprouts are young seedlings grown in the dark and used about a week after germination. Bean curd, soya cheese, tofu, a white or brownish cheese-like substance much used in Far Eastern cooking, are made from the flour. Soya 'milk' is a valuable supplement in infant or invalid diets. Soya flour is mixed with cereal flour for baking, and is an ingredient of ice-creams and many other food products. Soya sauce, which is used instead of salt on Chinese tables, is made from mature fermented beans boiled with salt, flour and other ingredients, and fermented for several days afterwards; it is the basis of Worcester and other English table sauces.

Origin, distribution and cultivation: Soya Bean does not exist in the wild; it is thought to have originated as a hybrid of two or more *Glycine* spp. in China, where it has been cultivated since the earliest dynasties. It reached Korea, Japan, Indonesia and other parts of S.E. Asia early on, and was first brought to Europe in the 18th century and to the USA in the early 19th century, but large commercial cultivation only began outside the Far East, particularly in the USA, in the 20th century. In Europe it is rarely sown as a field crop, but the fluctuations of commodity prices might well cause it to be cultivated in the future. It is grown to a small extent by market- and home-gardeners in France and in some other countries.

Similar plants: The hairiness of the plant distinguishes it from other European bean crops. In the tropics and sub-tropics, however, other similarly hairy legumes are cultivated.

Pigeon Pea *Cajanus cajan* is a short-lived perennial cultivated for its seeds in India, the Middle East and Africa, and perhaps occasionally in Cyprus and Turkey. It differs at first sight from Soya by its yellow flowers veined with red, and pods with diagonal depressions between the seeds. Black and Green Grams (see under Common Bean p. 55) also have yellow flowers, and much narrower pods.

Trigonella foenum-graecum
FENUGREEK

(p. 144)

Description: A small to medium-sized annual, usually erect, with little-branched stems. Lvs trifoliate, the leaflets oblanceolate to oblong, with slightly toothed margins. Fls small, solitary or in twos, yellowish-white tinged with violet at base, born in upper lf axils. Pods hairless, long and slender, slightly curved, with a beak, pale brown; seeds yellowish-brown, angular, smooth-skinned, with a deep furrow partly dividing them into two unequal parts. All parts of the plant are strongly aromatic.

Names: The specific epithet means 'Greek hay' in allusion to its ancient use as a fodder crop in Greece and the Levant. Fr.: Fenugrec, Trigonelle; It.: Fieno greco; Sp.: Alholva, Fenogreco; Ger.: Bockshornklee; Dtch.: Fenegriek; Dan.: Bukkerhorn; Russ.: Pazhitnik.

Uses: Fenugreek is cultivated for two distinct purposes: as a forage or fodder crop, and for its seeds, which are used as a spice.

The seeds are very mucilaginous, bitter to the taste, but with a fine characteristic aroma. It is most often encountered in western Europe in Indian cooking, as one of the ingredients of most curry powders, but it is widely used as a flavouring agent in Greece, the Balkans and throughout the Middle East. In one country it has become a pulse food in its own right, as *helba*, the national dish of North Yemen, in which the meal is boiled to a thick mucilaginous pea-green porridge, served still bubbling in clay pots and garnished with fried onion and a little meat. In this form it loses much of its aroma, but none of its bitterness.

The meal is sometimes used in Europe as a spice in cattle food, and also has a number of pharmaceutical uses. The young plants, grown only to the cotyledon stage like cress, make a fine salad. Older plants are bitter, and are only palatable when balanced with complementary spices in Indian cooking.

Origin, distribution and cultivation: Fenugreek is a native of the Near East, and has been cultivated since ancient times all over the Mediterranean and eastwards to India, and is naturalised in much of this range. When cultivated only for fodder, Fenugreek is usually sown in mixed herbage, and cut for hay, fresh fodder, or silage. When grown for the seeds it is sown alone; stock may be folded on the crop after harvesting, or the remains ploughed in as green manure. As a fodder crop it is cultivated in most of southern and central Europe, even to a small extent in Britain; crops grown for the spice are confined in Europe to the Mediterranean countries, Russia and the Balkans, especially Greece and Turkey.

Similar plants: Not to be confused with *T. ornithopodiodes*, also called Fenugreek in England, a creeping wild plant of sandy places, especially by the sea, in N.W. Europe, which resembles Subterranean Clover (see key, p. 38) more than it does Classical Fenugreek. It may be distinguished from the clover by its paler green and hairless leaves.

Several other species of *Trigonella* occur in the wild, especially in southern Europe; in these the flowers are more numerous, in heads; none of them is cultivated.

Phaseolus vulgaris
COMMON BEAN

(p. 138)

Description: The best known and most widely cultivated bean in the world. Plants may be either twining with stems up to 3 m long, or erect and bushy, needing no support; intermediate types also exist. Lvs trifoliate, often slightly hairy, on long stalks; leaflets ovate, pointed, 8–16 cm long by 5–12 cm broad, the lateral ones asymmetrical. Fls few in loose racemes, usually shorter than lvs; calyx 3–4 mm long with 1 upper and 3 lower teeth, and bracts as long or longer than calyx; petals white, cream, pink or violet, the standard 9–12 mm broad, notched. Pods variable but narrower than *Ph. lunatus*, at least 5 times as long as broad, mostly between 8–20 cm long, containing 4–7 seeds, up to 12 in some cvs, and very variable in colour: green, yellow, maroon, or green, yellow or red blotched with black. Seeds variable in shape, size and colour: kidney-shaped (typical), more or less flattened, to irregularly globose (Pea Bean), 7–18 mm long, white, yellow, pale green, buff to dark brown or black, pink to purple, or mottled or streaked, occasionally with a black mark around hylum as in *Vigna unguiculata* (see below).

Names: The many names by which this species or one or other of its varieties is known include: French Bean, Kidney –, Haricot –, Snap –, Frijoles, Berlotti –, Flageolet, Salad –, Chili –, Pinto –, Fazolia, Canellini, Arpajon, Mojhettes, Mexican Black –, Michelet, Pea –, Mangetout (in France), Runner –, String –, Field – (USA).
Fr.: Haricot commun; It.: Fagiolo; Sp.: Judia roja; Ger.: Braunbohn; Dtch.: Bruinboon; Dan.: Brunbønne; Gr.: Fassolios; Russ.: Fasol obiknovenaya; Yug.: Navadni fižol.

Uses: Different cultivars are grown for the immature pods which are consumed whole or sliced and cooked, and for the seeds, either mature and dried, or fresh and shelled.

Cultivars grown for pods can be classed in two categories: 'string' beans, which must be picked very young before the string (fibrous strands along the sutures) develops, and 'stringless' pods, which may be picked at a later stage. Many of the latter cultivars are known in France as 'mangetout' (literally, 'eat all of it'), whereas in England the term applies only to pea pods which are used in the same way.

Beans shelled and eaten fresh are consumed by the home-gardener, or sold in their pods by the grocer to be shelled at home. One of the finest of these is the pale green Flageolet, picked immature, and which can also be partly dried.

Much of the production of both pods and fresh shelled beans is canned or frozen.

The many varieties of dried beans have subtly different flavours suited to different dishes: Red Chili Beans for chili con carne, mottled Berlotti Beans for salads with fish and onions, green Flageolets cooked in butter with a lot of parsley to accompany roast lamb, etc. The best quality white Haricot or Canellini are the finest and most versatile, and essential for the delicate dishes of beans and cream of France and Italy, Greek fassoulia, the noble cassoulet, and Boston baked beans. Those chosen for canning the debased travesty of this dish which is so popular in Britain are selected for uniformity of size and appearance, rather than for flavour.

It is not generally appreciated that dried beans should be eaten within a year of picking; they lose much of their flavour thereafter.

Origin, distribution and cultivation: Like the two following species, *Ph. vulgaris* is a native of the New World. It probably derives from a wild, already variable species which was brought into cultivation independently in different parts of Central America at a very early date; beans from archaeological sites in Mexico have been dated to 5000 BC, and ones from Peru to over 2200 years. The Spaniards brought it to Europe in the 16th century, and it reached England in 1594.

The plant's origins at high altitudes in the tropics make it hardy in Europe, where it is now unrivalled as a pulse, being much preferred to the native but gastronomically inferior Broad Bean. It is grown in all European countries. In general dried bean cultivars are produced on a field scale in warmer countries, while the home- and market-gardeners of more northern parts concentrate on cultivars selected for their pods.

Similar plants: In view of the enormous range of variation in this species, it is fairly safe to assume that any edible bean cultivated in Europe that does not belong to one of the other three species (Broad –, Lima – and Scarlet Runner –) described below are varieties of Common Bean. However a number of imported beans belonging to exotic species are available in groceries. These include:

Very long (15–100 cm) pods, closely resembling some of the cylindrical podded 'green' beans, imported from the Far East, which belong to the genus *Vigna: V. unguiculata, V. sinensis, V. sesquipedalis*. They are used in the same way as green beans, and sometimes known as 'yard-long beans'.

The seeds of an erect bushy form of *V. unguiculata* grown in Africa and America, and largely imported from the latter, are called 'Black-eye Bean'. They are usually off-white with a finely wrinkled testa, and are readily recognisable by the black or dark brown mark which encircles the white hilum.

The seeds of Black Gram *Phaseolus mungo* and Green Gram *Ph. aureus*, two pulses widely cultivated in India but not in Europe, are currently available, especially in Asian groceries. They do not resemble any of the forms of Common Bean: Black Gram are small (4 mm long) oblong seeds with square ends, black with a conspicuous white hilum; Mung or Green Gram seeds are similar but usually green, sometimes brown or mottled, and have fine wavy ridges on the testa. Both are among the many pulses used in India for 'Dhal'.

Adzuki Bean *Ph. angularis*, is a native of Japan where it is the second most important pulse after Soya, and is imported from China and Thailand to Europe. The beans are small, ca. 8 x 4 mm, usually reddish-brown, with a long white hilum. The plant can be distinguished from Common Bean by its yellow fls and straw-coloured cylindrical pods constricted between the (5–12) seeds.

Pigeon Pea *Cajanus cajan* (see also under Soya Bean), known too as Red Gram, is the second most widely cultivated pulse crop in India, and sold by oriental grocers. The seeds are more globular than almost all forms of Common Bean, and smaller, ca. 8 mm in diameter, very variable in colour.

Lablab *Lablab niger*, known in Egypt as Lubia, is more difficult to differentiate from Common Bean because its seeds are equally variable. It is unlikely to be sold in European groceries, but the plant may occasionally be grown in eastern Mediterranean countries. The white or purple fls can be distinguished from those of *Phaseolus* spp. by the keel which is incurved at a right-angle, not coiled, and the style which is hairless around the stigma.

Egyptian 'Ful medames' is a variety of Broad Bean (p. 58).

Phaseolus lunatus
LIMA or BUTTER BEAN
(p. 138)

Description: A twining annual, biennial or perennial, depending on cvs, climate, etc. In Europe almost invariably grown as an annual. It closely resembles Common Bean, growing to 4 m high; small bush forms have also been developed. Lvs trifoliate, on long (7–18 cm) stalks; leaflets ovate, pointed, often slightly hairy beneath, 5–12 cm long; stipules minute, triangular. Fls many, 2–4 per node in long axillary racemes up to 15 cm long; fls small, ca. 12 mm long, with very shortly toothed calyx; petals white or cream, the standard often greenish, occasionally violet. Pods oblong, slightly curved, 5–12 cm long, generally broader and flatter than Common Bean, usually ripening to pale brown. Seeds large, 1–3 cm long, variable in shape from rounded 'potato' varieties to broad and flat (typical 'butter' bean), very variable in colour within the species, but almost always white in garden cvs; the testa has translucent lines radiating from hilum to outer edges.

Names: Synonyms: *Ph. limensis, Ph. inamoenus*. Also known as Madagascar Bean, Sieva Bean, Burma Bean. Fr.: Haricot de Lima, - du Cap; It.: Fagiolo di Lima; Sp.: Judia Lima; Ger.: Limabohn, Mond-Bohn; Dtch.: Limaboon; Dan.: Limabønne; Gr.: Fasóli limas; Russ.: Fasol limskaya.

Uses: Grown for dried shelled beans. In some countries the fresh beans, usually of the smaller-seeded forms, are used for canning.

Origin, distribution and cultivation: *Ph. lunatus* is a South American species believed to have been brought into cultivation separately in Peru and Guatamala, perhaps 6000 years or more ago. It was taken to the Philippines soon after the conquest of South America and is now widely distributed in the tropics and sub-tropics. Being less hardy than *Ph. coccineus* and *Ph. vulgaris* it is a marginal crop in Europe, grown under glass in Britain and northern Europe, and outdoors, but only on a limited scale, in South Europe. Most of the dry or canned beans of commerce are imported.

Similar plants: Common Bean; in addition to the characters given in the key, a useful distinguishing feature is the radiating translucent lines on the testa of the seed.

Phaseolus coccineus
SCARLET RUNNER or RUNNER BEAN
(p. 138)

Description: A perennial, grown as an annual, usually climbing, up to 3 m or more, but dwarf bushy forms also exist. Lvs trifoliate, the leaflets large, 7–15 cm long, and broad. Fl heads in axils, longer than lvs, with 20–30 fls; petals usually scarlet but may be white, or pink, or bicolorous red and white. Pods very large, 20–60 cm long, flattened with rough diagonally striate surfaces, green; seeds large, 10–25 mm long, convexly flattened, usually pink with black mottling, or white (in white flowered forms).

Names: Synonym: *Ph. multiflorus*. Fr.: Haricot d'Espagne; It.: Fagiolo di Spagna; Sp.: Judia escarlata; Ger.: Feuerbohn; Dtch.: Pronkboon; Dan.: Pralbønne; Gr.: Kokkinopó fasóli; Russ.: Fasol ognennokrasnaya; Yug.: Turški fižol.

Uses: The immature pods are cooked.

Origin, distribution and cultivation: *Ph. coccineus* is a native of the temperate high altitudes (ca. 2000 m) in Guatamala and neighbouring parts of Central America, where it still exists as a wild plant and has been harvested or cultivated for several thousand years.

In Britain the Scarlet Runner is by far the most popular green bean, and is cultivated in nearly every cottage garden and allotment, and extensively by market gardeners, sometimes even on a field scale, although the absence of a suitable method of mechanised harvesting makes this impractical. It is widely but less frequently grown on the continent, where superior green bean forms of the Common Bean are justly preferred. Most plants are trained on canes or strings to a height of ca. 2.5m, and the terminal buds are 'pinched' off to arrest vertical growth and encourage lateral spreading.

1	Fls usually coloured, pink and purple or red and purple. Stipules with a red spot at base. Pods small; seeds small, angular or round, grey or brownish, often mottled. Grown as a sprawling field crop=**Field Pea**	(2)
2	Fls white. Stipules without a red spot. Pods variable, usually large; seeds medium or large, round, smooth or wrinkled, usually green. Grown as a field crop or in gardens, with or without supports=**Garden Pea**	(1)

Similar plants: (See key), but the red fls and very large pods make this species readily recognisable.

Note that the term 'runner' bean is also used for varieties of the Common Bean grown for their pods.

Pisum sativum
PEAS
(p. 140)

Description: A climbing hairless, usually glaucous annual growing to 1.5 m. Stems round, slender, weak, therefore tall cvs are grown on supports. Lvs pinnate with 2, 4 or 6 ovate or elliptic leaflets 1.5–6 cm long and a branching terminal tendril; stipules larger than leaflets, leaf-like, ovate, toothed in basal half, 2–7 cm long. Fls in axils, solitary or in racemes of 2 or 3; calyx oblique, swollen on one side, with unequal lobes; petals white, or pink or purple, the wings longer than keel and adherent to it for about half their length. Pods cylindrical or flattened, straight or curved, 4–18 cm long, containing 2 to 10 seeds, with parchment-like lining which is absent in edible-podded types. Seeds globose or angled, smooth or wrinkled, green, grey or light brown, mottled in some cvs.

In recent years curious-looking 'leafless' and 'semi-leafless' cvs have been developed to facilitate harvesting and cultivation in areas of high rainfall. In the latter leaflets are absent, but the leaf-like stipules remain unaltered; in 'leafless' forms the stipules are minute, vestigial, leaving no foliage, but only stems, tendrils and fls/pods.

P. sativum is divided into two subspecies: ssp. *sativum*, Garden Peas, and ssp. *arvense*, Field Peas.

Field Peas are more homogenous in appearance, differing mainly in seed type: Dun Peas, with larger, dull brown seeds; Grey Peas, with small round pale grey seeds speckled with violet; and Maple or Partridge Peas, also small, brown and speckled.

Garden Peas are more variable in form. Sugar Pea or Mangetout is easily recognised by its very flat pod. Petit pois, by far the finest green pea for canning or for eating fresh, have narrower, more cylindrical pods containing more seeds than most other cvs.

Names: Synonyms: (Garden –): *P. hortense*; (Field –): *P. arvense*. Fr.: Pois; It.: Pisello; Sp.: Guisante; Ger.: Erbse; Dtch.: Erwt; Dan.: Haveaert; Gr.: Mpizeliá; Russ.: Gorokh; Yug.: Grah.

Uses: Field Peas are grown for feeding livestock, either with the whole plant, as forage, or cut for silage or in mixtures as hay, or else with the ripe seeds, split or ground to flour. They are also a useful green manure.

Garden Peas were formerly grown exclusively for the mature seeds which were dried and stored for use in winter. The use of green peas, the immature seeds eaten fresh, began in the 17th or 18th centuries but remained a seasonal delicacy until twentieth-century freezing and canning techniques transformed this pattern. Today the production of green peas, a much more valuable cash crop, takes precedence over other uses. Peas are grown under contract to the processors, who closely control all stages of growth and harvesting, as the peas must be canned or frozen within a few hours of picking. This industry has superseded the market for green pods for shelling at home; these are becoming more difficult to find in grocers, but are still produced by the home-gardener.

Peas grown for drying are mostly sold dry, either whole or split, in which form the two cotyledons separate after removal of the testa; but some are canned after soaking and marketed as 'processed' peas, as a cheap substitute for canned fresh peas. Dried peas can be divided into three main categories: Blue Peas, small round peas with green cotyledons used mainly for processing; Marrowfats, large peas with wrinkled skins and green cotyledons; White Peas, with round seeds and yellow cotyledons, grown for use as split peas.

Both Field Peas and Garden Peas are a useful green manure crop after harvesting the pods.

Origin, distribution and cultivation: *Pisum sativum* is not known in a truly wild state, but *P. arvense* occurs wild in Georgia. Peas are of very ancient cultivation, beginning in S.W. Asia, and reaching the Greeks over the Black Sea, and India and China via the ancient trade routes. From Greece they spread to the rest of Europe, and were introduced to Africa when the Axumite king of Abyssinia invaded S. Arabia in the 6th century. From Ethiopia they were taken to East Africa, where they were an established food crop by the time of the earliest European exploration.

Peas, including Garden Peas, are cultivated in Europe mainly on a field scale. Taller stemmed cultivars needing supports are grown in home- and market-gardens for the production of fresh green peas and mangetouts.

Similar plants: The only European plants which resemble *Pisum* belong to the genus *Lathyrus*, which includes the ornamental Sweet Pea and numerous wild vetchlings and 'peas' such as Everlasting Pea and Tuberous Pea. One *Lathyrus* sp., Grass or Chickling Pea *L. sativus* is widely cultivated in India and the Middle East as a forage crop, and the seeds are eaten by poorer people or in times of famine. It is a native of southern Europe as well as the Middle East, and is perhaps occasionally cultivated in the eastern Mediterranean. It is not unlike Pea in appearance, but has much narrower, linear-lanceolate lvs, blue or purple fls with a white keel, and small flattened pods 2.5–4 cm long which contain 3 to 5 white, brown or mottled seeds.

Vicia faba
BROAD BEAN and FIELD BEAN

(p. 138)

Description: An erect stout leafy hairless annual, up to 1.8 m tall, with thick hollow stems square in section and winged at angles, branching from basal nodes. Lvs pinnate, sometimes ending in a small point, with 2–3 pairs of large ovate, somewhat glaucous leaflets 5–10 cm long. Fls 1 to 6 on short axillary racemes, fragrant, 2.5–3.5 cm long; calyx bell-shaped, with triangular teeth; standard white often with thin black streaks on dorsal surface, wings usually with a purple blotch. Pods more or less cylindrical or flattened, 5–12 cm long in field cvs, up to 30 cm in garden cvs, thick walled with a white velvety lining when young, becoming hard and leathery later. Seeds variable in shape and colour, 1–2.5 cm long, globular or strongly flattened, usually brown, but may be white, buff, or purple to nearly black.

The species exists in two main forms: Broad Beans (often referred to as var. *major*) with flattened seeds, 15–25 mm in diameter, can be subdivided into two main groups: 'longpods' with 4–9 medium-sized seeds per pod, and 'Windsor' and similar forms, with 2–5 very large seeds per pod. Field Beans (var. *minor*) have smaller seeds which are cylindrical to almost spherical in shape, and vary in size according to cv.

Names: Other names by which some of the varieties of Field Bean are known include Winter Bean, Horse Bean and Tick Bean. Fr.: Fève, Fèverole; It.: Fava: Sp.: Haba; Ger.: Puffbohn, Saubohn; Dtch.: Tuinboon; Dan.: Hestebønne; Gr.: Kukia; Russ.: Bob; Yug.: Bob.

Uses: Broad Beans are a food crop cultivated for the seeds which are picked when almost mature, shelled and cooked fresh, or dried for later use. Field Beans may also be sold for human consumption, the most noteworthy example being the '*ful medames*' of Egypt, which is a round-seeded variety resembling the larger field beans of northern Europe, which are grown principally for livestock feeding. For this purpose they are usually dried and ground, and the meal combined with cereal or other flour.

V. faba is a valuable and traditional break crop and green manure on cereal land.

Origin, distribution and cultivation: This is the native edible bean of Europe, cultivated since early prehistoric times in northern and central Europe as well as by the Egyptians, Hebrews, Greeks and Romans. It was the only food bean known here before the introduction of the Common, Lima and Scarlet runner Beans in the 16th century.

Both Broad and Field Beans are cultivated in all European countries, the former in home-gardens, market-gardens and as a field crop, the latter only as a field crop, but sometimes on quite small plots purely as a green manure. The hardier cultivars (Winter Beans) can be sown in autumn for harvesting in spring, even in Britain.

Similar plants: None; *V. faba* is a much more robust plant than any other species of *Vicia* such as Common Vetch (below); the white and purple-black fls are particularly distinctive, although pure white-flowered cultivars exist, especially among long-pod varieties.

Vicia sativa
COMMON VETCH or TARE

(p. 142)

Description: An erect climbing or spreading downy annual with 4-sided stems, up to 60 cm. Lvs ending is long branched or simple tendrils, with from 4 to 8 pairs of oblong leaflets 20–30 mm long, their tips slightly concave and with a small mucron; stipules lanceolate, usually toothed and with a dark spot at centre. Fls solitary or in pairs, short-stalked, in leaf axils, 10–30 mm long, pale lilac to purple. Pods elongate, hairy or hairless, 5–8 cm long, narrow, somewhat flattened, containing 4 to 10 seeds. Seeds round, 4–6 cm in diameter, pale brown with dark mottling to dark brown.

The cultivated form described here is a larger plant than the wild form sometimes called ssp. *angustifolia* from which it is derived, which has smaller, narrower leaflets, and darker, purple fls.

Names: Fr.: Vesce commune; It.: Veccia commune; Sp.: Veza, Arveja común; Ger.: Futterwicke; Dtch.: Voederwikke; Dan.: Foderwikke; Gr.: Vikos; Russ.: Vika yarowaya; Yug.: Navadna grašica.

Uses: A fodder or forage crop.

Origin, distribution and cultivation: A common native of grasslands, hedges and scrub in most of Europe. Two main types are cultivated: Winter Vetch, a hardy plant sown in the autumn, and the faster growing but less hardy Spring Vetch.

Similar plants: *V. villosa* is another vetch, native of the Mediterranean, which is commonly cultivated in central and southern Europe, but not in Britain. It is similar to Tufted Vetch *V. cracca* in its pendulous blue-violet fls borne in large clusters. The long racemes are plume-like before flowering due to the very long hairy teeth on the calyx.

V. sativa can be distinguished from most of the many wild vetches by the combination of fl colour, the fls borne in ones or twos, erect bearing and hairiness. *V. bithynica*, a wild species which occurs in Britain, is similar but has winged stems and only 2–3 pairs of leaflets.

GROSSULARIACEAE

Currant Family

A family of small deciduous shrubs belonging to a single genus *Ribes*, which is widely distributed in Europe, northern Asia and North America. The species have alternate, palmately 3 or 5-lobed lvs and small greenish fls with 5 petals, 5 sepals and inferior ovary, which are borne singly or in racemes. The frt is a berry, with more or less translucent skin enclosing juicy pulp and a few seeds.

Some pink-flowered forms are grown for ornament. A number of wild spp. with frts too sour, insipid or small to be of use occur in Europe as well as the cultivated spp. The latter can be distinguished as follows:

KEY TO CURRANT FAMILY

1	Stems spiny=**2**	**(4)**
2	Frts larger, usually ovoid, green sometimes tinged with yellow or red, in 1s, 2s or 3s on all sides of stem=**Gooseberry**	**(3)**
3	Frts smaller, round, green ripening to black, hanging singly in rows on undersides of stems=**Worcesterberry**	**(2)**
4	Stems not spiny=**5**	**(1)**
5	Lvs glandular, smelling strongly of tom cat; frts purple-black=**Black Currant**	**(6)**
6	Lvs without a strong scent; frts white or red=**Red** and **White Currants**	**(5)**

Ribes uva-crispa
GOOSEBERRY
(p. 146)

Description: A shrub, variable in size and growth habit, from widely spreading or drooping to almost upright. Stems with spines at lf bases. Fls 1–3 together, tinged with purple, with spreading recurved petals. Frt ovoid, sometimes spherical, green, more or less translucent, often tinged with white, red or yellow, sometimes hairy, 1–4 cm long.

The many different cvs are commonly classed as white, red or yellow, the latter being considered the best.

Names: Synonym: *R. grossularia.* Fr.: Groseille à maquereau; It.: Uva spina; Sp.: Grosella espinosa; Ger.: Stachelbeere; Dtch.: Kruis; Dan.: Stikkelsbaer; Gr.: Fraskostafiliá; Rus.: Krizhovnik.

Uses: Gooseberries may be eaten fresh as a dessert fruit when quite ripe, usually with added sugar, but are more often picked slightly unripe for bottling or canning in syrup, jam making or cooking, for use in tarts, etc. They are more popular in Britain than in most European countries.

Origin, distribution and cultivation: This species occurs wild throughout most of northern and central Europe. Its cultivation is recorded in France and England in the Middle Ages; intensive selection of superior cultivars began in the 18th century, and nearly a thousand were listed by the end of the 19th century. Today only a few of the popular varieties are grown on a commercial scale. Gooseberries are cultivated in home-gardens and on a larger scale on fruit farms, sometimes as a second crop among orchard trees. Large plantations may exist to supply a single nearby jam factory.

Similar plants: Worcesterberry (below, and key, opposite).

A number of American hybrid berries resistant to gooseberry mildew, the most serious threat to crops, have come into cultivation in Europe. The frts of these are usually smaller than European gooseberries, and some have different habits, for instance 'Pixwell', in which the frts hang on long stalks well below the foliage.

Ribes divaricatum
WORCESTERBERRY

(p. 146)

Description: Similar to the spreading forms of Gooseberry, with long arching canes. The fls and frt are borne singly, in rows of up to 20 or more, hanging from the underside of canes. Frts are round, smaller than gooseberry, ripening to purplish-black.

Uses: As Gooseberry.

Origin, distribution and cultivation: Worcesterberry was once thought to be a cross between Gooseberry and Black Currant but is now acknowledged as a true species of American origin. It seems to have come into cultivation through a nursery in Worcester in the 19th century. It is rarely grown on a commercial scale, and is not normally available from fruiterers.

Similar plants: Gooseberry and American hybrids.

It resembles 'Currant Gooseberries' *R. hirtellus*, another American native with red to purple frts like small Gooseberries, rarely cultivated in Europe.

Ribes nigrum
BLACK CURRANT

(p. 146)

Description: A small shrub, similar to Gooseberry, but stems are spineless. Lvs hairless above, when crushed emitting a strong characteristic scent usually described as fragrant but distinctly reminiscent of tom cat spray. Fls inconspicuous, greenish, in spreading, drooping racemes of 5 to 20; receptable cups below the sepals 5-angled, proportionately larger in relation to petals and sepals than Gooseberry, the sepals reflexed. Frt 10–15 mm in diameter, round, purple-black.

Names: Synonym (together with Red and White Currants): *R. sativum*. Fr.: Cassis; It.: Ribes nero; Sp.: Grosella negra; Ger.: Schwartze Johannisbeere; Dtch.: Zwarte bes; Dan.: Solbaer; Gr.: Mauri stafila; Russ.: Smorodina chornaya; Yug.: Crni ribiz.

Uses: Black Currant is the most valuable of the cultivated currants, both because of its high vitamin C content which makes it a useful syrup drink for children, and because its distinctive flavour is widely appreciated. The frts are used like those of Gooseberry, cooked in tarts or made into jams and syrups, but also for flavouring yoghurts, ice-creams and many processed dessert foods.

Origin, distribution and cultivation: *R. nigrum* occurs wild in damp woodland in most of northern and central Europe, either naturally or as an escape from cultivation. It is the most extensively cultivated of the currants, often grown on large acreages by specialist fruit farmers.

Similar plants: See key, above. The aromatic lvs provide the best distinguishing character.

The word currant is also used for dried grapes (see p. 102).

Ribes sativum agg.
RED and WHITE CURRANTS
(p. 146)

Description: Similar to Blackcurrant, but usually with a stout main stem instead of having many stems, and lvs are downy above and without the latter's characteristic scent. Frts more or less translucent, red or white, globular, smaller (6–12 mm in diameter) than Black Currant.

Names: Synonyms: *R. vulgare*; *R. rubrum*; *R. sylvestre* (used for wild northern forms). Sometimes classed as an aggregate to include *R. nigrum* as well as the above and *R. petraeum.* Fr.: Groseille; It.: Ribes rosso; Sp.: Grosella; Ger.: Johannisbeere; Gr.: Kakkini stafila; Russ.: Smorodina krasnaya.

Uses: Both Red and White Currants are used, often with other fruits, for making jams and jellies. They may be eaten fresh, but Red Currants are rather too acid to be enjoyed on their own, and are best mixed with other, sweeter fruits such as Raspberries; White Currants are less attractive in appearance and being less acid are somewhat insipid.

Origin, distribution and cultivation: The members of this aggregate are European natives. *R. rubrum* occurs in mountain woodland in most of northern Europe and Asia; *R. petraeum*, distinguished by purple-tinged fls, lives in similar conditions in central and southern Europe, and plants of the cultivated forms may occur as escapes throughout its range. *R. rubrum* is more hardy, therefore much cultivated in Scandinavia and Russia. Red and White Currants are less often cultivated in southern Europe, where Black Currants and other fruits offer a more attractive alternative.

Similar plants: See key. Of the wild spp. with insipid fruits, the common *R. alpinum* may be recognised by its more deeply lobed lvs and erect racemes.

CORNACEAE

Dogwood Family

This small family is similar to the Umbelliferae, but distinguished by the typically woody stems, fleshy fruits and usually opposite leaves. Fls with 4 sepals, 4 petals and 4 stamens. It includes several species grown for ornament in Europe, but only one which can be considered economic.

Cornus mas
CORNELIAN CHERRY
(p. 146)

Description: A small deciduous tree or shrub up to 7 m. Twigs greyish-brown. Lvs opposite, oval or elliptic with 3 to 5 pairs of prominent veins. Fls minute, yellow, appearing in early spring before lvs in clusters of 10–25, each cluster only about 1 cm in diameter, and with 4 yellowish-green bracts at base. Frt an ovoid fleshy drupe ca 1.5 cm long, ripening to bright red.

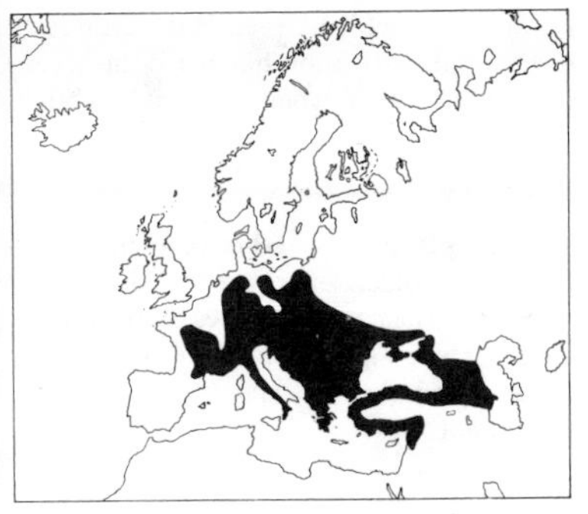

Natural distribution of Cornelian Cherry

Names: Fr.: Cornouiller; It.: Corniolo; Sp.: Cornejo, Corno; Ger.: Dürrlilitze, Herlitze; Dtch.: Kornoelje; Dan.: Kornel; Russ.: Kizil muzhskoi; Yug.: Drijen.

Uses: The fruit is used to make sweet jellies, and in some countries an alcoholic drink (*vin de cornouille* in France).

Origin, distribution and cultivation: A widely distributed native of Europe, Cornelian Cherry is common in the wild, especially on calcareous soils, in thickets and at the edge of woods. It is cultivated as much for ornament as for its fruit, although never on a large scale, usually as single trees in gardens.

Similar plants: The lvs resemble those of other members of the Dogwood Family, but the fls and frt are distinctive. Harvested frt might be confused with that of Oleaster (p. 100) but are a brighter red, and lack the latter's small silvery scales.

CAPRIFOLIACEAE

Honeysuckle Family

A small family of mostly woody shrubs or climbers, distinguished by their opposite, usually simple lvs. Fls with calyx and corolla 4–5 lobed, with stamens attached to the corolla tube; the ovary is inferior, the frt a drupe or berry.

Apart from Elder, the family is of no economic importance, but includes several common ornamentals such as Viburnum and Honeysuckle.

Sambucus nigra
ELDER
(p. 146)

Description: A familiar large shrub, much branched, the trunk with very rough crevassed bark. Lvs compound, with 5–7 oval or lanceolate, toothed leaflets which smell strongly when crushed. Fls about 5 mm in diameter, creamy-white, in flat-topped clusters up to 20 cm across; the weight of frt clusters causes them to droop. Frts purplish-black when ripe, but occasionally remaining greenish-white, ca. 7 mm in diameter, on red stalks.

Names: Fr.: Sureau noir; It.: Sambuco; Sp.: Saúco; Ger.: (schwarzer) Holunder; Dtch.: Vlier; Dan.: Hyld; Russ.: Buzina chornaya; Yug.: Bazga.

Uses: Both the flower and fruit are widely used in Europe to produce fermented drinks.

Elderberry wine is dark red, and has been compared to port. Elderflower wine, still or sparkling, is made from the corollas after carefully removing the stalks which are unpalatable. These wines are often distilled on the continent, the most famous spirit produced being the Italian *sambuca romana.* The berries are also used in combination with other fruits for making sweet jellies.

Origin, distribution and cultivation: Elder is so common in northern and central Europe on waste land, even in the centres of towns, that cultivation has not been necessary for the limited economic use it has, but it is often cultivated on a small scale in southern Europe.

Similar plants: No other economic plant resembles Elder. Red-berried Elder *S. racemosa* – the name describes its most striking difference – also has more yellowish fls in dense round clusters, and the pith is pale brown, not white.

FAGACEAE

Beech Family

A family of primordial ecological importance in temperate countries, where its deciduous or evergreen trees dominate the forests. The family is characterised by its nut which is surrounded by a ring of fused bracts which completely envelop several nuts in Beech or Chestnut, and in Oak is reduced to a cup encircling the base of a single nut. One member of each genus is described in this book.

Fagus sylvatica
BEECH
(p. 148)

Description: A familiar very large tree with smooth grey bark, purplish-brown shoots and long slender scaled buds. Lvs ovate, the blade thin, pale green with fine silky hairs and 5–8 pairs of side veins. Fls unisexual, appearing with lvs in late spring, male fls are borne round, in yellow catkins on long (2 cm) drooping stalks, the females are inconspicuous, greenish, on a short stiff stalk. Frt (known as 'mast') woody, triangular in section, covered in slender spines, splitting into 4 halves when ripe.

Names: Fr.: Hêtre; It.: Faggio; Sp.: Haya; Ger.: Buche; Dtch.: Beuk; Dan.: Bøg; Gr.: Beuki; Russ.: Buk; Yug.: Bukva.

Uses: The inclusion of Beech in this book is justified on historical grounds rather than on present economic use of the fruit. The nut is edible, contaiing 46% oil and was formerly harvested in great quantities for feeding pigs and poultry, making cattle-cake, and for the production of oil (lighting, etc.). The principal economic use of Beech today is timber.

Origin, distribution and cultivation: Beech is a native of the whole of Europe except northern Scandinavia, forming entire forests especially on calcareous or other well drained land, and in mountain areas; it is of great ecological importance. Forests are maintained by the governments of many countries for timber. Nuts are still harvested locally in some parts of southern Europe, particularly in a good or 'mast' year: the trees tend to produce small quantities of fruits for several years and then have a bumper year; this is known as a 'mast' year.

Similar plants: In S. Bulgaria, eastern Greece and Turkey *F. sylvatica* is replaced by Oriental Beech *F. orientalis* which differs in its more distant branching and larger, more spreading lvs which have 7–12 pairs of lateral veins.

The smooth grey bark and similarly shaped lvs of Hornbeams (*Carpinus* spp.) often cause them to be confused with Beech, but the lvs have double-toothed margins, and twice as many veins, and the fls and frt are quite different.

Castanea sativa
CHESTNUT
(p. 148)

Description: A large tree, older specimens have characteristic vertically fissured bark, the ridges often spirally twisted. Shoots thick, purplish-brown, at first with long grey pubescence, without a terminal bud. Lvs large, ca. 15–35 x 8–10 cm, glossy, the conspicuous side veins ending in large spined teeth. Fls in axillary branches of catkins which appear in summer, long after the lvs; male fls in small clusters near tip of shoot, female fls near base. Frts in bunches of 2–3 in pale green densely spiny cups which split when ripe (in autumn) to reveal the familiar glossy red-brown nuts, usually 2, one more developed, rounded, the other smaller with one concave face.

Names: Fr.: Châtaignier; It.: Castagno; Sp.: Castaño; Ger.: Kastanie; Dtch.: Kastanje; Dan.: Kastanie; Gr.: Kastaniá; Russ.: Kastan; Yug.: Kesten.

Uses: Roasted chestnuts in season are familiar all over Europe, and chestnut puree is tinned and used as an accompaniment to game and poultry, but these uses are of minor economic importance. The nuts, used for flour, breadmaking, or boiled and mashed, formerly provided a staple food in the poorer mountainous parts of central and southern Europe such as the southern Massif Central of France and the Appenines; they are still extensively used for feeding cattle, and particularly pigs.

Origin, distribution and cultivation: Chestnut is a native of S.E. Europe, but was extensively planted elsewhere as early as Roman times, and now forms entire forests in some areas. In northern Europe nuts only ripen after an exceptionally hot summer, and trees are planted mainly for ornament.

Similar plants: Not to be confused with Horse Chestnut *Aesculus hippocastanum* which bears the same vernacular name in many languages. For instance 'purée de marrons' in French ought to be 'purée de châtaignes'.

Quercus suber
CORK OAK
(pp. 148, 219)

Description: A medium-sized evergreen oak with very thick rough spongy bark, pale grey on the surface, pinkish-buff inside. The under-bark of freshly stripped trees is bright brownish pink which darkens within a few weeks through chestnut-red to black; the first layers of new growth are pale grey like mature bark, but with a smoother surface. Lvs small, shiny, with greyish hairs beneath, the edges more or less spiny-toothed, the mid-vein characteristically slightly sinuate. Frt an acorn with large elongate nut, the upper scales of mature cup slightly spreading (not adpressed to cup as in Holm Oak. which the lvs and acorn otherwise resemble).

Names: Fr.: Chêne liège; It.: Sughera; Sp.: Alcornoque; Ger.: Korkeiche; Dtch.: Kurkboom; Dan.: Korkbom; Gr.: Velanidiá felloy; Russ.: Dub probkovi.

Uses: Because of its exceptional combination of lightness and impermeability, and therefore buoyancy, cork has lost none of its importance in its best-known use as bottle-stoppers, especially for wine. For this purpose the corks are cut out of solid pieces of better quality, fine-grained bark, in the axis of lenticels, ie. parallel to the tree trunk. The left-over pieces and inferior quality barks are reduced to flakes or granules and amalgamated to make large bottle bungs, shoe soles, linoleums, cork tiles, sound insulating panels, life buoys, floats for fishing nets, etc., though in many of these uses it has been superseded by synthetic products, such as expanded polystyrene.

Origin, distribution and cultivation: Cork Oak is a native of the western Mediterranean, from Morocco and Portugal eastward to Yugoslavia. It may be seen in plantations, but more usually in semi-natural stands cleared of scrub. The main producing areas in Europe are Spain and Portugal, with some woods still exploited in Corsica and Italy. In France it is no longer commercially viable.

The tree is remarkable in that it is resistant to the complete stripping of bark from the bole, and rapidly grows new layers, a faculty no doubt developed to resist forest fires. Trees are stripped for the first time when they are at least 70 cm in diameter, thereafter about every 10 years; they may withstand the treatment for centuries.

Similar plants: The pink to black stripped trunks of trees that are exploited make this species unmistakable in the field. It most closely resembles Holm Oak, a very variable species with smoother acorn cups (see description above) and straighter mid-vein of lvs.

Of the more than 20 species of oak native to Europe, several others have been of limited economic importance for products other than timber. In the Périgord and the Vaucluse in France stands of Hairy Oak *Q. lanuginosa* are planted or encouraged for the propagation of truffles (see p. 340). The bark of Holm Oak *Q. ilex* and of Kermes Oak *Q. coccifera* is rich in tannins, and still used for tanning and dying, as are the large acorn cups with widely spreading scales, rather like little pine cones, of Valonia Oak *Q. macrolepis* which are still imported from Turkey and Eastern Europe for that purpose.

CORYLACEAE

Hazel Family

A small family of deciduous, catkin-bearing trees and shrubs with nuts enclosed in a thin greenish bract, or involucre. Apart from the species described below, the family includes only 2 other genera in Europe: *Ostrya* (Hop Hornbeam) and *Carpinus* (Hornbeams).

Corylus avellana
HAZEL NUT
(p. 148)

Description: A familiar large spreading shrub, rarely with a short bole, often coppiced, with shiny grey-brown bark raised in small curling strips on older wood. Twigs densely covered in stiff club-shaped hairs; buds ovoid, blunt and smooth. Lvs up to 10 cm long, almost as broad, obovate, the margins with sharp triangular unequal teeth. Male catkins brownish-yellow in autumn, pale yellow when opening between December and April; female fls ovoid, brown, 3–5 mm long, with bright red styles. Nuts in clusters of 1–4, slightly flattened, ovoid, 1.5–2 cm long, pale green ripening to rich brown, with bases enclosed in a spreading involucre cut into broad teeth and with sparse white hairs.

A number of cvs exist, as well as hybrids

with other *Corylus* spp. Cultivated plants are usually pruned to encourage fl and frt production and to facilitate harvesting.

Names: Fr.: Noisetier; It.: Nocciolo; Sp.: Avellano; Ger.: Haselnuss; Dtch.: Hazel; Dan.: Hassel; Gr.: Fountoukiá; Russ.: Leshia obiknovenaya; Yug.: Lijeska.

Uses: Principally a dessert nut, but also widely used in cooking, pastry, or ground to flavour processed dessert foods.

Origin, distribution and cultivation: Hazel is a very common inhabitant of woods, coppices and hedgerows, tolerant of all soils except the most acid, found in the whole of Europe except the extreme north and the driest parts of the Mediterranean. Many nuts are harvested in the wild, but those intended for commercial use are cultivated. Commercial production in Britain is restricted to Kent, and is insufficient for the home market, so large imports are made from the major producing countries: France, Spain, Italy and Turkey.

Similar plants: Common or European Hazel is distinguished from all other *Corylus* spp., except American Hazel *C. americana*, by the shape of the involucre; this has partially free lobes and does not form a tube extending to the tip of the nut as in Turkish Hazel and Filbert. Some hybrid forms may be difficult to determine.

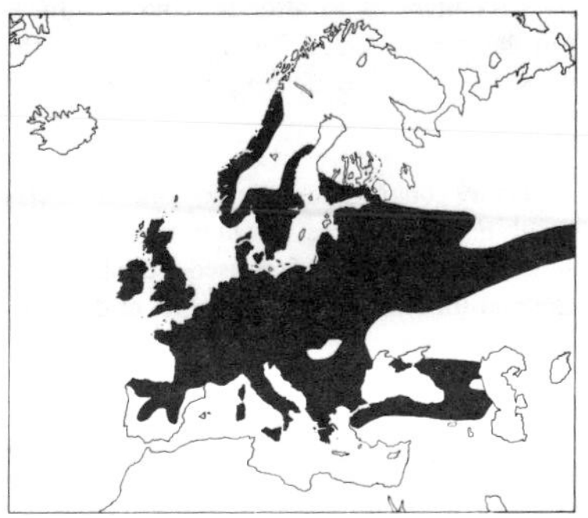

Natural distribution of Hazel

Corylus maxima
FILBERT, KENTISH COB

(p. 148)

Description: Similar to Hazel, but more robust, taller in its natural habit. The nuts are larger, more elongate, with an involucre of characteristic shape, long, tubular, completely enclosing the nut, somewhat constricted and fluted near apex, with toothed margins, and downy.

English Filbert or Cobnut, of which there are several varieties, is grown exclusively in Kent.

Names: Fr.: Avelinier; It.: Nocciolo di Dalmazia; Sp.: Avellana de Lambert; Ger.: Lambertnuss; Dtch.: Tamme hazel; Dan.: Slags stor hassel; Gr.: Tourkiki fountoukiá; Russ.: Leshia krupnaya; Yug.: Pitom ljesnjak.

Uses: As Hazel and Turkish Hazel.

Origin, distribution and cultivation: *C. maxima* is a native of the Balkans. It is widely cultivated in most of the countries which produce and export Hazel Nuts, but more particularly in southern Europe.

Similar plants: Hazel and Turkish Hazel (see descriptions below). The frt is readily identifiable by the downy involucre which extends beyond the tip of the nut and is not deeply lacerated as in Turkish Hazel.

Confusion may be caused by lax use of the word Cobnut, sometimes applied by fruiterers to Turkish Hazel or even to large Common Hazel Nuts.

Corylus colurna
TURKISH HAZEL

(p. 148)

Description: Basically like the preceding two species, but recognisable because it is the only large *Corylus* forming a stout trunk, and the bark is strongly furrowed on wood more than 2 years old, becoming 'corky' with age. Fts large, like Filbert, but the involucre is characteristic, long, deeply cut into long linear pointed, somewhat curling lobes.

Names: Fr.: Noisetier de Bizance; It.: Nocciolo di Turchia; Sp.: Avellana de Turquia; Ger.: Türkische Baumhazel; Dtch.: Turkse hazel; Dan.: Tyrkisk hassel; Gr.: Fountoukiá; Russ.: Leshia drevovidnaya; Yug.: Pitom izeshjak.

Uses: As Hazel Nut.

Similar plants: Hazel and Filbert.

Origin, distribution and cultivation: This species, like Filbert, is a native of the Balkans. It is less widely cultivated than the latter, and not in Britain, where the only trees are to be found in parks and botanical collections. The nuts are often available from fruiterers, many imported from Cyprus.

JUGLANDACEAE

Walnut Family

A small family of catkin- and nut-bearing trees with large pinnate leaves. Of the sixty or so species it contains, only Walnut is native to Europe, but several others are cultivated for ornament or timber or naturalised, such as the Caucasian Wingnut (*Pterocarya*) and the American Hickories (*Carya* spp.). *Juglans* (Walnut and related American or Oriental species) have unbranched catkins, while those of Hickories are divided into 3 lobes.

Juglans regia
WALNUT

(p. 148)

Description: A large, handsome, slow-growing tree, to 30 m in height, with a broad crown and bright, clear green deciduous foliage. Bark very pale grey, turning paler with age. Lvs up to 45 cm long, with usually 7 (sometimes 3, 5 or 9) large (up to 20 cm) untoothed leaflets, the terminal one larger than others, on a long stalk. Catkins 5–10 cm long, dark yellow, in axils. Frt a globose, smooth, dark green, more or less speckled drupe 4–5 cm in diameter, containing a 2-valved nut with characteristic lumpy surface which splits when ripe and contains the wrinkled kernel.

Names: Fr.: Noix; It.: Noce; Sp.: Nogal; Ger.: Walnuss; Dtch.: Okkernoot, Walnoot; Dan.: Valnød; Gr.: Karudiá; Russ.: Greski orekh; Yug.: Orah.

Uses: Walnut is the finest and most nutritious of the European nuts. It is sold as a dessert nut, but also has many uses in flavouring confectioneries and pastries, and in cooking, as for instance in Middle Eastern chicken dishes, *raito*, a salt cod dish of Provence, or Italian *pesto.* The kernels make an excellent hors d'oeuvre salad after soaking in diluted vinegar for 24 hours. Young frts, before the nuts have developed, are pickled and eaten whole.

Walnut oil, expressed from the kernels, is a superior cooking and salad oil, formerly much used in France, but now largely superseded by cheaper oils. It is used industrially in the manufacture of artists' paints and in cosmetics.

The wood is of great value in furniture and cabinet-making, but 'walnut' gunstocks, veneers, furniture, etc. may be made from the wood of many of the related American or oriental species.

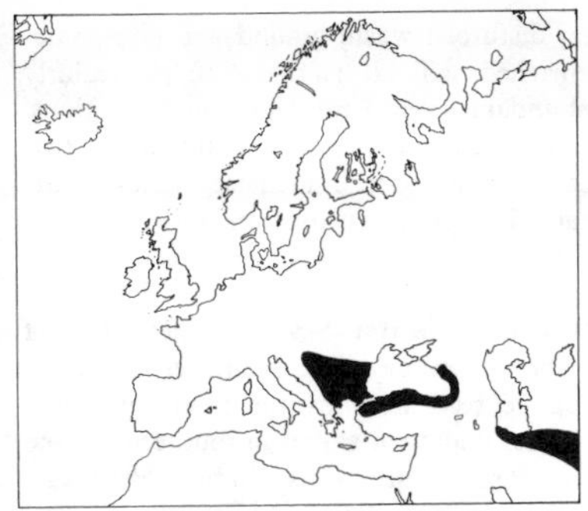

Natural distribution of Walnut

Origin, distribution and cultivation: Common, European, Persian or 'English' Walnut is a native of warm-temperate Eurasia, from S.E. Europe to western China, but it is naturalised in most of Europe as a result of ancient cultivation. It has been in France at least since Roman times, but probably only reached England in the 14th century. The main producing and exporting country in Europe is France, with large quantities grown in Italy, Rumania and Turkey. Although the quality of English Walnuts has been vaunted, Britain is at the limit of the climatic range necessary for ripening fruit, and commercial production has decreased to an insignificant level.

Similar plants: Black Walnut *J. nigra* and Butternut *J. cinerea* are North American species both cultivated in their homeland for nuts which are sometimes imported to Europe. The former is also extensively grown in parts of central and southern Europe for timber. Black Walnut shells are extremely thick and hard, with closer, rougher ridges than Walnut. Butternut has strong raised ridges in an irregular reticulate pattern.

Pecan Nut *Carya illinoensis* is more widely cultivated than either Black Walnut or Butternut in the USA. The kernel resembles Walnut, but the nut is smooth with four sharp longitudinal ridges. It is often available from grocers, together with other exotic nuts, at Christmas time.

Walnut differs from these 3 species and from all other *Juglans* and *Carya* spp. in having entire, not toothed leaflets.

URTICACEAE

Nettle Family

A family of mainly tropical herbs, shrubs and some trees, often with stinging hairs. Fls are minute, inconspicuous, unisexual; the frt usually a dry achene. The only plant of economic importance is Ramie *Boehmeria nivea*, cultivated in China and some other tropical countries for one of the strongest and most durable of all plant fibres.

Urtica dioica
STINGING NETTLE

This all too familiar plant needs no description.

Names: Fr.: Ortie; It.: Ortica; Sp.: Ortiga; Ger.: Nessel; Dtch.: Netel; Dan.: Braendemaelde; Gr.: Tsouknida; Russ.: Krapiva; Yug.: Kopriva.

Uses: Nettle has a tenuous claim to inclusion in this book because it has lost less favour than many other plants which were formerly cultivated or gathered in the wild to be used as pot herbs.

Nettles are rich in vitamin C and are still picked when young and tender, before the fls develop, particularly in France. They may be blanched and added to salads, or treated as spinach, or used in soups.

Country children in France, and no doubt elsewhere, are still threatened with 'nettle spankings' in some families, and pious young women in Greece flagellate themselves with nettles during Holy Week, as a reminder of Christ's suffering. Victims of such atrocities may derive some comfort from the belief that nettle stings are a cure for rheumatism.

Origin, distribution and cultivation: Nettle occurs throughout Europe, especially on disturbed waste ground and phosphate-enriched soils. It is therefore particularly abundant around rural human habitations, farmyards, and the edges of cultivation. It is so common that its limited use has never warranted deliberate cultivation, nor is it offered for sale.

Similar plants: Several other spp. of *Urtica* occur in Europe: Small Nettle *U. urens* can be recognised by the lower lvs being shorter than their stalks; in southern Europe the commonest sp. is Roman Nettle *U. pillulifera*, conspicuous by its large (1 cm) round frts borne on long drooping stalks. Both these species may be used for the same purposes as Common or Stinging Nettle.

Deadnettle is not related, but belongs to the Labiate Family, as can be seen by the structure of its large fls.

CANNABACEAE

Hemp Family

A small family related to the Nettles, containing only two genera. Plants are herbaceous and dioecious. The male plants have axillary panicles of fls with 5 perianth segments and 5 stamens; female fls in dense clusters, with small entire perianth and 2 large stigmas, later surrounded by conspicuous bracts and bracteoles; lvs palmately lobed, stipulate. Only two species, Hop and Hemp, are cultivated.

Humulus lupulus
HOP
(pp. 150, 222)

Description: A perennial climber, up to 6 m, twining clockwise around support. Stems angular and hairy, bearing opposite palmately lobed lvs and pointed stipules at bases of lf stalks. Mature male plants with panicles of small (4–5 mm) fls in axils and tips; female plants with smaller panicles of strobili which at first resemble burrs, later developing into cone-like structures covered with pale green bracts and bracteoles, about 4 cm long.

The many cvs developed in response to commercial needs do not differ substantially in appearance.

Names: Fr.: Houblon; It.: Luppulo; Sp.: Lupulo; Ger.: Hopfen; Dtch.: Hop; Dan.:

Humle; gr.: Agióklima; Russ.: Khmel; Yug.: Hmelj.

Uses: Grown exclusively for the strobili, which contains a substance, lupulin, which gives the bitter flavour to beer and acts as a preservative by checking bacterial growth. The strobili have to be dried in kilns (oast houses in Britain), and treated with sulphur dioxide before being marketed.

The young shoots of wild or cultivated plants may be steamed as a fresh vegetable.

Origin, distribution and cultivation: A native of northern Europe where it is still common in the wild, although most plants are probably escapes from cultivation. Hop has gradually replaced many other plants as a flavouring agent for beer, and was introduced to Britain from Germany or Flanders in the 16th century. It is now grown in suitable areas of Britain, northern France, the Low Countries and Scandinavia eastwards through central Europe to Russia. It is a localised crop which requires much attention in the preparation of wire frameworks for the strings that support the plants, and in pruning, clearing spreading rhizomes and manuring. Picking, formerly done by hand, once required extra seasonal labour, but is now mostly done mechanically with some damage to the plants. Propagation is done vegetatively, by cuttings (setts) from stem bases. Only female plants are grown, as it is the strobilus which is used, and in many places wild plants must be cleared from hedgerows to prevent pollination and the growth of seeds.

Similar plants: None. The wire frameworks supporting the plants make it unmistakeable in cultivation.

Cannabis sativa
HEMP
(p. 150)

Description: An erect, slender, rather tender dioecious annual herb, 1–4 m tall. Stems and lvs finely hairy; lvs alternate, palmately divided into 3–11 lanceolate toothed leaflets. Male fl similar to that of Hop, yellow-green, ca. 5 mm in diameter, borne in small panicles; female plants a darker green, with denser foliage and tightly bunched panicles, and longer lived, to about 1 month after pollination, until seeds are ripe; fls closely surrounded by tubular bracteoles. Frt a mottled brown achene ca. 4 mm long.

Names: Fr.: Chanvre; It.: Canapa; Sp.: Canamo; Ger.: Hanf; Dtch.: Hennep; Dan.: Hamp; Gr.: Kannavi; Russ.: Konoplya; Yug.: Konoplja.

Uses: Hemp is cultivated for three products: fibre from the stems; a narcotic, Cannabis, from the leaves, flowers and seeds; and oil from the seeds. Fibre crops require a temperate, moister climate; the strong but soft fibres, 1–4 m in length, are used for coarse fabrics such as canvas and for the manufacture of twines and ropes.

Plants grown in these conditions do not usually produce enough narcotic resin for use as a drug, but abuse has caused the World Health Organisation to try to develop 'harmless' cvs. The production of narcotic resin depends on hotter, drier conditions; for this purpose male plants are uprooted from the crop at an early stage, and the leaves and flowers of the female plant harvested alone. The drug is used in two forms: dried resin fashioned into small bars or cubes from which the required dose is cut off and smoked or swallowed, or simply the dried leaves and seeds, which are smoked.

The oil, used as a drying oil in paints and varnishes in the same way as Linseed oil, or in soap manufacture, is expressed from the seeds, which are harvested after male plants have been pulled from the crop for fibre. The seeds have a secondary but widespread use as bird feed.

Origin, distribution and cultivation: The species is a native of central Asia, where it is of very ancient cultivation. It came into use in Europe later than flax, but soon became established as one of the most important fibre crops, and was extensively cultivated throughout the region, including Britain, until recently. It is an expensive crop to grow and to harvest, as male plants, which produce the best fibre, mature earlier than the females and for best results must be hand pulled a month or so before the final harvest.

Competition with imported fibres of other plants and with synthetic fibres has reduced its economic importance, and its increasing use as a drug in the last twenty-five years has led some countries to ban cultivation altogether. The USSR is the major producer in Europe today, and the crop may still be seen in extensive cultivation in other East European countries. Yugoslavia and Italy are the world's biggest exporters of hemp, mainly to France and W. Germany. The decline of Cannabis as a fibre crop has been concurrent with its growing importance as a narcotic and it has become in some countries a valuable, albeit illegal, cash crop. Although the climate of the Mediterranean countries in Europe is suitable to the production of high resin content, Cannabis is little cultivated, most of the drug being imported from North Africa and the Middle East.

Similar plants: Among cultivated species: none.

MORACEAE

Mulberry Family

A family of tropical and sub-tropical trees distinguished by the milky latex in stems and leaves, and by the structure of the usually compound fleshy fruits. The latter are so different in appearance in the various genera that they are not at first sight obviously related.

In the mulberries the frt is a head of drupelets resembling the frts of Raspberry and other brambles, while the false fruit (syconium) of figs is a botanical oddity. It is a flask-shaped container with many fls packed on the inside walls. The fls are of 3 kinds: male, female with long styles, and short-styled females adapted as an egg case and brooding chamber for the larvae of the fig insect, on which the plant depends for fertilisation. The Common Fig insect *Blastophaga psenes* is a minute wasp, but it is thought that each of the 2000 or so *Ficus* species depends on its own species of *Blastophaga*.

There is only one native fig in Europe, but in the tropics the numerous spp. are of considerable ecological importance. Familiar species include the Banyan of Asia *F. bengalensis*, the Peepul or Bo Tree sacred to Bhuddists and the rubber plant *F. elastica*, a large forest tree extensively cultivated for its latex before being superseded by the Para Rubber Tree *Hevea brasiliensis* in the mid 19th century, and whose seedling is a common house plant in Europe.

Other members of the family include the Osage Orange *Maclura pomifera*, with its odd inedible frt superficially resembling a green orange, and Paper Mulberries *Broussonetia* used in the Far East for making paper. Both are grown as ornamentals in southern Europe. *Artocarpus* spp. including the giant Jackfruit and the Breadfruit will be familiar to anyone who has lived in the damp tropics.

Morus nigra
BLACK MULBERRY
(p. 150)

Description: A small spreading tree, to 10 m, with stout rough trunk and branches. Twigs thick, dark brown, with dense velvety hairs. Lvs thick, dark green, up to 20 cm long, ovate with deeply cordate base and pointed tip, toothed margins, rarely lobed, the surface rough above, hairy beneath. Fls unisexual, small, individually inconspicuous, clustered into drooping green male or female catkins borne on the same tree. Frt raspberry-like, ripening to dark red or purple to almost black, and almost stalkless.

Names: Also known as Persian or English Mulberry. Fr.: Mûrier noir; It.: Gelso nero; Sp.: Mora negra; Ger.: Schwarzer Maulbeere; Dtch.: Zwarte Moerbei; Dan.: Morbaer; Gr.: Maúri mouriá; Russ.: Sholkovitsa chornaya; Yug.: Dud.

Uses: Grown as an ornamental and for its fruits which are eaten fresh, and more commonly used for making jams, jellies and mulberry wine. The raw frt is rarely if ever available from fruiterers, but are sometimes offered for sale by small farmers on markets in southern Europe. Mulberry jam, however, is produced commercially.

Mulberries, like apricots and figs, are a valuable winter food in the poorer areas of their homeland – Afghanistan, Iran, Pakistan, providing a source of sugar and vitamins in an otherwise poor diet. For this purpose the fruits are preserved in the form of semi-dried cakes.

Origin, distribution and cultivation: Black Mulberry is a native of Iran and neighbouring countries. It is widely cultivated for its fruit in southern Europe, either as single trees or in small stands. In Britain and northern Europe it is more often planted for ornament, and the fruit only harvested by the home-gardener for his own use.

Similar plants: Red or American Mulberry *M. rubra* is a larger tree with frts 3–4 cm across which are sweet even before ripening. Although superior to *M. nigra* as a fruit tree, it is seldom seen in Europe. See also White Mulberry, below.

Mulberry frts superficially resemble Raspberry and other brambles, but close examination will show that the structure of the drupelets is different. In brambles they are simple, whereas in mulberries they are composed of 4 cup-shaped segments, the outer 2 partially enfolding the inner pair, the divisions showing as pale H-shaped impressed lines.

Morus alba
WHITE MULBERRY
(p. 150)

Description: White Mulberry differs from Black in having hairless twigs, thinner, often deeply lobed lvs, (in var. *heterophylla* lobed and unlobed lvs occurring on the same branch) which have smooth upper surfaces and are hairy beneath. Ripe frts may be white, pink or purple, always distinguished by being borne on stalks about as long (1–2 cm) as the frt itself.

'Downing' Mulberry is an American cv of this species selected for its fruit, which might be brought into cultivation in Europe.

Names: Fr.: Mûrier blanc; It.: Gelso bianco; Sp.: Mora blanca; Ger.: Weisser Maulbeere; Dtch.: Witte moerbei; Dan.: Hvid morbaer; Gr.: Aspri mouriá; Russ.: Sholkovitsa belaya; Yug.: Beli dud.

Uses: The primary use of this tree in its homeland is for feeding silkworms. It is used for this purpose in Europe in the few areas where sericulture still exists on a small scale, for instance in Italy. The frts, although edible, are rarely used in Europe.

Origin, distribution and cultivation: White Mulberry is a native of China, where it is extensively planted in towns, private gardens, farmland, and on a larger scale on silk farms.

The spread of this species outside China began when the secret of the origin of silk was leaked, and China lost her monopoly of manufacture, first to India and the Middle East. Justinian is said to have established the first European silkworm farms at Constantinople in the 6th century. Silkworms (the larvae of a moth, *Bombyx mori*) were later taken to Sicily and to Italy, and in the 13th century to Avignon, which with Lyon and other towns in the Rhône valley became a major centre of sericulture during the reign of Henri IV of France.

White Mulberry is naturalised in many areas of former or extant silk production such as Turkey, Italy and south-east France. In Britain only a few trees exist in botanical collections and gardens.

Similar plants: See other Mulberries, above.

Ficus carica
FIG

(p. 150)

Description: A deciduous, spreading large shrub or tree 2–5 m tall, in some circumstances growing to 10 m or more, with thick knobbly shoots and smooth pale grey bark marked with darker grey. Lvs large, up to 30 cm long by 25 cm broad, palmately lobed, the terminal lobe larger than others, and conspicuously palmately veined. Frts borne near tips of shoots, small (1–2 cm), dark grey, pear-shaped in the first winter, ripening in second year to a broad flask shape with green or dark purple skins. The mass of internal fls pink to purplish-red.

Cultivated figs do not differ markedly in appearance from wild forms, but long cultivation has induced an important change in their reproductive process. The Common or Adriatic Fig has no male fls, so the frt develops without being pollinated, or 'parthenocarpically'. The Smyrna Fig also has no male fls, but requires pollination for the frt to develop. To this end bundles of wild Caprifigs, *F.c. sylvestris*, containing fig insects (see introduction to Moraceae, p. 72) are suspended in the branches of the cultivated trees.

Names: Fr.: Figuier; It.: Fico; Sp.: Higuera; Ger.: Feige; Dtch.: Vijg; Dan.: Figen; Gr.: Sykiá; Russ.: Smokovnitsa; Yug.: Smokva.

Uses: The fruits are eaten fresh, or stewed, tinned in syrup or dried. Fresh fruits are delicate and travel badly, and are therefore expensive outside the areas of production.

Origin, distribution and cultivation: *F. carica* is a native of Asia Minor, and spread to the Mediterranean region at an early date. It is known to have been cultivated in Egypt 6000 years ago, and has been so continuously ever since.

The trees are sufficiently hardy to grow even in northern Europe, where they are often planted for ornament. Trees grown in hotter climates produce several crops a year, and it is only in southern Europe that they are cultivated on a commercial scale. Those grown in the North produce a single autumn crop, and the fruits only ripen in sheltered situations after an exceptionally hot summer. Figs are planted in very stony ground; in deep humus the tree responds by excessive vegetative development and produces fewer frts. In these situations the roots of young plants, obtained from cuttings, can be surrounded by a concrete casing.

CAPPARACEAE

Caper Family

A small family of herbs and shrubs with stipules and alternate simple or compound leaves. Fls have sepals and petals usually in 4s, and 6 to many stamens; the superior ovary is borne on a long stalk. Only one species, *Capparis spinosa*, is of economic interest.

Capparis spinosa
CAPER
(p. 150)

Description: A small shrub with numerous long slender trailing stems up to 1.5 m long. Lvs with thick ovate blades borne on a short stalk, at the base of which are two thick downward curving spines. Fls showy, 4–6 cm across, with many red stamens much longer than the 4 rounded white or pinkish petals; fls are very short-lived, borne along the entire length of stems, opening first near the bases then in succession towards the tips.

Wild spineless forms called var. *inermis* have more drooping stems, and the stipules are straight, scarcely spiny, and drop off at an early stage. Most of the cultivated capers are of this type.

Names: Synonyms: *C. rupestris*; *C. inermis*. (These are sometimes treated as distinct species).
Fr.: Caprier; It.: Cappero; Sp.: Alcaparra; Ger.: Kaper; Dtch.: Kapper; Dan.: Kapers; Gr.: Kappari; Russ.: Kapersi; Yug.: Kopar.

Uses: Grown for the capers of commerce, which are the unopened flower buds, wilted and pickled in salted vinegar, for use as a condiment.

Caper sauce sometimes accompanies lamb in Britain, but is particularly successful with fish, and capers are essential for many French and Mediterranean dishes including *sauce ravigote*, *rémoulade*, *gribiche*, *tartare*, and with raw meat (steak tartare). Its slightly astringent taste usefully counterbalances any dish that might otherwise seem too oily.

Origin, distribution and cultivation: Capers belong to a complex of species which occur in the wild throughout the Mediterranean, into the deserts of North Africa, and eastwards through Asia Minor to the Gobi Desert. It has been used as a condiment for thousands of years, but was probably mostly harvested in the wild, for the plants are quite common. They may be found today growing on ancient monuments, or on the rubble of new building developments and on waste land in all the hotter parts of the Mediterranean. They are cultivated on a commercial scale in most of these countries, with the finest quality buds (*nonpareille*) produced in France. The lower-grade capers are sometimes dry-salted. The plants are also widely grown as ornamentals, on walls, rock gardens, patios, etc.

PASSIFLORACEAE

Passion Flower Family

A family of about 10 genera and 500 species of herbs and woody, usually climbing plants of the tropics and sub-tropics, mostly from South America. Four-fifths of the species belong to the genus *Passiflora*, perennial woody vines with unbranched axillary tendrils, spectacular flowers of an unusual structure (see below) and large, many-seeded berries. Several species are grown for ornament in Europe, under glass or in sheltered sunny situations, and one is cultivated for its fruit. Other edible species are cultivated in the tropics, particularly in the West Indies and South America.

Passiflora edulis
PURPLE PASSION FRUIT

(p. 152)

Description: A woody perennial climber with green, hairless, grooved stems up to 12 m long, and long cylindrical spirally coiling axillary tendrils. Lvs deeply 3-lobed, sometimes ovate and unlobed on young shoots, 12–25 cm long, borne on long (2–5 cm) stalks which are grooved on upper surface; stipules ca. 1 cm long, lanceolate. Fls solitary, 7–10 cm in diameter, with 5 sepals and 5 petals alternating, so that the fl appears to have 10 petals; sepals white above and below; corona composed of a double row of radiating thread-like filaments, purple at base, white above, 2–3 cm long, and several inner rows of purple-tipped nipple-like protuberances; the 5 large radiating stamens are surmounted by the ovoid yellow-green ovary and 3 large yellow anthers. All these structures, from calyx to anthers, form a striking radiating geometric pattern which makes the fl unmistakeable. Frt a large (4–6 cm long) ovoid berry with a thin hard wall which turns deep purple and wrinkled or buckled when ripe and contains numerous small seeds embedded in the yellowish, translucent, sweet-scented juicy pulp.

Names: Also known as Purple Granadilla. Fr.: Barbadine, Fruit de la passion; It.: Granadiglia purpurea; Sp.: Granadilla; Ger.: Purpurgranadille; Dtch.: Passievrucht; Dan.: Passionsfrugt; Russ.: Passiflora; Yug.: Božja krunica.

The generic name does not owe its origin to any supposed aphrodisiac property, but to a fanciful comparison of the fl structures with the implements of the crucifixion: the corona represents the crown of thorns, the anthers the nails, and the stamens the hammers, or alternately the 5 stigmata.

Uses: The fruits, which are the best and most widely cultivated of all the passion fruits, are eaten raw, the flesh spooned directly from the shell, or used in fruit salads, as topping for ice-creams, for sorbets or for making jams and jellies. The small seeds are not easily separable from the pulp, and must be eaten too. The main industrial use is as canned fruit juice, made after the seeds have been strained from the pulp.

Origin, distribution and cultivation: *P. edulis* is a native of southern Brazil, and was taken to many tropical and warm-temperate parts of all continents in the 19th century. It is grown on a large scale in some countries, notably Australia, New Zealand, S. Africa and Kenya. In the tropics it can only be cultivated in the highlands, being replaced by other *Passiflora* spp. in the hot lowlands. It is cultivated to a small extent in the Mediterranean countries as a commercial crop, but more often by the home-gardener. Further north it will flower, but will not produce ripe fruit unless grown under glass. Plants are supported on wires or trellises.

Similar plants: Blue Passion Flower *P. coerulea* and hybrids of this and other spp. are much more frequently seen in Europe than *P. edulis*, but are only grown as ornamentals. Blue Passion Flower differs from *P. edulis* in having mostly 5- or 6-lobed lvs, in the fl with corona filaments purple-red at base, white in the middle, purple at tips and with dark purple styles, and the ripe frt is greenish-yellow.

A yellow-fruited variety of *P. edulis* is cultivated in the tropics, but not in Europe.

CUCURBITACEAE

Marrow Family

A family of tropical and sub-tropical plants, several of which are of considerable economic importance in temperate countries, including Europe. None, however, are resistant to frost, so they can only be grown as annuals during the summer months, or under glass.

Other familiar members restricted to the tropics include the Luffa *L. cylindrica* cultivated in the East for the fruits which are edible when immature, but later develop a network of tough fibres which after the rind and flesh have been removed are sold as 'vegetable sponges', and the Bottle Gourd *Lagenaria siceraria* grown for the light hard dry shells used as containers. These are often called Calabashes, but the true Calabash *Crescentia cujete*, which is used for the same purpose, is globular or broadly ovoid, never bottle-necked, and belongs to an entirely different family of plants.

The cultivated Cucurbitaceae are fast-growing, trailing or climbing plants with mostly soft, hairy, prickly or smooth stems and large, more or less lobed lvs arranged spirally. Fls are unisexual, yellow in all but one of the spp. seen in Europe, with inferior ovaries. The frt is typically a 'pepo', a large or very large fleshy structure like a berry, with many seeds embedded in soft flesh enclosed in a hard rind, but some are 1-seeded.

Most of the fruits of this family are well known, but the lax use of the words 'pumpkin' and 'squash' to describe fruits of all the *Cucurbita* spp. is confusing. Herklots suggests the following definitions of these words: Summer Squash: any *Cucurbita* (mostly *C. pepo*) used immature as a table vegetable. Winter Squash: Any *Cucurbita* used ripe as a vegetable or for feeding livestock.

Since no specific English terms exist for the species of *Cucurbita*, and because other species include more than one produce (eg. *Cucumis sativus*: Cucumber and Gherkin), the scientific names are used in the following key. Note that British or North European *Cucurbita* spp. are almost bound to be *C. pepo* or *C. maxima*. *C. moschata* and *C. mixta* are mainly grown in central and southern Europe and in the Soviet Union.

KEY TO MARROW FAMILY

1	Fls small, white or green; frt pear-shaped, 10–20 cm long, smooth-skinned with deep longitudinal furrows, containing a single large flat white seed=*Sechium edule*	(2)
2	Fls larger, yellow or orange. Frt many-seeded with a hard rind=**3**	(1)
3	Lvs deeply, pinnately lobed; tendrils branched=*Citrullus lanatus*	(4)
4	Lvs more or less deeply, palmately lobed; tendrils simple=**5**	(3)
5	Fls with 5 petals completely fused from base to middle=**6**	(12)
6	Stems soft, round in section, bristly, but more softly so than *C. pepo*; frt stalk round in section, enlarged by corky tissue=*Cucurbita maxima*	(7)
7	Stems hard, angular; frt stalk angular in section, grooved=**8**	(6)
8	Stems and lvs bristly. Frt stalk sharply angular, grooved, not enlarged by corky tissue and not or only slightly flared at attachment to frt=*Cucurbita pepo*	(9)
9	Stems and lvs without bristles=**10**	(8)
10	Frt stalk smoothly grooved, not enlarged by corky tissue, often greatly flared at attachment to frt; frt soft-shelled=*Cucurbita moschata*	(11)
11	Frt stalks 5-angled, often enlarged by corky tissue, but not flared at attachment to frt; frt hard or soft-shelled=*Cucurbita mixta*	(10)
12	Fls with 5 petals separated almost to base=**13**	(5)
13	Frt sweet, the rind smooth or netted or scaly, hairless or with downy hairs=*Cucumis melo*	(14)
14	Frt not or less sweet, used as a vegetable, the rind rough with short blunt projections or prickles=**15**	(13)
15	Lvs not or shallowly lobed, the fundus of spaces between lobes acute; frts long and potentially large=*Cucumis sativus*	(16)
16	Lvs deeply palmately lobed, the fundus of spaces between lobes rounded; frts small, under 7 cm, less elongate=*Cucumis anguria*	(15)

Cucurbita pepo
MARROWS, PUMPKINS and SUMMER SQUASHES

(p. 154)

Description: A very variable species in size, reproductive characters and in habit, either slightly bushy, or more usually with long trailing stems. Stems and lvs rough to the touch, with spiny bristles, the stem hard, often 5-angled; lvs with heart-shaped base and narrow acute spaces between usually deep lobes, and margins saw-toothed; frt very variable according to cv, but with stalk hard, little swollen, not flared at attachment to frt, sharply angular and grooved.

The main cvs of this species can be grouped in 7 main categories:

1. Vegetable Marrows 'English' Vegetable Marrows are either bushy plants (White Bush, Green Bush) or trailing plants bearing large cylindrical or round frts with green or cream skins and greenish-white, rarely yellowy flesh; they are usually grown to a large size. Cvs include Long White; Long Green; Table Dainty (a smaller, striped, cylindrical frt); Cream; Rotherside Orange (with yellow flesh); Tender and True (round, mottled green); Pen-y-bryd (round, cream-coloured).

'Italian' Vegetable Marrows are bushy plants producing cylindrical mottled green frts which are picked young. Cocozelle, also known as Asparagus Squash, Eggplant Squash or Italian Green Striped, are cut when 35–40 cm long; Caserta are cut earlier, when 15–20 cm long, and true French Courgettes when only 12–15 cm long. Courgette and Zucchini are names commonly applied to all 'baby' squashes of this type, but the latter is properly a darker green frt growing on a more vigorous plant and is cut when 25–30 cm long; it is sometimes also known as Italian or Spanish Squash.

Vegetable Spaghetti or Spaghetti Marrow, a pale oblong frt with flesh forming loose strands, also belongs to the 'Vegetable Marrow' category.

2. Pie Pumpkins This is the common Pumpkin of New England, growing on trailing plants, which we have come to associate with Halloween. Frts are either large (8–12 kg in weight), globose or slightly flattened, pale orange with pale cream flesh; or more oblong, with drier, dark yellow flesh (Golden Oblong); or small, globose and flattened, 2.5–3 kg in weight, dull orange skin and sweet firm orange flesh (Small Sugar Pumpkin); the last of these are the best for pies, etc.

3. Fordhook These are bush or trailing plants with frts 20–25 cm long, cylindrical, with skins whitish mottled with yellow, and yellow flesh.

4. Summer Crook-necks and Straight-necks Bush-type plants. Crook-necks are club-shaped and curved between the stem and middle, 20–35 cm long, the skin ribbed and warty, orange, yellow or white according to cv; Straight-necks are similar but not curved in basal half, usually with yellow skin and greenish-white flesh.

5. Custard Marrows Also known as Scallops or Patty Pan. Frts are white or yellow 'flying saucer'-shaped with a wavy rim, cut when about 15 cm across.

6. Table Queen Squash Small (12–15 cm in diameter, 600–800 gr) frts with dark green skin and dull yellow to pale orange flesh.

7. Small hard inedible fruits Variously shaped with smooth or very warty skins, patterned in combinations of cream, green, yellow, orange and black, grown only for ornament, as the frts dry and will keep. These are called Coloquinte in France, but are not to be confused with the true Colocynth *Citrullus colocynthis*, a species related to the Water Melon which was formerly cultivated in Asia for medicinal purposes.

Names: Fr.: Courge, Citrouille; It.: Zucca, Zucchino; Sp.: Calabaza; Ger.: Kürbis; Dtch.: Pompoen; Dan.: Mandelgraeskar, Centnergraeskar; Gr.: Kolokythi; Russ.: Tikva; Yug.: Navadna buče.

Uses: Large Vegetable Marrows are used for feeding livestock, or as an inferior vegetable in soups, stews, or stuffed with meat and spices. The smaller Courgettes, Zucchini, are a respectable vegetable in their own right. Pumpkins are used for soup, stews, and in American Pumpkin Pie. Mature frts may be used for jam. Unless competing for prizes for size, amateur growers of English marrows would be well advised to cut the frts at courgette or zucchini size; although not selected for this purpose, in this form they make a far better table vegetable than the tasteless mushy mature frt.

Origin, distribution and cultivation: *C. pepo* has been cultivated in its native Mexico and the southern United States for at least 8000 years. It has been widely distributed in the world, and some of its cvs are the hardiest members of the genus, and therefore the most commonly cultivated in Britain and northern Europe. Custard Marrows have been cultivated in Britain and on the continent since the 16th century, but are now rarely seen. Large Vegetable Marrows are the most widely grown form in Britain, while Courgette and Zucchini type plants are favoured in France and the Mediterranean countries. The hot summers of central and eastern Europe allow the cultivation of Pie Pumpkins on a large scale as well as the larger Vegetable Marrows. 'Vegetable Spaghetti', first developed in N.E. China, is now grown commercially under glass in Britain and Holland as are Courgettes, for which there is an increasing demand. The other types – Fordhook, Crook-necks and Table Queen – are rarely grown in Europe.

Similar plants: See key and descriptions of other *Cucurbita* spp. (p. 78).

Cucurbita maxima
PUMPKINS and WINTER SQUASHES

(p. 154)

Description: A long-running annual, trailing or climbing vine, rarely a bush, rough to the touch but much less so than *C. pepo*, the bristles sparser and finer. Stems round in cross-section. Lvs usually kidney-shaped, with finely saw-toothed margins, not or only shallowly lobed; frt variable, but stalk soft, round in section, not angled or grooved, enlarged by corky tissue.

The cvs may be classed into several groups according to the type of frt.:

1. Turban Squashes These are readily identifiable, because the ovaries protrude prominently from the apex of the frt, shaping it like a turban sitting on a head or an acorn in its cup. They are typically small to medium, with smooth skins, often red or mottled. Synonyms and cvs of these include Bishop's Head; Turk's Cap; Buttercup. Essex Hybrid has characteristics of both this type and of Hubbard (see below). The group also includes the Warty or Pebbled Squashes, similar in shape but with a hard thick shell with a bumpy surface.

2. Mammoth or Show Squashes Very large (16–50 kg) globular frts with soft thin shells coloured orange, in some cvs with pale brown stripes, and thick yellow flesh.

3. Banana Squashes Frts weighing 5 or 6 kg, shaped like a very large courgette, with skins grey-green becoming pink in storage, and yellow flesh.

4. Hubbard These are pear-shaped frts, 30–40 cm long and weighing 4–6 kg, with very hard thick green shells and dull yellow flesh. They are considered to be among the best table squashes.

5. Boston Marrow Also known as Orange Marrow. The frts are similar to Hubbards, but more globose, less constricted near the stalk, with a softer, orange shell. 'Delicious' Marrows are smaller, top-shaped frts with green skins mottled with grey; 'Golden Delicious', a cross between this and the Golden Marrow, has orange skin.

Names: Fr.: Potiron, Giraumon, Pâtisson; It.: Zucca torta; Sp.: Calabaza amarilla; Ger.: Riesenkürbis; Dtch.: Pompoen; Dan.: Centnergraeskar; Russ.: Tikva bolshaya; Yug.: Jedilne buce.

Uses: Mammoth Squashes are used for feeding livestock; the other types are used in the same way as other squashes and pumpkins.

Origin, distribution and cultivation: It is thought that *C. maxima* was first cultivated in Peru, where seeds 700 years old have been found, and was not taken to the northern hemisphere until after the Spanish conquest. It is now widely distributed on all continents, and is the second most commonly cultivated species in Europe, after *C. pepo.* Mammoth Squashes are grown on a field scale in France and other parts of the continent, and Turban Squashes are widely cultivated in Europe, but the other types are rarely seen here. Some of the many superior cvs developed in Japan may well be adopted in the future.

Similar plants: See key and description of other *Cucurbita* spp. (p. 78).

Cucurbita moschata
PUMPKINS and WINTER SQUASHES

Description: An annual, long-stemmed trailing vine with softly hairy, not prickly, stems which are round or smoothly 5-angled. Lvs large, shallowly lobed, sometimes with white blotches, up to 30 cm broad. Frt variable, hard or soft shelled, dull in colour, with yellow to orange flesh.

Cvs belong to three main categories:

1. Bell or Gourd-shaped The best known cv is Buttersquash, a dull orange frt in which the flesh is solid in the basal (nearest stalk) half, the seed cavity lying in the broader distal half.

2. Crook-necks In shape resembling the *C. pepo* Crook-necks, but with smooth, not warty or ribbed shells, and larger, weighing 5–7 kg. Golden Cushaw and Canada Crook-necks belong to this category.

3. Large Cheese Pumpkin-type frts with cream or buff-coloured skins resembling *C. pepo* Pumpkins. 5–7 kg in weight; they can sometimes be pear-shaped, as with Quaker Pie frts.

Names: Fr.: Courge musquée; It.: Zucca moscata; Sp.: Calabaza moscada; Ger.: Moschuskürbis; Dtch.: Pompoen; Dan.: Moskusgraeskar; Russ.: Tikva muskatnaya;.

Uses: As other squashes and pumpkins.

Origin, distribution and cultivation: *C. moschata* is thought to have been cultivated first in Mexico or central America. It was widely distributed in both N. and S. America at least 5000 years ago. It has been taken to all continents since the Spanish conquest, and is the most commonly cultivated *Cucurbita* sp. in the tropics. It is rarely grown in Europe, but 'Buttersquash' frts imported from the USA have become available in supermarkets.

Similar plants: See key to *Cucurbita* spp. (p. 78).

Cucurbita mixta
PUMPKINS and WINTER SQUASHES

Description: Formerly treated as a variety of *C. moschata* to which it is very similar. Stems are softly hairy, not rough, and hard, distinctly 5-angled. Lvs similar to *C. moschata*, usually with white blotches. Frt variable; frt stalk much enlarged by corky tissue, but never flared at point of attachment.

The best known cvs belong to the type called Cushaw Pumpkins, oblong frts usually curved in the middle or near the neck, cream or cream with green stripes, or pale green with darker green stripes (Japanese Pie). Tennessee Sweet Potato, a broader, slightly pear-shaped frt of a uniform yellow, 5–8 kg, also belongs to this species, as do a number of recently developed Japanese squashes.

Uses: As other squashes. Some are used for feeding livestock.

Origin, distribution and cultivation: This species also originated in Mexico or central America, and although widely distributed in the region and in the southern United States in pre-Columbian times, is probably of less ancient cultivation than the other species. It is grown throughout N. America, the Far East and the drier tropics; in Europe mostly in the Mediterranean and in the central and eastern countries.

Similar plants: See key to *Cucurbita* spp. (p. 78).

Cucumis melo
MELONS
(p. 152)

Description: A variable softly hairy annual trailing vine. Stems ridged: tendrils simple, unbranched. Lvs 10–15 cm in diameter, ovate to slightly kidney-shaped, angled or shallowly 5- or 7-lobed. Fls 1.2–3 cm across, yellow, the corolla deeply divided into 5 petals; male fls in clusters, female fls solitary. Frt very variable in size, shape, colour, type of rind and flavour according to cv. In Asia a number of varieties with elongate frts resembling cucumbers are grown and used as vegetables, but only sweet cvs are grown in

Europe. The main types are the following:

1. Cantaloupe These are medium-sized globose or ovoid frts with a thick rough rind, often with deep longitudinal grooves suggesting segments, without a network or rough pale lines, usually yellow or orange in colour. The French Charantais belongs to this type.

2. Ogen Melon Derived from the Cantaloupe types; these are very small (15 cm or less) bright orange-yellow globose frts with vertical green stripes, and green flesh with a fine flavour.

3. Musk Melon Also known as Netted Melons because of the tracery of rough whitish lines which covers the yellow, pinkish, orange or green rind. The flesh is green to salmon pink and very aromatic. Cvs include the Cavaillon Yellow, Sucrins, Dutch Net and Superlative.

4. Winter Melons Globose or more often ovoid to strongly elongate, medium to large frts with smooth or slightly bumpy or ridged rinds of a uniform pale or dark green, and pale green flesh. They are of inferior quality to the other 3 categories, but are harder skinned and keep longer. Honeydew, a whitish or pale green skinned variety, and the elongate dark green melons imported from Spain under the same name both belong to this group.

Names: Fr.: Melon; It.: Popone; Sp.: Melon; Ger.: Melone; Dtch.: Meloen; Dan.: Melon; Gr.: Peponi; Russ.: Dinya; Yug.: Melone.

Uses: The flesh is eaten fresh as a dessert. Powdered ginger, lemon juice, pepper or other condiments may be added, but the best quality Cantaloupes or Musk Melons should be eaten unadulterated. Very small young frts may be pickled in vinegar like gherkins, or candied.

Origin, distribution and cultivation: *C. melo*, like most members of the genus, is a native of tropical Africa. One primitive type, with scarcely palatable frts ca. 7.5 cm in diameter, is cultivated as a vegetable in Malawi. The spread in cultivation of melons outside Africa is relatively recent. They do not appear to have been known to the Greeks or to the ancient Egyptians, but it is certainly via the Nile Valley that they reached the Mediterranean and Asia. Melons were brought to Italy in the later years of the Roman empire, and only reached France in 1495, as a result of Charles VIII's campaigns in Italy. (The name Cantaloupe dates from this period, Cantalupo being a summer residence of the pope where this variety was cultivated.)

Melons are now grown on a field scale in all Mediterranean countries and in France as far north as the Loire. Further North, including Britain, they are grown under glass.

Similar plants: *Cucurbita* spp. and Cucumber *Cucumis sativus* (see key p. 78).

Cucumis sativus
CUCUMBER and GHERKIN

(p. 152)

Description: A trailing or climbing annual with stiff bristly hairs on lvs and stems. Stems markedly 4-angled. Lvs on long (5–15 cm) stalks, 3 or 5-angled, ovate or shallowly lobed, 8–20 cm long, the base deeply emarginate, the apex acute, and margins finely toothed. Fls 3–4 cm in diameter, yellow, the corolla deeply divided into 5 hairy crinkled petals; male fls in clusters, female fls in 1s or 2s. Frt variable (see below), green, ovoid to very elongate, with numerous spiny tubercles and warts, especially when young, the flesh pale green with distinctive cucumber smell.

The cvs grown in Europe may be divided into three main categories:

1. 'English', 'Forcing' or 'Indoor' Cucumbers Large frts, up to 90 cm long, which reproduce parthenocarpically, grown in hot houses.

2. Ridge or Field Cucumbers Generally smaller frts (exceptions are some of the Japanese cvs, eg. Suyo, Kaga, Kariha), which require pollination, grown out of doors.

3. Gherkins Small fruited cvs picked when very young for pickling.

The Apple Cucumber is a form with globose frts which is not grown commercially.

Names: (Cucumber): Fr.: Concombre; It.: Cetriolo; Sp.: Pepino; Ger.: Gurke; Dtch.: Komkommer; Dan.: Salatagurk; Gr.: Anguri; Russ.: Ogurts; Yug.: Kumare.

Uses: All cucumber frts are picked before they are fully mature. Large Indoor and Ridge Cucumbers are generally eaten raw, in salads, but may be cooked or pickled. The very young frts of small fruited cvs are pickled as Gherkins. In central and eastern Europe especially, larger frts are pickled in sweeter solutions, often with dill; the French prefer very small frts pickled in a more acid solution (sometimes known as 'cocktail gherkins' in Britain).

Origin, distribution and cultivation: *C. sativus* is a native of India, where it has been in cultivation since the remotest times. It was known in ancient Egypt, and to the Greeks and Romans, and has been grown in Europe ever since.

Ridge Cucumbers are only grown on ridges by home-gardeners and in some market gardens. They are more widely sown as an ordinary field crop. Indoor varieties require higher temperatures and humidity than most crops (tomatoes, etc) grown under glass, and should be protected from pollination by insects, so they are usually grown apart in 'cucumber houses'. Cvs grown for pickling gherkins are cultivated under glass or outdoors, depending on the local climate.

Similar plants: See key to the Cucurbitaceae, (p. 78).

The West Indian Gherkin *C. anguria* is a related species, originally of African origin, but which developed its present form, both in the wild and in cultivation, in the West Indies and central America. It is now rarely seen in Europe, but was once fairly extensively cultivated in France, and might again be adopted as a hot-house crop. The frts resemble gherkins of *C. sativus*, but are usually less elongate, sometimes almost globose, and never exceed 10 cm even when mature; the plant is readily identifiable by the deeply 3- or 5-lobed lvs.

Citrullus lanatus
WATER MELON
(p. 154)

Description: A much-branched trailing annual, with stems 1.5–5 m long. Stems slender, angled and grooved, and covered in long white hairs. Lvs 5–20 cm long, with 2, 3 or 4 pairs of pinnate lobes which are again once subdivided, on stalks 2–8 cm long; tendrils branching once or twice. Fls unisexual, solitary, axillary, pale yellow, 2.5–3 cm in diameter, with corolla deeply divided into 5 petals; male fl with 3 to 5 stamens, the filaments short and free; female fl with 3 staminodes, the ovary ovoid, densely hairy, the style 5 mm long with 3 lobes. Frt large or very large, up to 70 cm long, globose or oblong, with hard smooth rind variously patterned in green and cream or different shades of green; the flesh very watery, typically deep pink, sometimes white, yellow or greenish.

Names: Fr.: Pastèque; It.: Cocomero; Sp.: Sandia; Ger.: Wassermelone; Dtch.: Watermeloen; Dan.: Vandmelon; Gr.: Karpusi; Russ.: Arbuz; Yug.: Lubenice.

Uses: The fruit is eaten fresh. It has the virtue of remaining cool and therefore refreshing even when the fruit has stood all day in the sun in the hottest climates. It is a useful way of quenching thirst in places where the water may be unsafe or unavailable. The fruits are rather fragile and will not keep for long; they are consequently mostly eaten in the areas of production, and exports are limited.

Origin, distribution and cultivation: Water melon is a native of tropical Africa, where a wild form with small bitter frts still occurs. It was cultivated in Ancient Egypt whence it spread throughout the Mediterranean and eastwards to India in prehistoric times. Today it is cultivated in all tropical and sub-tropical countries, and in temperate countries with a continental climate. In Europe it is grown in all the Mediterranean countries and in central and eastern Europe where hot summers prevail. It favours light but fertile soils, and will often be seen on sandy river banks.

Similar plants: The pinnately lobed lvs distinguish the plant from other European Cucurbitaceae. None of the *Cucumis melo* Melons cultivated in Europe has frt patterned in the same way; in this respect Water Melons more closely resemble Vegetable Marrow, but are much less elongate.

Sechium edule
CHAYOTE

Description: A sprawling or (almost always in cultivation) climbing non-woody perennial vine with stems growing to 10 m, and tuberous roots. Stems grooved. Tendrils axillary, large, and branched. Lvs large, 12–25 cm in diameter, ovate or (mostly) angled, sometimes shallowly lobed, on stalks 5–15 cm long. Fls small, in axils; male fls in small clusters, female fls solitary, both greenish or white, the corolla deeply divided, the petals free almost to base. Frts irregularly pear-shaped, with deep longitudinal furrows and smooth white or green skin, containing a single large (3–5 cm) flattened white seed near the base; flesh whitish.

Names: Also known as Christophene. Fr.: Sechium, Chayote; It.: Chayote; Sp.: Chayote; Ger.: Chayote; Dtch.: Chayote; Dan.: Chajote; Russ.: Chayota.

Uses: Cultivated for the fruits which are boiled or used in stews as a vegetable.

In many tropical countries the tuberous root is eaten in the same way, and the young shoots may be used as a spinach or pot herb.

The stems yield a brilliant silvery-white fibre sometimes used in hat-making.

Origin, distribution and cultivation: Chayote is a native of Mexico and central America where it was commonly cultivated in pre-Columbian times. It has been widely distributed in the tropics and sub-tropics, sometimes grown as a commercial crop but more usually in the vegetable garden. Fruits available in European shops are imported, mainly from the West Indies, but the plant is cultivated by a few home-gardeners in the Mediterranean, often under glass.

Similar plants: See key. The fls and frt are unlike any other European Cucurbitaceae.

Chayote

CACTACEAE

Cactus Family

A family of typically succulent and spiny plants endemic to the New World.

All native European, African or Asian plants which resemble them, for instance the succulent spiny Euphorbias which cover dry hillsides in some parts of the Mediterranean, belong to other families, their resemblance to cacti being an example of 'convergent' evolution, whereby plants of different origins develop similar forms and structures in response to the same ecological or physical factors.

Many cacti are grown as ornamentals in Europe, but only *Opuntia* is of economic use.

Opuntia ficus-indica
BARBARY FIG or **PRICKLY PEAR**

(p. 156)

Description: A leafless succulent spiny plant growing erect, often tree-like, to 5 m. Trunk rounded, brownish, slightly fissured, bearing oval flatted, racket-shaped stem joints 15–45 cm long, sparsely covered in small bosses covered in many small yellow spines and often 1 or 2 larger pale spines, up to 5 cm long. Fls bright yellow, large (6–10 cm across) with many petals and stamens, borne on upper stem joints. Frt ovoid, 5–10 cm long, yellow, red or purple, sweet-tasting.

Names: Fr.: Figuier de Barbarie, Nopal; It.: Fico d'India; Sp.: Chumbera; Ger.: Feigendistel; Dtch.: Vijgecactus; Dan.: Figenkaktus; Gr.: Fragosykia; Russ.: Opuntsia indiskaya.

Uses: Planted for hedges and boundaries, and for the edible fruits which may be eaten raw, but are usually fried in oil or cooked in stews. The tufts of minute hair-like barbed spines scattered on the surface of the frt must be thoroughly removed before use, and care must be taken in handling the frts, as the spines cause serious irritation.

Origin, distribution and cultivation: Like all cacti, this plant is a native of the New World, introduced to Spain by Christopher Columbus or shortly thereafter. It has been naturalised in many parts of Africa, Asia and Australia, often becoming a pest, as it forms impenetrable thickets over vast tracts of land, rendering them useless for grazing or any other purpose.

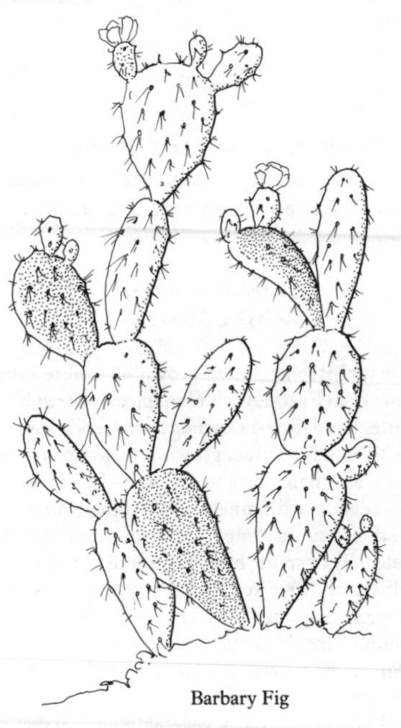

Barbary Fig

Prickly Pear occurs in cultivation or in the wild throughout the drier parts of the Mediterranean, and its fruits, either harvested in the wild or from small family plantations, are offered for sale on markets in all Mediterranean countries. They are of minor economic importance, and are not exported.

Similar plants: In parts of Spain and in the Canary Islands a closely related species, *O. coccinellifera*, is cultivated as the food of the cochineal insect, farmed for the carmine dye used to colour confectioneries, ink, liqueurs and fabrics.

At least two other Opuntia spp. occur, but more rarely in the Mediterranean. *O. monocantha* is distinguished by its brighter green joints with darker – yellow to dark red – spines. *O. maxima* has a more upright, less spreading habit than *O. ficus-indica*, dull green leaf joints, and whitish spines in clusters of 1–4 amid shorter brown spines.

TILIACEAE

Lime Family

A family of tropical and temperate trees, shrubs and a few herbs. Jute *Corchorus capsularis*, grown mainly in the Ganges valley for its fibre, is one of the few members which has any economic importance.

Corchorus olitorius
MELOKHIA

Description: When grown as a fibre crop (never in Europe) this plant closely resembles Jute. It is a little-branched herbaceous annual with slender stems, growing to 4 m or more. Lvs alternate, bright green, 5–15 cm long, lanceolate with finely saw-toothed margins and a pair of long fine auricles spreading laterally from the base. Fls solitary or in small clusters, with 5 sepals and 5 yellow petals ca. 8 mm long and 10 to many stamens. Frt a round capsule (a cylindrical pod in Jute) 1–2 cm in diameter, wrinkled, with 10 vertical ridges.

Plants grown as a vegetable are harvested when very young and tender, not or little over 30 cm in height. Taller plants (1–2 m) may be grown for seed.

Melokhia leaf

Names: Fibre crops are called Tossa Jute or Jew's Mallow; Melokhia (also spelled Molokhia or Mulokhia) applies to the plant as a vegetable. Fr.: Corette potagère; Ger.: Gemüsepappel; Gr.: Melokhia, Molokha.

Uses: As a vegetable the tender, very mucilaginous leaves are used like spinach, or in soups. They may be used either fresh or dried.

	KEY TO LIMES	
	These three species may be distinguished from other European Limes and from each other by the nature of the pubescence, or short downy hairs on the undersides of the lvs:	
1	Underside of lf entirely pubescent, silvery or grey=**other spp.**	**(2)**
2	Underside of lf pubescent only on veins or in tufts in axils of lf veins=**3**	**(1)**
3	Both sides of lf pubescent on veins; lf stalk hairy when young=**Large-leafed Lime**	**(4)**
4	Underside of lf pubescent in tufts of brownish or orange hairs in axils of veins=**5**	**(3)**
5	Lf, bract, fls and frt larger; lf somewhat asymmetrical; buds green or reddish-brown=**Common Lime**	**(6)**
6	Lf, bract, fls and frt smaller; lf more symmetrically heart-shaped; buds red=**Small-leafed Lime**	**(5)**

Origin, distribution and cultivation: Egypt is the main producer and consumer of this plant, where it has been cultivated since the earliest pharaonic dynasties and still provides a staple vegetable for the fellaheen. Although it is rarely cultivated in Europe, except in Turkey and Cyprus, the plant deserves mention in this book because it is used in Greek and Turkish cooking, and the dried leaves are often available from Cypriot grocers in Western Europe.

Similar plants: In Europe, none. The auricles at the base of the leaf make it unmistakeable.

Tilia spp.
LIME or **LINDEN**
(p. 156)

Description: Familiar medium to very large trees widely planted for ornament in parks, and avenues, etc., with tall domed crowns in branches arising at narrow angles with trunk, and dark grey closely fissured bark. Lvs variable, round-ovate, with pointed tip, 6–15 cm long and broad, finely hairy above. Fls in cymes of 3–6 on a long stalk adhering to the centre of a large elongate pale green bract. Frt globose, finely and densely hairy, with 5 more or less prominent ribs, 6–10 mm across.

About 10 closely related spp., some of them introductions, occur in Europe. The most commonly used are Large-leaved Lime, *T. platyphyllos,* and Common Lime *T.* x *europaea,* a natural established hybrid between *T. platyphyllos* and *T. cordata,* Small-leaved Lime.

Names: Fr.: Tilleul; It.: Tiglio; Sp.: Tilo; Ger.: Linde; Dtch.: Linde; Dan.: Lind; Russ.: Lipa; Yug.: Lipa.

Uses: The flowers are picked when in full bloom, together with the 'wing' or bract, and dried for making an infusion: Lime 'tea'. The dried fls are sold in chemists and food markets all over France and elsewhere. This drink has been recognised as a mild sedative and was used by doctors during the 2nd World War for this purpose.

Origin, distribution and cultivation: These three species are all native to most of Europe, and are widely planted for ornament. Trees from which the fls are regularly harvested are usually pollarded for easier access. France is the main producer and consumer of Lime tea, but the fls are also sold in Germany, Switzerland, etc.

Similar plants: The dried fls with attendant bract are unmistakeable.

MALVACEAE

Mallow Family

A family of some 1000 species of herbs and shrubs distributed in all the major regions of the world. In Europe it is familiar through the many wild and ornamental mallows (*Malva*, *Lavatera* and *Althaea* spp.) and Hibiscus.

It contains one genus of outstanding economic importance: *Gossypium*, the Cotton plant, and a few others of only minor importance. Three species are cultivated in the tropics and subtropics for fibres from their stems (whereas cotton produces seed-fibres); these are Kenaf *Hibiscus cannabinus*, grown mainly in Asia, including the Soviet Union, Aramina fibre *Urena lobata* in Brazil and central Africa, and Roselle *Hibiscus sabdariffa* in Egypt, Africa and the West Indies; the calyx tubes of this plant are boiled to produce kakardé, or sorrel drink. One species, Okra, is cultivated in Europe and throughout the tropics as a vegetable.

The plants of this family are usually hairy or downy, the stems often fibrous. Lvs usually large, simple, palmately veined. Fls are usually showy, in 1–6s in lf axils, with 5 petals and 5 sepals and an epicalyx of 3 to 9 bracteoles, according to genus.

Hibiscus esculentus
OKRA
(p. 156)

Description: A stout annual herb, 1–2 m tall, with stems sometimes tinged with red. Stipules narrow, dropping off. Lvs alternate, 15–30 cm long, broadly heart-shaped and more or less, sometimes very deeply, palmately 3–7 lobed, hairy, with finely saw-toothed margins, and paler green below. Fls solitary, in axils, with 5 broad, ca. 6-cm-long yellow petals each with a dark red spot at base. Epicalyx formed of 5–10 narrow bracteoles ca. 1 cm long. Stamens numerous, on a column joined to bases of petals. Frt an angled elongate conical and beaked capsule 10–30 cm long with shallow longitudinal furrows, green, with or without hairs, soft when harvested, hardening and splitting open if left to ripen.

Names: syn: *Abelmoschus esculentus.* Also known as Gumbo (America, W. Indies), Lady's Finger, and by the Arabic name *Bamya*; it is the *Bhindi* of Indian restaurant menus.
Fr.: Gombo; It.: Ocra; Sp.: Quesillo; Ger.: Okra, Rosenpappel; Dtch.: Okra; Dan.: Okra; Gr.: Bamia; Russ.: Bamia; Yug.: Jedilni oslez, Okra.

Uses: The tender immature frts are picked when 5–12 cm long for use as a cooked vegetable. They are usually boiled or included in stews, for they are highly mucilaginous, but may also be sliced and fried. The mucilage has various minor industrial uses.

Origin, distribution and cultivation: Okra is a native of tropical Africa, and was widely distributed in the tropics and subtropics in the 19th century. In Europe it is cultivated mainly in Turkey, Cyprus, Greece and Spain, and is commonly available from Cypriot and Indian grocers in western Europe. It is grown on a small field scale or, more usually, on market-garden plots.

Similar plants: Roselle *Hibiscus sabdariffa* usually has more deeply lobed lvs, a darker, brownish-red spot at the base of petals, and the frt is an ovoid capsule, not elongate and pyramidal.

Okra might also be mistaken for Cotton (below). The latter has characteristic frt (bolls); the fl has an epicalyx of 3 large leaf-like toothed bracteoles; the lvs of cvs grown in Europe are never divided to more than half-way to base, and the whole plant is covered in black spots.

Gossypium spp.
COTTON
(p. 156)

Description: Annual or perennial shrubs, variable in size and growth habit, the whole plant irregularly spotted with black oil glands. Branches round in section, slender, hairy. Lvs large, more or less deeply palmately lobed; fl/frt with 3 large, very conspicuous leaf-like toothed bracteoles. Fls with cup-shaped calyx, 5 partly overlapping yellow petals and numerous stamens. Frt a large globose or oval dry dehiscent capsule (the 'boll') which opens to reveal the fluffy white mass of lint.

Of the 30 or so spp. of *Gossypium*, some of the wild ones are devoid of lint. The many cultivated varieties belong to one of 4 spp.: *G. herbaceum* (which includes the forms grown in Europe) and *G. arboreum*, both from Asia and Africa, and *G. barbadense* and *G. hirsutum*, originally from America. The Old World spp. can be recognised by their entire or toothed bracteoles, those of *G. herbaceum* being widely flared, whereas they hug the fl in *G. arboreum.* The New World spp. have bracteoles deeply divided, the lobes more than 3 times as long as broad. 'Sea Island' and Egyptian cottons belong to the latter spp.

Names: Fr.: Coton; It.: Cottone; Sp.: Algodon; Ger.: Baumwolle, Katun; Dtch.: Katoen; Dan.: Bomuld; Gr.: Vamvaki; Russ.: Khlopchatnik; Yug.: Bombaž.

Uses: Cotton is the world's most important textile fibre. The fibres are the lint: unicellular ribbon-like hairs of varying length in different cvs, the longest being the most desirable, that grow in a dense mass on the seeds inside the frt capsule. A good edible oil is expressed from the seeds.

Origin, distribution and cultivation: Cotton has been used as a textile both in Asia and in America since prehistoric times. When Alexander the Great invaded western Asia clad in linen, he conquered peoples dressed in cotton, but this superior fibre did not become known in Europe until twelve centuries later, when the Arabs introduced the plant and the art of spinning and weaving the fibre to Spain, Sicily, Cyprus and the Levant.

Cotton did not achieve any importance in Europe until it was widely planted in America and Africa, and new American varieties were introduced in Asia by the colonial powers in the seventeenth and eighteenth centuries. By the early nineteenth century, following the invention of mechanical mills and looms, the Lancashire spinners and weavers dominated the world trade, selling cotton cloth to India and other producer countries more cheaply than it could be produced locally.

Cotton is now an obsolescent crop in Europe. Fields of the crop may still be seen in the Balkans, Cyprus, Turkey and a few other areas of S. Europe, but in general these countries cannot compete with the major producers with semi-tropical climates: the USA, the Soviet Union, Egypt, Sudan, Brazil, India and China. European and Soviet production is based mainly on cultivars belonging to the Old World *G. herbaceum*, but Egypt grows a cross of forms of the American *G. barbadensis.*

Similar plants: Cotton spp. differ from Okra and other *Hibiscus* spp. by the large epicalyx of 3-toothed bracteoles. The black oil glands, and the characteristic withering of lvs when the crop is ripe, give the foliage a characteristic 'unhealthy' appearance.

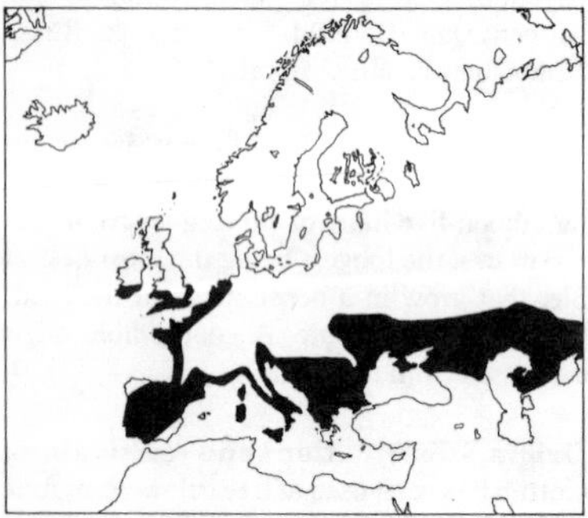

Natural distribution of Marshmallow

Althaea officinalis
MARSHMALLOW

Description: An erect herb 60–120 cm tall with little-branched stem; stem and lvs velvety. Lvs ovate, broad at base, irregularly lobed and toothed, the upper lvs partly folded like fans. Fls 2.5–4 cm across, 1–3 together in lf axils; petals 5 in number, broad, slightly notched or concave at apex, pale or bright pink; sepals 5, velvety; epicalyx a cup of 8–9 narrow triangular lobes.

Names: Fr.: Guimauve; It.: Altea, Bismalva; Sp.: Malvavisco; Ger.: Althee, Eibisch; Dtch.: Heemst, Soort snoepgoed; Dan.: Laege-stokrose; Gr.: Dentromolokha; Russ.: Altei aptechni.

Uses: Marshmallow is cultivated as a medicinal plant. All parts are mucilaginous and have other properties used in herbal preparations and proprietary medicines as an emollient, demulcent and expectorant for the treatment of respiratory, gastric and intestinal disorders. The roots are sometimes eaten as a boiled vegetable.

Marshmallows, the sickly white or pink sponge-rubbery confection made of water, sugar and gelatine, are so called because they were originally made with Marshmallow root.

Origin, distribution and cultivation: Marshmallow has a widespread natural distribution in Europe, from Britain to Siberia. It occurs mainly near coasts and by brackish marshes, and ditches, and has been gathered in the wild for medicinal purposes since classical times. It is cultivated as a field crop for the pharmaceutic industry in Belgium, Germany and parts of central Europe.

Marshmallow

LINACEAE

Flax Family

A small family of herbaceous plants with simple, alternate leaves. Flowers are usually 5-petalled, conspicuous, pollinated by insects. Only one species is of any agricultural importance.

Linum usitatissimum
FLAX and **LINSEED**
(pp. 156, 215)

Description: An annual herb. Stems erect, very slender, 80–160 cm tall; as a cultivated plant in closely-spaced field conditions little-branched except at apex. Lvs alternate, entire, lanceolate, greyish-green, with 3 veins. Fls 5-petalled, in a cluster, bright blue, white in some forms; sepals lanceolate, nearly as long as the pointed frt. Frt a spherical, somewhat flattened, more or less indehiscent capsule; seeds oval, flattened, 4–6 mm long, pale to dark brown, shiny.

Flax tends to be taller, is less branched, with fewer fls/frt.

Linseed is usually shorter, much more branched at apex, bearing more frt.

Names: Fr.: Lin; It.: Lino; Sp.: Lino; Ger.: Flachs; Dtch.: Vlas; Dan.: Hor; Gr.: Linari; Russ.: Len; Yug.: Lan.

Uses:
Flax The soft but very strong fibres are extracted from the stem by retting, formerly done by soaking the plants in water or by exposing them to very damp air, but now done more efficiently in factories, to give linen fibre.
Linseed The seeds, rich in oil and protein, are a valuable animal fodder, either fed complete or more usually as linseed cake, which is the compressed residue from the seeds which have been pressed for oil. The oil is used in human food and in the manufacture of paints, linoleum, etc.

Origin, distribution and cultivation: *Linum usitatissimum*, one of the world's oldest cultivated plants, is usually considered to be a cultigen of one of the wild Levantine spp., *L. angustifolia* or *L. perenne.* As a source of flax, it was the most important vegetable textile fibre of Europe and the Near East until trade with the East brought it into competition with the great oriental fibre plants, hemp and cotton. For this reason it was never taken into cultivation in India and China, except to a limited extent as an oil seed. In Europe cultivation for both purposes continues to this day.

Although most crops are used for both fibre and oil, two distinct forms of the plant were evolved early on, as high-seed yields are not entirely compatible with good quality fibre. Flax is typically grown in the cooler and moister northern countries, while the faster maturing, shorter and more branched linseed is a crop of warm summer conditions, and was principally grown in the Mediterranean, the Levant and Asia Minor, but both forms have been extensively grown in northern Europe. It is always grown on a field-crop scale.

Similar plants: Several wild European spp. of *Linum* are very close, but the taller, much less branched *L. usitatissimum* cannot be confused with any other crop species.

ACTINIDIACEAE

Yang Tao Family

A small family of tropical and sub-tropical woody shrubs or climbers, some of which are grown for ornament. Only one is of economic importance.

Actinidia chinensis
YANG TAO or **KIWI**
(p. 156)

Description: A vigorous deciduous woody climber with stems up to 10 m long. The plant does not have tendrils but climbs by twining around its supports. Shoots are conspicuously covered in dense reddish-brown hairs. Lvs alternate, heart-shaped, 12–20 cm long, almost as broad, but narrower on fruiting shoots, downy beneath and covered by stiff erect hairs above. Fls in clusters on short axillary stalks, ca. 4 cm across, white darkening to cream, sweetly scented; male and female fls on separate plants (female fls recognisable by swollen ovary) so that compatible pairs must be grown together to obtain frt. Frt a fuzzy brown ovoid berry with thin walls, containing bright green juicy flesh and small dark seeds arranged in a radial pattern around a yellow core.

Names: Also known as Chinese Gooseberry.
Fr.: Kiwi, Souris végétale; It.: Kiwi; Sp.: Kiwi; Ger.: Strahlengriffel, Kiwi; Dtch.: Kiwi; Dan.: Kiwi; Gr.: Kioyi; Russ.: Kivi.

Uses: The sweet, slightly acid flesh, variously compared to melon, pineapple, strawberry, etc. and usually qualified as delicious, is eaten raw after peeling the frt, or used in fruit salads, garnishes on ice-creams, cakes, etc. The plants are sometimes grown indoors purely for ornament.

Origin, distribution and cultivation: Yang Tao is a native of the Yangtze Valley and has been cultivated in China for many centuries. It was first introduced to European gardens in 1900 but did not become a commercial crop outside China until 1960, when New Zealand began to export from the large plantations then newly established in the Bay of Plenty. The name Kiwi, suggesting that the plant is native to New Zealand, was invented at this time as part of the marketing strategy for a new product. Since then, commercial production has flourished in southern France, Italy, Spain and the Soviet Union, and the plant has doubtless been introduced to other warm European countries. In these it is grown on trellises out of doors, but in colder climates, including Britain, the plants will only fruit under glass.

Similar plants: The densely hairy shoots and lvs distinguish this species from other cultivated vines. The frt is likewise unmistakeable.

Two other, inferior, spp. of *Actinidia*, *A. arguta* and *A. kolomikta* are sometimes cultivated in the Far East, but not in Europe.

ERICACEAE

Heather Family

A family of shrublets and shrubs with simple, usually evergreen leaves and no stipules. The flowers are solitary or in clusters, with 4 or 5 sepals and petals, the latter usually forming a characteristic bell-shaped corolla. The superior ovary develops into a capsule, a berry or a drupe.

The family is best known by the many species of heather (*Erica* and *Calluna* spp.) which cover extensive wild areas in Europe, and are sometimes grown for ornament. One of these, Tree Heath *Erica arborea* deserves particular mention, for the roots are gathered in the wild for the manufacture of Briar pipe bowls (in this context Briar should not be confused with the wild rose *Rosa rubiginosa*, also called Briar or Sweet Briar).

Members of the genus *Vaccinium* (Cranberries and Blueberries) are treated by some authors as a separate family, the Vacciniaceae, but the distinctions are slight. The following key may help to identify the European economic species:

KEY TO VACCINIUM spp.		
1	Slender prostrate plants; mature frt red=**2**	**(6)**
2	Stems creeping with erect branched shoots up to 30 cm tall; lvs large (10–30 mm) closely spaced on erect shoots; frt 5–10 mm in diameter=**Cowberry**	**(3)**
3	Stems creeping with only fl- and frt-stalks erect=**4**	**(2)**
4	Lvs pointed, smaller, 4–10 mm long, with edges strongly down-curled; frt smaller, 6–10 mm in diameter=**Cranberry**	**(5)**
5	Lvs blunt, larger, 6–18 mm, with edges less strongly down-curved; frts larger, 12–20 mm in diameter=**American Cranberry**	**(4)**
6	Plants erect, bushy; mature frts blue-black=**7**	**(1)**
7	Larger shrub, 1 m or more (up to 5 m in the wild); lvs large, 2.5–5 cm long=**Highbush Blueberry**	**(8)**
8	Smaller shrubs, under 65 cm tall; lvs smaller, 1–3 cm long=**9**	**(7)**

KEY TO VACCINIUM spp.		
9	Lvs finely toothed; stems angled; fls and frts solitary or in pairs=**Bilberry**	**(10)**
10	Lvs untoothed; stems rounded; fls and frts solitary or in clusters of up to 4=**Northern Bilberry**	**(9)**

Vaccinium oxycoccus
CRANBERRY
(p. 158)

Description: A tiny prostrate creeping sub-shrub with string-like hairy stems. Lvs widely spaced, alternate, dark green above, greyish below, oblong to narrowly elliptical, 4–10 mm long. Fls cyclamen-like, solitary or in pairs, drooping on long erect stalks, with 4 strongly recurved dark pink petals 5–6 mm long and darker stamens projecting in a column. Frt globose or oval, 6–8 mm across, red or yellowish spotted with brown.

Names: Fr.: Airelle, Canneberge; It.: Mortella di Palude; Sp.: Arandano; Ger.: Kronsbeere, Moosbeere; Dtch.: Veenbes; Dan.: Tranebaer; Gr.: Koúmaro; Russ.: Kliukva; Yug.: Brusnica.

Uses: The berries are used to make a savoury jelly or cranberry sauce, traditionally used to accompany venison and roast turkey, in Britain, North Europe and North America. Cranberry is virtually unknown as a food in southern Europe.

Origin, distribution and cultivation: Cranberry has a holarctic distribution: North Europe, North Asia and North America. It is an inhabitant of peat bogs, and is widespread but rare in Britain, Northern France, Germany, etc., much commoner in Scandinavia and Russia. Some frts are gathered in the wild. Small-scale cultivation of this sp. is generally being abandoned in favour of the larger American Cranberry.

Similar plants: *V. microcarpum* is a closely related wild European sp. with more lanceolate lvs, hairless stems and darker pink fls. It is of no economic importance. See American Cranberry, below.

Vaccinium macrocarpon
AMERICAN CRANBERRY
(p. 158)

Description: Similar in structure and habit to *V. oxycoccus* but more robust, with large (6–18 mm) blunt lvs with margins strongly downcurved, and much larger (12–20 mm across) frts.

Names: As an imported crop and product this sp. is generally known throughout Europe by the English name 'Cranberry', or by the local name for cranberry qualified by 'American'.

Uses: As Cranberry.

Origin, distribution and cultivation: This sp. is a native of the United States and Canada, where it occurs in similar acid bog situations to *V. oxycoccus.* It was gathered as a food plant by Indians, and adopted by the earliest European settlers. Although European Cranberries have probably been gathered for food since prehistoric times, the present popularity of cranberry sauce in Britain is largely due to its traditional association with turkey in America. American Cranberry is cultivated on a large scale in the north-eastern states of America, in Canada, and recently in parts of Europe, especially Britain, where it is now virtually the only commercial cranberry. The plant occurs locally in Britain as an escape.

Similar plants: *V. oxycoccus*, above.

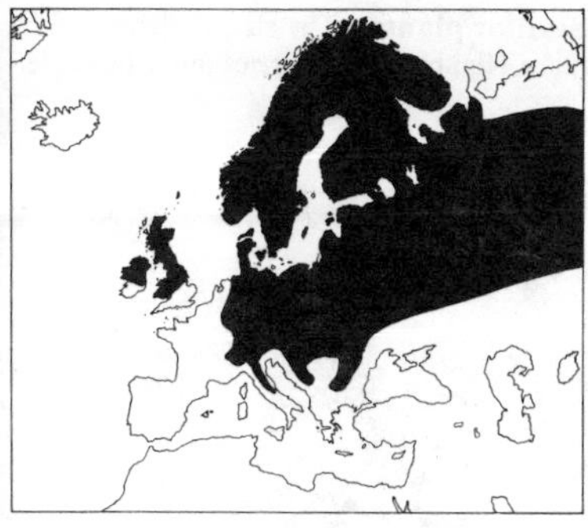

Natural distribution of Cowberry

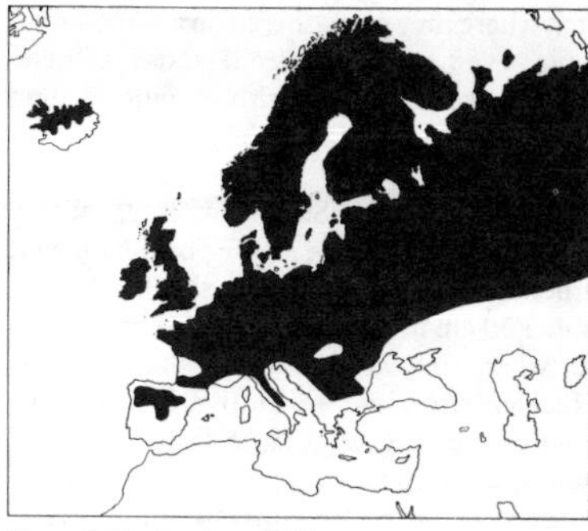

Natural distribution of Bilberry

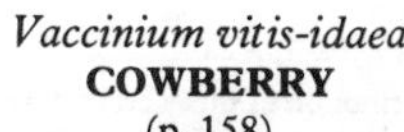

Vaccinium vitis-idaea
COWBERRY

(p. 158)

Description: Somewhat intermediate in structure and habit between cranberries and blueberries, with creeping stems giving rise to more or less erect branching shoots up to 30 cm in height. Lvs resemble Box, blunt-ovate to obovate, evergreen, leathery, with strongly downcurved margins. Fls few in short drooping racemes, white or flushed with pink, broadly bell-shaped with long recurved corolla lobes. Frt globose, red, ca. 6–8 mm across, resembling unripe Bilberry.

Names: Also known as Mountain Cranberry or Red Whortleberry.
Fr.: Airelle rouge; It.: Mirtillo rosso; Sp.: Arandano encarnado; Ger.: Hölperchen; Dtch.: Rode bosbes; Dan.: Tyttebaer; Russ.: Brusnika; Yug.: Crevena borovnica.

Uses: The frts are used locally in northern and central Europe to make jellies and jams.

Origin, distribution and cultivation: Cowberry occurs throughout northern and central Europe on moors, heaths and especially in mountain regions. It has no commercial value, but is gathered locally for home use.

Similar plants: This plant sometimes hybridises with Bilberry, producing plants with intermediate characters.

Vaccinium myrtillus
BILBERRY

(p. 158)

Description: A low hairless deciduous undershrub 20–60 cm tall with erect quadrangular green twigs. Lvs ovate, 1–3 cm long, bright green, finely toothed, flat. Fls solitary or in pairs in lf axils, the corolla greenish-pink, urn-shaped, with 5 minute teeth. Frt pale red ripening to blue-black with a bloom.

Names: Also known as Whortleberry, Blueberry, or Blaeberry (Scotland).
Fr.: Myrtille, Airelle; It.: Mitillo; Sp.: Arandano; Ger.: Blaubeere, Heidelbeere; Dtch.: Blauwe basbes; Dan.: Blåbaer; Gr.: Filli; Russ.: Chornika; Yug.: Borovnica.

Uses: The acid berries are used to make savoury or sweet jellies and jams, in tarts and other desserts, for flavouring various sweets and confectioneries, and in parts of central Europe for the production of Bilberry 'wine'.

Origin, distribution and cultivation: Bilberry occurs on heaths, moors and in open woodland over the whole of northern Europe and in all the mountain ranges of central Europe. Frts are harvested in the wild, sometimes as commercial exploitation on leased or privately-owned land, but the plant is scarcely ever cultivated. Recently established cultivation has favoured the larger-fruited American Blueberries (below).

The laborious task of picking frt by hand deters many from making use of them, but in eastern France, Germany, central Europe, etc., where they are gathered on a commercial scale, even weekend strollers use a 'rake' shaped like a dustpan with a comb of long teeth to harvest the frt in large quantities.

Similar plants: See Cowberry, above. Lowbush Blueberries *V. angustifolium* and others are very low-growing shrubs, usually under 30 cm in height. All come from America, where they are known as Blueberries or Huckleberries, and are cultivated and gathered in the wild on a large scale. They are high-ground spp., hardier than Bilberry, and so may be taken into cultivation in parts of Europe such as northern Scandinavia which are unsuitable for Bilberry.

Europe has its own native spp. of hardy upland blueberries such as Northern Bilberry *V. uliginosum* which occurs in Britain, but the frts are inferior to those of Bilberry or *V. angustifolium. V. uliginosum* differs from Bilberry in its rounded stems, blue-green untoothed lvs, and bluer berries.

Vaccinium corymbosum
HIGHBUSH BLUEBERRY
(p. 158)

Description: Similar in structure to Bilberry, but plants are very much larger, at least 1 m, sometimes several m high. Lvs at least 2.5 x 1.3 cm, often much larger. Fls in short racemes, up to 1.3 cm long. Frts blue or blue-black, 8–12 mm or more across.

Names: Also known in America as Swamp or Tall Blueberry.

Uses: As Bilberry.

Origin, distribution and cultivation: Highbush Blueberries are a complex aggregate formed by multiple natural hybridisations and back crosses of several North American spp. over many centuries. They are cultivated on a large scale in the United States, and have recently been adopted in parts of Europe, especially in Britain. *V. corymbosum* is less hardy than the other commercial spp., and requires higher summer temperatures.

Similar plants: The size of plants and frt make Highbush Blueberries unmistakeable.

Natural distribution of Strawberry Tree

Arbutus unedo
STRAWBERRY TREE
(p. 158)

Description: A small tree or shrub with very short trunk, sinuous branches and dense foliage. Lvs evergreen, slightly obovate, with sharp forward-pointing teeth on margins, dark green above, pale green with prominent white midrib below, ca. 7 x 2.5 cm. Lf-stalks pink above, ca. 6 cm long; young shoots dark pink. Fls urn-shaped, in clusters of 15 or more, greenish-white, appearing in autumn with previous year's frt. Frt globose, 1–2 cm in diameter, bright red and dotted with tiny papillae.

Names: Fr.: Arbousier; It.: Albatro, Corbezzolo; Sp.: Madroño; Ger.: Erdbeerbaum; Dtch.: Arrdbeizieboom; Gr.: Koumariá, Lagomiliá; Russ.: Zemlyanichnik.

Uses: The attractive but sweet, insipid, even mildly distasteful fruits (*unedo* means 'I eat one', alluding to the disappointing taste) are made into jams, and in several countries the pulp is distilled into alcoholic drinks, the most famous being the Portuguese *madrongho*.

Origin, distribution and cultivation: *A. unedo* is native to the western and central

Mediterranean region, its natural range extending up the warm Atlantic coast as far north as Ireland. It is not cultivated except as an ornamental, but the frt is gathered and sometimes sold on markets in some countries.

Similar plants: The serrate lvs distinguish *A. unedo* from the Greek Strawberry Tree, *A. andrachne*, a native of the eastern Mediterranean which has larger, entire lvs. A natural hybrid between these two spp. occurs in Greece with larger but serrate lvs. Both *A. andrachne* and the hybrid differ from the common Strawberry Tree by their red bark (soon turning brown in *A. unedo*).

A. unedo bears a vague resemblance to Bay (see p. 16).

MYRTACEAE

Myrtle Family

A tropical family of some 3000 species of trees and shrubs especially abundant in S. America and Australia. It includes such exotic economic species as Cloves *Eugenia caryophylla*, native to the Moluccas and cultivated in Indonesia, Zanzibar, etc., Guava *Psidium guajava*, originally from S. America but grown all over the tropics, and Allspice *Pimenta dioica* grown mainly in its homeland in the West Indies.

The family takes its name from the only European representative, Myrtle *Myrtus communis*, a large Mediterranean shrub with many classical associations. The plant's lvs, fls and frt all contain an aromatic oil (*Eau d'Anges*) used in perfumery, while the frt is often made into a condiment or fermented to produce alcoholic drinks. The roots and bark are used for tanning the finest Russian leather, giving it a characteristic sweet scent.

The genus *Eucalyptus* also belongs to this family. Its 600 or so species are all natives of Australia, but have been widely distributed around the world, and at least ten species are commonly planted in the Mediterranean.

One member of the myrtle family is cultivated to a small extent in Europe for its edible fruit.

Feijoa sellowiana
FEIJOA
(p. 160)

Description: A small tree, up to 6 m, in its natural state with several slender trunks and widely spreading supple slender branches, but may be pruned to any shape, so is more often seen as a bushy shrub. Young shoots are covered in whitish velvety hairs. Lvs ovate, 4–8 cm long, entire, dark glossy green above, velvety whitish below. Fls (early summer) numerous, solitary or in pairs at base of current year's shoots, ca. 4 cm across, with 4 velvety sepals, 4 round concave petals of a pale grey-violet marked with dark red near base, and erect crimson stamens and yellow anthers. Frt (ripening October–January) ovoid, 2–8 cm long, the skin thin, dark green with a waxy bloom, and conspicuous velvety whitish persistent calyx, contain yellowish-white slightly gritty flesh surrounding a jelly-like pulp in which the small seeds are embedded.

Names: Often called Pineapple Guava in the USA. In all European countries the generic name *Feijoa* is used.

Uses: The sweet, slightly acid flesh, reminiscent of pineapple with a hint of peppermint, is eaten raw, spooned directly out of the halved frt, or used in fruit salads.

Origin, distribution and cultivation: This plant, the sole representative of the genus, was discovered in southern Brazil in 1819 by the German explorer Sellow, and was first introduced to Europe by the French horticulturalist André who planted it in his Côte d'Azur garden in 1890. It has since been taken into commercial cultivation in Australia, New Zealand, California and other countries with a similar climate. Feijoa is cultivated on a small scale in S.E. France, where it also occurs in the wild as an escape, and in Italy, and the frts are sometimes offered for sale on local markets.

Similar plants: None.

PUNICACEAE

Pomegranate Family

A monogeneric family of only two species, Pomegranate and a wild shrub native to the island of Socotra. It is characterised by its fl and frt structure, and recognisable by the large persistent calyx that crowns the frt.

Punica granatum
POMEGRANATE

(p. 160)

Description: A large shrub, usually grown as a bush 2–4 m in height, deciduous in Europe but evergreen in some tropical countries. Lvs opposite, dark green turning to yellow in autumn, oblong, 4–8 cm long; fls orange-red with a very large concolorous calyx with 5–7 lobes, 5–7 crumpled petals and ca. 20 stamens. Frt a berry with a leathery skin 6–12 cm in diameter, dark yellow to crimson, sometimes flushed with red only on one side, with long persistent calyx tube; the inside is divided by thin yellow septa into irregular cells, each containing a number of seeds surrounded by a bright pink juicy pulp.

Many cvs exist, including ones with white, or variegated white and red, or 'double' fls.

Names: Fr.: Grenadier; It.: Melograno; Sp.: Granado; Ger.: Granatapfel; Dtch.: Granaat; Dan.: Granataeble; Gr.: Rodiá, Roidiá; Russ.: Granat; Yug.: Mogranj.

Uses: The pulp surrounding the seeds is the edible part of the plant, the rind and septa being bitter and inedible. The pulp may be scooped out and eaten fresh, or the juice used in sherbets and other drinks, including pomegranate 'wine', and for making syrup (eg. *grenadine*) or jams.

The high esteem in which this frt was held from antiquity until quite recent times is perhaps explained by the absence of so many other refreshing juicy fruits – citrus, superior melon varieties, etc. – which we take for granted today, for compared to these it is rather disappointing.

Origin, distribution and cultivation: Pomegranate is a native of Persia where it has been cultivated since prehistoric times. It was grown in the hanging gardens of Babylon and in ancient Egypt, and spread in classical times to all parts of the Mediterranean, eastwards to N. India, central Asia and China, and south to Ethiopia, where, as in Arabic, it is still known as *roman*, the 'Roman fruit'. It has long been a symbol of fertility or plenty, and as such is only rivalled by the grapevine.

Pomegranates are now cultivated, usually on a small scale, in most tropical and subtropical countries. They require a long hot summer to produce ripe frt, but yield a heavier crop in climates with a cool winter.

Similar plants: None. The vegetative parts of the plant are unremarkable, but the fl and frt are unmistakeable.

RHAMNACEAE

Buckthorn Family

A small family of some 600 species of shrubs or small trees, a few of which are native to Europe; and includes a few which are or were of minor economic value. Buckthorns (*Rhamnus* sp.) have various medicinal uses, and their bark and fruits provided yellow, green or blue-grey dyes. Persian Berries, formerly imported to Europe for that use, are the fruits of Middle-Eastern *Rhamnus* spp. Two members of the family, *Paliurus spina-christi* and *Zizyphus lotus* have been named as the plant from which Christ's crown of thorns was made.

The family may be recognised by the perigynous fls in which the ovary is ringed by a lip from which the sepals, petals and stamens, all in fours or fives, arise. The fruits are in most cases fleshy drupes.

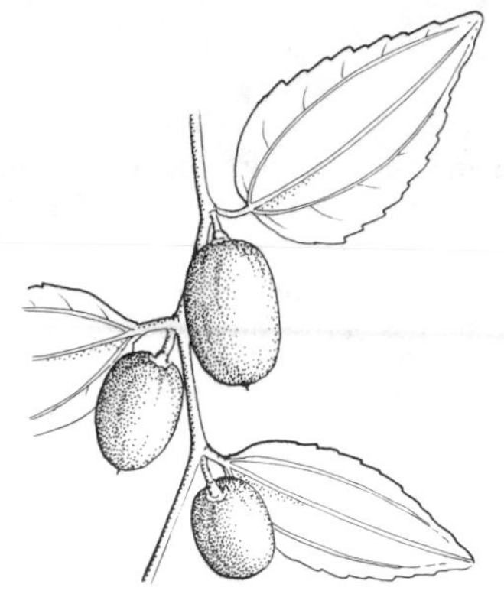

Common Jujube: leaves and fruit

Zizyphus jujuba
COMMON JUJUBE

(p. 212)

Description: A deciduous tree growing to about 8 m, but usually smaller in cultivation. Branches, and especially twigs, zigzag in shape and except in a few cvs are armed with spines arising in pairs at the nodes. Lvs 2–6 cm long, ovate-lanceolate with bluntly toothed or wavy margins, hairless beneath. Fls in dense clusters by two or threes, in lf axils of current year's growth, small, greenish or yellow, with 5 petals and stamens. Frt an ovoid drupe 2–5 cm long with shiny skin ripening to dark brownish-red to almost black, and containing a hard, longitudinally wrinkled and slightly beaked stone.

Names: Also sometimes called Chinese Date.
Synonyms: *Z. vulgaris*; *Z. sativa.* This species was described by Miller; it is not *Z. jujuba* (L.) Lam. which is a synonym of *Z. mauritania* Lam. (see below under Similar Plants).
Fr.: Jujubier; It.: Giuggiolo, Zizzolo; Sp.: Azufaifo; Ger.: Brustbeere; Dtch.: Jujube; Dan.: Jødetorn; Gr.: Titjifia; Russ.: Unabi, Yuyuba.

Uses: The fruit may be eaten fresh, but is more often dried and used as a dessert frt, or in cooking. The wrinkled dried frts are sometimes offered for sale in Mediterranean markets but are not exported or processed in any way.

Origin, distribution and cultivation: *Z. jujuba* is variously described as originating in China and in Syria. It is likely that the latter provenance is correct, and that the tree spread in cultivation at a very early date across the arid lands along the central Asian trade routes and westward to the Mediterranean. The tree is resistant to heat and drought and to very cold winters. The frt has little economic value in Europe today, and most trees seen, either singly or in small stands in dry barren situations, are remnants of former cultivation.

Similar plants: Indian Jujube *Z. mauritania*, a species widespread in Africa, Arabia and India, is not frost-tolerant. European jujubes are sometimes referred to this species, and it is possible that it exists in some areas, though the trees I have seen (in Italy, Greece) certainly belong to *Z. jujuba.* Indian jujube frts are similar, but the plant can be identified by its densely hairy young shoots and undersides of lvs.

Jew's Thorn *Z. lotus* is a commoner tree than Jujube, especially in the E. Mediterranean, with more broadly ovate lvs and smaller, spherical, inedible yellow-brown frts. Christ's Thorn or Jerusalem Thorn *Paliurus spina-christi*, sometimes planted for hedging in the Mediterranean, has quite different, non-fleshy frts girdled with a broad papery rim, recalling a broad-brimmed hat.

ELAEAGNACEAE

Oleaster Family

A small family of fewer than 50 species of shrubs and trees, readily recognised by the silvery or rust-brown scales or minute clusters of hairs which cover shoots, lvs, fls and frts.

Sea Buckthorn *Hippophae rhamnoides* is the only native European member. Its small orange, very acid frts have most of the properties of rose hips, and are sometimes used in the same way to make syrup.

Eleagnus angustifolia L.
OLEASTER

Description: A usually spiny large shrub or small tree, to 10 m. Young shoots and undersides of lvs silvery-white. Lvs elongate, willow-like, greyish-green above. Fls small, about as broad as lvs, with a long tubular calyx spreading in 4 yellow petal-like lobes, and 4 stamens. Frt ovoid, 1–2 cm long, yellow-green with silvery scales ripening to orange or reddish-brown, in clusters.

Names: This species is also called Wild Olive, but so are small-fruited feral forms of Olive.
Fr.: Olivier de Bohème, Olinet; It.: Oleastro, Olirastro; Sp.: Acebuche; Ger.: Silberbaum; Dtch.: Wildeolijfboom; Dan.: Solvblad; Gr.: Agreliá; Russ.: Dikaya maslina; Yug.: Oleaster.

Uses: The sweetish edible frts are used to make jams, etc.

Origin, distribution and cultivation: Oleaster is a native of central and western Asia. It spread to Europe in cultivation as a food plant in the Middle Ages and is now naturalised in sandy areas of the Mediterranean coast, usually near ditches. It is no longer of economic importance, and frts are harvested only for home use from trees grown mainly for ornament.

Similar plants: The foliage bears a superficial resemblance to that of Willow and Olive, but even from a distance the pallor, especially of lf undersides, make it unmistakeable.

VITACEAE

Vine Family

A family of mostly climbing shrubs with tendrils which represent modified stems. Lvs simple, heart-shaped to palmate or pinnate, often with glandular pores. Fls in clusters at nodes opposite lf-stalks, minute, greenish, with parts in fours or fives; ovary usually 2-celled, with 1–2 seeds in each cell.

The family, and the genus *Vitis* to which the European Grapevine belongs, is of worldwide distribution. Besides this genus, a few other members, such as Virginia Creeper and *Cissus* spp. are familiar as introduced ornamentals.

Vitis vinifera
GRAPEVINE
(pp. 162, 216)

Description: A familiar woody climber with a twisted trunk and stems with rough bark which peels off in longitudinal strips; branched tendrils arising opposite the large, heart-shaped, more or less deeply palmately lobed lvs. Fls minute, greenish. Frts green ('White'), or flushed with red, or dark blueish or purple ('Black' or 'Red'), with or without seeds according to cv.

Many hundreds of cvs exist, which do not differ greatly in structure; appearance is most noticeably determined by growth habits

Distribution of Grapevine

induced by the various methods of pruning. Structural variation mainly affects the shape and size of lvs and frt, the most unusual of the latter being the white Italian dessert grape 'cornicella', which is conical and curved. The varieties illustrated on plate are: *Chardonnay*, or *Pinot Blanc*, a classic white Burgundy, Chablis, and Champagne grape; *Muller Thurgau*, or *Riesling Sylvaner*, is one of the most widely planted variety in Germany, the Moselle and Alsace, and probably also in England. *Riesling* is a collective term for this and less 'soft' varieties which yield the finest German wines, known as 'hock' in Britain; they have been widely introduced to other parts of Europe, notably Yugoslavia *Scheurebe* is another of these. *Cabernet Sauvignon* is one of the classic red Bordeaux grapes; it is now grown in many other European countries, and in all the good red-wine-producing areas of other continents; *Seyval Blanc* and *Cascade Seibel* are respectively white and red wine grapes, while Black Hamburg is a dessert grape.

Names: Fr.: Vigne, Raisin; It.: Vite, Uva; Sp.: Vid, Parra, Uva; Ger.: Weinstock, Rebe; Dtch.: Wijnstock; Dan.: Vinstock; Gr.: Ampeli; Russ.: Vini vinograd; Yug.: Loza, Trs.

Uses: The principal economic use of the grape in Europe is the production of wine, mostly table wine, but also sweet 'dessert' and apéritif wines, and fortified wines such as Sherry and Port. Wine is also an important culinary flavouring ingredient, especially in French and Mediterranean cooking, and it is the source of the best table vinegars. A small quantity of unfermented juice is bottled or canned as a beverage, and verjuice, the acid juice of unripe grapes, is used locally in the mustard industry. Many cvs are grown exclusively as dessert grapes, and others, always seedless varieties, are dried as currants, raisins or sultanas. A fine salad oil is expressed from the pips.

Origin, distribution and cultivation: The European Grapevine originated on the south-west coast of the Caspian Sea, and spread westward in cultivation at a very early date. It was grown in Egypt more than 4000 years ago; the oldest Greek and Roman records testify that viticulture had already been developed to a high degree of sophistication. The Phoenicians, Greeks and Romans introduced the vine to their western colonies, the latter being the first to bring it to Burgundy, the Rhineland and Britain.

Although, unlike staple food crops such as wheat, wine is not vital to human survival (although many Europeans would dispute this), no other plant has so ancient or powerful a symbolic association with Mediterranean and European civilization. It is the first cultivated plant mentioned in the Bible; wine remained central to Jewish tradition and ritual, and assumes equal importance to bread in the Eucharist – a recognition that notwithstanding widespread and ancient abuse (And Noah . . . planted a vineyard. And he drank of the wine, and was drunken: *Genesis* 9:20), wine is a healthy and nutritious drink.

Grapes are grown commercially in the whole area shown on the map on p. 101, with minor pockets of cultivation north of the boundary, such as the few vineyards that have been re-established in England. Italy leads production, followed by Spain and France, which from the great (but sometimes exiguous in terms of acreage) vineyards of Burgundy and Bordeaux produce the finest wines in the world.

In the 1860s and 70s European vineyards were devastated by an aphid, *Phylloxera vastatrix*, accidentally introduced with one of the American vine spp. which were being tried experimentally. Fortunately other American *Vitis* spp. proved immune to *Phylloxera*, and the great vineyards of France and elsewhere were soon reconstituted using the American spp. as rootstock on which to graft the original varieties.

The various ways of training and pruning vines are partly determined by the need for optimum exposure to sunlight. In northern areas such as the Rhineland, maximum exposure is achieved by training the vines on tall wires with the rows aligned facing south or east. In the hottest parts of the Mediterranean grapes produced for drying as raisins, in which a high sugar content is desirable, may be grown in the same way, but wine grapevines will be trained in such a way that the ripening grapes are protected from excessive insolation by the plant's foliage. Methods of husbandry are also dictated by the exigencies of mechanical harvesting, or by climate: in Provence, where the cold mistral wind is a menace, the plants are trained very low on the ground.

Similar plants: The genus *Vitis* is represented by many spp., some occurring even in the humid tropics. Many have edible berries, but none, except a few North American spp., is cultivated. The best American wines, from California and Arizona, are made from the European grape, but some of the native spp., especially *V. labrusca*, are cultivated in the east and mid-west and other areas unsuited to *V. vinifera.* The frts of these spp., sometimes called 'slip-skin grapes', are easily distinguished from the European grapes because the skin does not adhere strongly to the flesh, but slips away easily. These spp. are not grown commercially in Europe, although they are widely used as rootstock, and certain hybrids have been produced in France.

EBENACEAE

Ebony Family

Diospyros is a genus of some 450 tropical and warm-temperate trees with shoots that do not form terminal buds. Most species are unisexual, with small inconspicuous whitish fls with petals and sepals usually in fours, and from one to four times as many stamens. Frts are large, juicy berries with a large persistent calyx.

The family's principal economic importance lies in the several species felled for the various ebonies of commerce. Two species are cultivated in Europe for their fruits.

Diospyros kaki
CHINESE PERSIMMON
(p. 160)

Description: A deciduous tree, in cultivation not exceeding 6–7 m in height, with a broad rounded dome. Young twigs and undersides of lvs softly hairy. Lvs ovate, entire, 8–20 cm long, glossy dark green above, with depressed mid-rib. Fls ca. 4 cm across, yellowish-white. Frt yellow to red when ripe, globose or slightly elongate, like a tomato in appearance but with large persistent calyx, 5–10 cm in diameter, ripening in autumn and remaining on tree long after lvs have fallen.

Names: Also called Date Plum, Kaki, and Oriental or Japanese Persimmon. Fr.: Plaqueminier kaki; It.: Cachi; Sp.: Kaki, Placa minera; Ger.: Kakipflaume; Dtch.: Kaki; Dan.: Kaki; Gr.: Kaki; Russ.: Khurma yaponskaya.

Uses: The frts are extremely astringent when unripe but when soft are sweet with a fine flavour; they may be eaten fresh or cooked, pureed or iced and used for desserts and for making jam.

Origin, distribution and cultivation: *D. kaki* is a native of both China and Japan where it has long been cultivated on a large scale; it is now grown in the subtropics throughout the world. It was introduced to Europe in 1766 but remained little-known except as an ornamental until after the last war. Commercial production is under way in S. France, Spain, Italy, Cyprus, etc. and is likely to increase to meet rising demand.

Similar plants: See *D. lotus*, below.

The true Persimmon, *D. virginiana* is not cultivated in Europe. It occurs in deciduous forest in most of the United States where it is rarely cultivated, but large quantities of frt are harvested in the wild.

Diospyros lotus
DATE-PLUM
(p. 160)

Description: A tree similar to *D. kaki*, but with smaller (5–13 cm long) lvs, which lose most of the pubescence of the undersides with age. Fls smaller, white tinged with orange. Frts much smaller, 1–2 cms in diameter, yellow, often turning purple-black.

Names: Fr.: Plaqueminier lotus; It.: Loto d'Italia; Sp.: Placa minera del Europa; Ger.: Dattelpflaume; Dtch.: Dadelpruim; Dan.: Daddelblomme; Russ.: Khurma evropeskaya.

Uses: As *D. kaki.* The frt flesh is firm and sweet, with a scent recalling dates.

Origin, distribution and cultivation: This species also originated in Asia, where it has a natural range from China to Japan to Iran. It was introduced to Europe at a much earlier, unknown date than *D. Kaki*, and for this reason is sometimes assumed to be native. The main centre of cultivation is Italy, but it may be seen in gardens throughout the Mediterranean, and the frts are often available in winter from local grocers and markets. The species is being eclipsed by the increasing cultivation of the larger and more valuable Chinese Persimmon, but it may hold its own as a fruit, owing to the distinctive flavour.

Similar plants: See Chinese Persimmon, above. The large persistent calyx lobes distinguishes the frt from others of similar size.

RUTACEAE

Rue Family

The cultivated members of this family of some 1500 species of herbs, shrubs and trees, mostly from the warm-temperate and old world tropics, are distinguished by the glands (clearly visible when a leaf is held against the light) containing aromatic oils; in the leaves and fruit peel; by the more or less broadly winged leaf-stalks; and in many species of *Citrus*, a spine borne in the leaf axil.

The family derives its name from Rue *Ruta graveolens*, a shrub up to 1 m in height with blue-green lvs twice divided into small (0.5–1.5 mm) obovate, strongly aromatic, foetid leaflets and yellow fls with 4 sepals and petals. This common native of the Mediterranean was widely cultivated as a medicinal and kitchen herb plant from early classical times until the 19th century. Today it is only grown as an ornamental, except to a very small extent in south-east France where it has a minor use in the perfume industry, and in Italy where it is the main flavouring agent for the spirit *grappa*. A related species, *R. chalepensis*, called *Ruta frangiata* by the Italians and distinguished from common Rue by the presence of long erect tooth-like hairs on the petals, is commonly used for the same purpose.

All the commercial species in Europe belong to the woody genus *Citrus*, and come from the drier parts of S.E. Asia where a number of other species are in cultivation. Man has selected and improved those species containing the greatest quantity of water-storing pulp, and those with particular aromatic rinds (evolved by the wild plants as protection), for the production of essential oils used in perfumery and soap-making. Commercial production in Europe is limited to the Mediterranean, where fruits ripen in autumn and are harvested in winter.

The fruits of these species are too well known to require lengthy descriptions, although Sweet and Seville Oranges are often confused. The following key, based partly on vegetative characters, should help to distinguish the plants, but it should be borne in mind that the characters are variable.

KEY TO CITRUS FRUITS

1	Lf-stalks narrowly winged and articulated or wingless=**2**	**(10)**
2	Frts yellow=**3**	**(7)**
3	Frt large, up to 20 cm, oblong, with very thick rough rind and scant acid juice; lf-stalks either narrowly winged or round, wingless; twigs with long stout spines=**Citron**	**(4)**
4	Frts smaller, under 12 cm. Lf-stalks with narrow wings=**5**	**(3)**
5	Fls tinged with purple outside; twigs spiny; frt oblong-ovoid with a nipple-like swelling at apex; flesh acid=**Lemon**	**(6)**
6	Fls pure white; twigs without spines; frt more globose, without a nipple-like swelling; flesh insipidly sweet=**Sweet Lime**	**(5)**
7	Frts orange, with juicy sweet flesh=**8**	**(2)**
8	Lvs larger and broader; frts larger, globose, with smoother, strongly adherent rind=**Sweet Orange**	**(9)**
9	Lvs smaller and narrower; frts smaller, distinctly flattened at each end, with rougher, loose rind=**Tangerine**	**(8)**
10	Lf-stalks broadly winged=**11**	**(1)**
11	Frts smaller (5–10 cm), with hollow core and small segments, the flesh sour and bitter=**12**	**(14)**
12	Frt globose, orange, with very rough warty rind=**Seville Orange**	**(13)**

KEY TO CITRUS FRUITS

13	Frt slightly pear-shaped, distinctly flattened at apex, pale yellow, the rind rough but thinner, very fragrant = **Bergamot Orange**	**(12)**
14	Frts larger (10–25 cm), yellow, with large segments and sweet flesh = **15**	**(11)**
15	Underside of lf-veins and stalk slightly hairy; frt very large, up to 25 cm, like Grapefruit but with coarser rind, and segments separating more easily = **Pomelo**	**(16)**
16	Undersides of lf-veins and stalks hairless; frt large (10–15 cm), the segments coherent = **Grapefruit**	**(15)**

Citrus sinensis
SWEET ORANGE
(p. 164)

Description: A tree, 6–12 m tall, with small or medium spines. Lvs ovate, up to 15 x 8 cm, dark green, sometimes slightly saw-toothed. Lf-stalk short, narrowly winged, articulated. Fls white, with 5 petals and 20–25 stamens. Frts globose, 4–12 cm in diameter, the rind thin, not exceeding 5 mm, strongly adherent, orange when ripe, the flesh juicy and sweet.

Many local varieties have been cultivated by the Chinese for centuries, but these are rarely exported. Oranges, like other yellow- or orange-fruited *Citrus* frts, usually remain green even when ripe in the moist tropics, but these do not constitute varieties, and the orange colour may be induced artificially by a gas treatment. The commonest European cv is 'Valencia' which also forms the basis of the Californian and South African production. It is a vigorous and prolific plant giving medium-sized frts with only 5–6 seeds and excellent flesh. Jaffa Orange, a large cv from Palestine, is also grown in Cyprus and parts of south-east Europe. Washington Navel, a large seedless variety said to have originated in Brazil, is the best-known of the navel oranges, in which a second row of carpels develops at the frt apex. Blood oranges have entirely or partly blood-red flesh; well-known cvs include 'Maltese' and 'St. Michael'.

Names: Fr.: Orange douce; It.: Arancia dolce; Sp.: Naranja dulce; Ger.: Orange; Dtch.: Orange; Dan.: Orange; Gr.: Portokaliá; Russ.: Portokal; Yug.: Naranča.

Uses: Principally as fresh fruit, canned juices and orange squash drinks. Secondary uses include flavouring for marmalade, and the production of essential oils: *Meroli* and *Petit Grain* oils are extracted from the Sweet Orange as well as from the following two spp. (below). Pectin is obtained from the rind, but citric acid is now mostly made synthetically.

Origin, distribution and cultivation: Sweet Orange is a native of S. China and Vietnam. This is the most important species in the genus, but only reached Europe five centuries after the Seville Orange, when Portugal opened the direct trade route to the Far East. (The name Orange is derived from the Arabic *Naranja*, and was transferred from the Seville Orange, but the Arabs themselves, and the Greeks and Russians still make the distinction between the two species, calling this one the 'Portuguese' – see names, above.)

Sweet Oranges are cultivated in all warm or tropical countries, although like most of the *Citrus* spp. it does best in drier climates. Spain and Italy are respectively the world's third and fourth largest producers, after the USA and Brazil, while Britain, France and W. Germany are the biggest importers of oranges and other citrus frts. In Europe it may be seen either in small orchards or large plantations in all the Mediterranean countries. Propagation is almost invariably by budding; rootstocks are grown from seed.

Similar plants: *C. aurantium* (below) and other *Citrus* spp. (see key, p. 106).

Citrus aurantium
SEVILLE or **SOUR ORANGE**
(p. 164)

Description: A tree up to 10 m. Lvs medium-sized, up to 10 x 6 cm, ovate, the margins sometimes with blunt teeth, the stalks broadly winged. Fls large, white, very fragrant. Frts globose, with thick rough highly aromatic rind, the segments small, arranged around a usually hollow core, the flesh very sour and bitter.

C. bergamia, considered by some botanists to be a variety of *C. aurantium*, is here treated as a distinct species. The Bigaradia Orange of Italy and France is a small var. of this species, but does not differ notably in appearance. Bitter-Sweet Oranges, not widely available now, are probably hybrids of the Sweet and Seville Oranges.

Names: Fr.: Orange amère, Bigarade; It.: Arancia amara, Bigaradia; Sp.: Narancia agria; Ger.: Pomeranze; Dtch.: Pomerans; Dan.: Pomerans; Gr.: Pikroportokaliá; Russ.: Bigardia.

Uses: This is the best of all oranges for the manufacture of marmalade, and is principally cultivated for that purpose. Britain is the main manufacturer and consumer of this conserve, and imports largely from Spain. The rootstock is widely used for Sweet Orange cvs, Lemons and Grapefruit. *Petit Grain* oil is obtained from the lvs of plants bearing unripe frt.

Origin, distribution and cultivation: The Seville Orange was brought to Europe by the Arabs in the 10th century, long before the Sweet Orange. It is grown on a large scale in Spain, and to a lesser extent in France, Italy and the Balkan peninsula, often merely for ornament.

Similar plants: Sweet Orange, from which it may be distinguished by the broadly winged lf-stalks, the much coarser rind, and small segments of bitter, sour flesh.

Citrus bergamia
BERGAMOT ORANGE
(p. 164)

Description: A tree, similar in size and appearance to the preceding sp., but with relatively broader lvs.

Names: Fr.: Bergamote; It.: Bergamotto; Sp.: Bergamota; Ger.: Bergamotte; Dtch.: Bergamotcitoen; Dan.: Bergamot; Gr.: Kitros tó pergmeion; Russ.: Bergamot.

Uses: Grown exclusively for the production of essential oils: Bergamot, obtained from the rind by expression, and Neroli oil, from the fls, by distillation with steam.

Origin, distribution and cultivation: The origin of this orange is uncertain, but it is thought to have developed in Europe from primitive stock which also included *C. aurantium.* It was formerly common in Italy and France, but commercial cultivation is now restricted to S. Italy.

Similar plants: *C. aurantium* (see key). *C. bergamia* differs from all other *Citrus* spp. by its scent.

Citrus reticulata
TANGERINE, MANDARIN
(p. 164)

Description: A small spreading tree, 2–8 m in height, often spiny. Lvs small, narrow, up to 8 x 4 cm, the margins usually with blunt teeth, dark green above, yellowish below; lf-stalks narrowly winged. Fls small, under 2.5 cm across, white. Frt small, 5–8 cms in diameter, flattened at base and apex, the rind easily separated from segments, the flesh sweet, little acid. The more bushy aspect of plants, with smaller lvs than other *Citrus* spp., helps to distinguish it at a distance.

The names Mandarin and Tangarine have been used loosely to distinguish the pale or yellow cvs (Mandarin) from the deep orange ones, following the Chinese distinction between their two main varieties, the Swatow (Mandarin) and Fuchow 'Orange', but too many cvs exist for the distinction to be valid. The Clementine, developed in Algeria and widely cultivated in S. Europe, has small deep orange frts and peel that is less easily detachable. Outside Europe the species includes such cvs as the Satsuma Orange of Japan, and 'Emperor' and 'Dancy' in Australia and the USA. Tangelos are hybrids between the tangerine and grapefruit; the Ugli from the West Indies is an example, and is now frequently seen on European food stalls. Tangors are hybrids between the Tangerine and the Sweet Orange, and include the 'Ortanique' from the USA.

Names: Fr.: Mandarine; It.: Tangerino; Sp.: Mandarina; Ger.: Mandarine; Dtch.: Mandaijntje orange; Dan.: Mandarin; Russ.: Mandarina; Yug.: Mandarin.

Uses: Used as a fresh fruit and to a lesser extent canned segments, or mixed with other *Citrus* fruits in juices, the pure juice being rather insipid. The hardy variety known as Calamondin (sometimes treated as a distinct sp., *C. mitis*) is often used as rootstock for other *Citrus* species, and because *C. reticulata* is a relatively unstable species, it has been used to produce many hybrids.

Origin, distribution and cultivation: *C. reticulata* probably arose as a cv from *C. aurantium* in China, where its main forms are extensively cultivated. It only reached Europe in the 19th century, although it was known earlier in N. Africa. It is the hardiest of the citrus plants and is therefore found further north and in colder areas of Europe than other species.

Similar plants: See key, p. 106. Typical bushy plants of this species are the most distinctive of the European citrus.

Citrus limon
LEMON
(pp. 166, 212)

Description: A small thorny, bushy tree, 3–6 m in height. Lvs 5–10 cm long x 3–6 cm broad; lf-stalks short, with narrow margins, distinctly articulated. Fls solitary or in clusters, 4–5 cm across, pink in bud, white tinged with purple when open, with 20–40 stamens. Frt ovoid, 5–12 cm long, with a distinct apical nipple, light yellow when ripe.

In addition to the characters used in the key, Lemon can be distinguished from all other European *Citrus* spp. by the greater number of stamens, always more than 4 times the number of petals; in other spp. the stamens number 20–25, 4 times or less than the number of petals.

Rough Lemon, a form with very coarse rinds and rather dry flesh, probably originated as a hybrid between Lemon and Citron. It is not cultivated for frt, but widely used as rootstock for Lemons and other *Citrus* spp.

Names: Fr.: Citron; It.: Limone; Sp.: Limón; Ger.: Zitrone; Dtch.: Citroen; Dan.: Citron; Gr.: Lemoniá; Russ.: Limon; Yug.: Limun.

Uses: Lemon is the most important acid citrus frt, and second only to Sweet Orange in overall economic importance. Both the juice and the peel, which have different properties and uses, are important flavouring ingredients in cooking, in salad dressings, etc. The juice is widely used, fresh or preserved, for lemonades, squashes, for flavouring confectionery, etc. Candied peel is made from the rind which is also the source of lemon oil, while lemon pip oil is used industrially in the manufacture of soaps and cosmetics. The juice is also a major commercial source of citric acid.

Origin, distribution and cultivation: *C. limon* does not exist in the wild, but is thought to have originated in the region comprising the eastern Himalayas and the mountains of Sichuan and Yunnan. It was introduced to Europe by the Arabs in the Middle Ages, and has since spread in cultivation to all the regions of the world with Mediterranean or dry sub-tropical climates. Commercial cultivation first began in Italy and Spain; these remain the largest European producers, followed by Greece, Cyprus and Turkey.

Similar plants: Sweet Lime *C. limetta* closely resembles Lemon, but the fls are pure white, the frt is usually less elongate, without an apical nipple, the scent is quite different, and the flesh is insipidly sweet. It has no commercial value but is sometimes planted for ornament in Mediterranean gardens.

Sweet Lime has nothing to do with true Lime *C. aurantifolia*, a yellow to dark green frt which is imported but never cultivated in Europe. Limes replace Lemons in the humid tropics, and are used for the same purpose; the flavour and scent are however quite different, and Lemons should not be substituted, if possible, in any recipe for dishes or drinks calling for Lime.

Citrus medica
CITRON
(p. 166)

Description: A spiny shrub to about 3 m in height. Lvs ovate, 8–20 cm long, the margins more or less bluntly toothed; lf-stalks short, not margined or winged and not articulated. Fls 3–4 cm in diameter, with petals tinged pink or mauve, and 30–40 stamens. Frt 10–20 cm long, like a large Lemon but without a distinct nipple at apex and skin rougher, bumpy, often with longitudinal furrows; rind very thick, enclosing small segments of greenish-yellow sour pulp.

Names: Fr.: Cedrat; It.: Cedrone, Cedro; Sp.: Cidra; Ger.: Zitronat; Dtch.: Muskuscitroen; Dan.: Tykskalletcitron; Gr.: Kitrodentro; Russ.: Tsitron; Yug.: Četrun.

Uses: Grown almost exclusively for the peel which is candied and used for flavouring confectioneries, or in marmalade-type preserves. *Etrog* is a variety of this species used ritually by Jews at the feast of the Tabernacles.

Origin, distribution and cultivation: Citron originally occupied the westernmost part of the natural distribution range of the genus, either in India or in western Asia, where it was cultivated in pre-classical times. It was the first citrus fruit to reach Europe, about 300 BC, and the Mediterranean remains to this day the main centre of cultivation. Citron is even more intolerant than Lemon of heat and cold, and is grown mainly on islands or in coastal areas with the least extreme temperatures. Corsica, Sicily, the Genoese coast, Corfu and parts of Greece are the only centres of commercial cultivation.

Similar plants: Lemon (see p. 108, and key p. 106).

Citrus grandis
POMELO
(p. 166)

Description: A rather spreading tree, to 12 m in height, with hairy twigs. Lvs large, up to 20 x 12 cm, broad, often notched at apex, and with mid-rib usually hairy beneath. Lf-stalks broadly winged. Fls large, 3–7 cm in diameter, creamy-white, with 20–25 stamens. Frt very large, 12–30 cm in diameter, globose or pear-shaped, similar to Grapefruit but with thicker rind, greenish or yellow when ripe, and smaller, pale yellow or pinkish and less acid pulp segments which detach more easily.

Names: Synonyms: *C. decumana*, *C. maxima.* Also spelled Pummelo, and called Shaddock.
Fr.: Pamplemousse, Pomelo; It.: Pomelo; Sp.: Toronja; Ger.: Pompelmus; Dtch.: Pompelmoes; Dan.: Pompelmus; Gr.: Frapa; Russ.: Pompelmus.

Uses: The pulp segments are eaten fresh. The species is of no economic importance in Europe where its sweeter, relatively insipid and less juicy flesh cannot rival Grapefruit. Frts sometimes available in supermarkets and luxury grocers are imported, although locally-grown frts are occasionally seen on markets in Greece and Cyprus.

Origin, distribution and cultivation: *C. grandis*, a native of S.E. Asia, is widely cultivated in the whole of southern Asia, from the Middle East to Japan, with the best frts produced in Thailand. It is not grown on a commercial scale anywhere in Europe, but has been cultivated as a curiosity in Mediterranean gardens ever since its introduction by the Arabs in the Middle Ages, long before the existence of Grapefruit (see overleaf).

Similar plants: Grapefruit, from which it is distinguished by hairy young twigs and undersides of lf mid-ribs, and by the qualities of the frt.

Citrus paradisi
GRAPEFRUIT
(p. 166)

Description: A spreading tree growing to 8–15 m in height, similar to Pomelo but with hairless twigs. Lvs generally smaller, broad, with midrib hairless beneath, and stalks short but fairly broadly winged. Fls 4–5 cm in diameter, white, usually with 5 petals, and 20–25 stamens, borne singly or in clusters. Frt large, globose or slightly flattened at poles, with yellow rind and yellowish or pinkish flesh of a distinctive, rather bitter flavour.

Names: Sometimes erroneously listed as *C. grandis*, *C maxima*, or *C. decumana*, which are all synonyms of Pomelo.
Fr.: Pamplemousse, Grapefruit; It.: Pompelmo; Sp.: Toronja; Ger.: Pomelie, Pampelmuse; Dtch.: Soort Pompelmoes; Dan.: Pompelmus; Gr.: Gkéipfrout; Russ.: Grepfrut.

Uses: Eaten as a fresh fruit, especially at breakfast when the refreshing, slightly bitter flavour is most appealing. Uninspired hosts in Anglo-Saxon countries also serve it as a first course at lunch or dinner. The juice is canned or bottled commercially on a large scale.

Origin, distribution and cultivation: There has been some confusion about the taxonomic status and origin of Grapefruit, but it is now generally believed to have arisen as a chance mutation from the Pomelo in the West Indies in the 17th or early 18th centuries.

Odet Philippe, chief surgeon of Napoleon's navy, was captured at Trafalgar and imprisoned in the Bahamas. After his release he settled in the United States, and later planted grapefruit seeds which he had brought with him or had sent from the Bahamas in Florida. Thereafter it spread and was developed in the United States, which remains the world's main producer. Grapefruits require very hot summers to ripen satisfactorily, and in Europe are grown commercially in Spain, Greece and Cyprus, but Israel, with the advantage of a more suitable climate, supplies most of the frts consumed in Europe.

Similar plants: Pomelo – see descriptions and key (p. 106).

Fortunella margarita
OVAL KUMQUAT
(p. 160)

Description: A much-branching evergreen shrub resembling Orange and other *Citrus* spp., but with much smaller lvs, fls and frt. Most cultivated plants are dwarf varieties growing to 1 or 2 m in height, but standard plants may grow to more than twice that size. Twigs spiny. Lvs variable in size, elongate with pointed tips, the stalks more or less broadly winged. Fls white. Frt small, ca. 4 cm long, ovoid, with thick edible dark yellow or orange peel, and 3–5, usually 4, pulp segments.

Names: Also known as 'Nagami' Kumquat.
Fr.: Kumquat; It.: Kumquat; Sp.: Kumquat, Quinoto; Ger.: Kumquat; Dtch.: Kumquat; Dan.: Kumquat; Gr.: Koumkouat; Russ.: Kinkan, Kumquat.

Uses: Kumquats are mainly cultivated for ornament, but the frts are also used by the home-gardener, and occasionally marketed in Europe. They are eaten whole, including the skin, either fresh, or more usually pickled in vinegar or preserved in syrup or candied. In these forms they are useful in many sweet and sour dishes, with duck, etc.

Origin, distribution and cultivation: Neither *F. margarita* nor *F. japonica* (see below) is known in the wild, but both have been cultivated for many centuries in China and Japan, which remain the main centres of commercial production. Kumquats are the hardiest of all citrus type frts, and do well in the Mediterranean, but unlike the Far East and the United States there is little commercial growing, although Spanish frts are sometimes exported, and small growers may offer frts on local markets in other countries.

Similar plants: Round Kumquats, also known as Marumi or Meiwa Kumquats, belong to a different species, *F. japonica*. It is less often grown for fruit than *F. margarita*, although the fruits are preferred for eating raw. Plants of the two species are indistinguishable, but the frts of *F. japonica* are globose, not ovoid.

Limequats are a cross between Kumquat and Lime *C. aurantifolia*; Orangequats are a hybrid of Kumquat and Sweet Orange. Neither is grown in Europe.

Calamondin Orange, mentioned above under Tangerine, is also believed by many botanists to be a Kumquat hybrid.

ANACARDIACEAE

Cashew Family

A small family (ca. 400 spp.) of mainly tropical trees and shrubs. Lvs are alternate, pinnate (in all the European spp.), without stipules. Fls are small, in panicles, with 3–7 sepals and petals, or without petals. Frts are drupes. All the members of this family have resinous sap which is often poisonous or vesicant, even in the few species which yield edible fruits, of which the best known are Cashew *Anacardium occidentale*, a tree cultivated for its 'nuts' in Brazil, E. Africa and S. India, and Mango *Mangifera indica*. The most notorious of the vesicant species are the *rengas* trees of Malaya and the poison ivies of the United States.

The resin of several species is exploited. Mastic, obtained from the Lentisc (see below) is now largely superseded by synthetic products, but no aesthetically acceptable substitute exists for the oriental lacquers, the poisonous sap of at least two different spp.; Burmese lacquer is obtained from *Melanorrhea usitata*, and Chinese lacquer from *Rhus verniciflua*.

The genus *Rhus*, Sumachs, are best known in Europe as ornamentals, but one species, *R. coriaria*, is cultivated in S. Italy, Sicily, etc. as a source of tannin and dye for the leather industry. The seeds of this species are widely used as a souring agent in Middle-Eastern cooking, as it was in Europe from classical times until the introduction of Lemons. It can be obtained in some Lebanese and Jewish shops in the form of a red powder called *sammak*. The plant is a hairy, evergreen shrub growing to 3 m, with large pinnate lvs, dense erect spikes of greenish fls, and purple-brown frts which distinguish it at once from the more commonly seen ornamental *R. typhina*.

The Peruvian Mastic, or Pepper Tree *Schinus mollis*, widely planted as an ornamental in southern Europe, is mentioned here only because it is sometimes mistaken for the source of peppercorns. True pepper is the frt of several spp. of *Piper*, vines belonging to 2 different families, only cultivated in the humid tropics. But the frts of *Schinus* can and sometimes are used as a pepper substitute, although they are never sold commercially. The same applies to those of Prickly Ash *Zanthoxylum alatum*, which does not belong to this family but to the previous one, the Rutaceae. *Schinus mollis* is an elegant tree with pendulous branches bearing pinnate lvs of 15–27 small narrow leaflets and loose-hanging bunches of pink frts. *Zanthoxylum alatum* is a fiercely thorny tree with usually 3–5 pinnate lvs with winged stalks, and red frts drying to black.

Pistacia vera PISTACHIO

(p. 168)

Description: A deciduous tree growing to 10 m with grey stems and, in older specimens, a thick trunk. Lvs with 3 to 7 large (10–15 cm long) broadly ovate leaflets which are finely hairy when young. Fls individually inconspicuous, without petals, in spreading racemes borne in axils; male and female fls on separate trees. Frt a drupe ca. 2–5 cm long with a hard thin 2-valved pale brown shell containing a bright green kernel enveloped in a thin papery reddish-brown skin.

Names: Fr.: Pistache; It.: Pistacchio; Sp.: Pistacho, Alfoncigo; Ger.: Pistazie; Dtch.: Pistache, Pimpernoot; Dan.: Pistacie; Gr.: Fystikiá; Russ.: Fistashka.

Uses: In the countries in which they are produced Pistachio nuts are eaten lightly roasted and salted, like peanuts, as a snack, and are used in many Middle-Eastern meat dishes. Pistachios have a delicate and subtle flavour, and are much more expensive than other commercial nuts. The chopped kernels are the green flecks in nougat and Turkish delight, and are (or should be) the flavouring and colouring agent in Italian pistachio ice-cream. The kernels are also widely used in pastries, cakes and confectioneries.

Origin, distribution and cultivation: *P. vera* is a native of Iran and neighbouring countries which remain the principal producers. It has been cultivated since ancient times in the Levant, and was introduced to Europe in the first century of our era. It has been grown in all parts of the Mediterranean, but today commercial production is limited to small stands in S. Spain, Sicily, Malta, and more extensively in Greece, Cyprus and Turkey. Most of the nuts marketed in northern Europe are imported from the Middle East.

Sumach

Similar plants: The much larger leaflets and frt distinguish *P. vera* from other European *Pistacia* spp.

Pistacia lentiscus MASTIC TREE or LENTISC

(p. 168)

Description: Usually seen as a low evergreen shrub, but if left ungrazed in favourable conditions may reach 8 m. All parts have a strong, rather unpleasant resinous smell. Lvs pinnate with 4–12 more or less narrow ovate, blunt-tipped leaflets, shiny above, without a terminal leaflet. Fls very small, with red anthers and no petals, in dense spike-like racemes in lf axils. Fruits small pea-sized, red ripening to black.

Names: Fr.: Lentisque, Mastique; It.: Lentischio, Mastice; Sp.: Lentisco, Almaciga; Ger.: Mastix; Dtch.: Mastiekboom; Gr.: Skinari, Mastika; Russ.: Fistasha lentiskus.

Uses: Mastic is a resin which exudes from incisions in the stems and dries in the form of 'tears'. It was once used for a variety of industrial purposes and as filling material by dentists, but with the exception of the manufacture of some varnishes has been replaced by synthetic resins. Mastic is used in Greece and the Levant as a chewing gum and sweetmeat, and for flavouring pastries, bread, and the Greek liqueur *mastike*. Lentisc is often used as a rootstock for Pistachio.

Origin, distribution and cultivation: Lentisc is one of the commonest shrubs of Mediterranean scrub, found throughout the region. Its abundance has always made cultivation unnecessary, except on the island of Chios, where a local variety, var. *latifolia*, or *chia*, is grown commercially for its superior mastic.

Similar plants: The absence of a terminal leaflet distinguishes *P. lentiscus* from Turpentine Tree *P. terebinthus*, which has also been exploited for its resinous gum. Turpentine Tree is a generally larger tree than Lentisc, with broader leaflets which are deciduous. It occurs throughout the Mediterranean, spreading north along the Atlantic coast and into parts of central Europe.

A similar, yet larger tree, native to the Canary Islands but occurring in various parts of the Mediterranean, is *P. atlantica*. It differs from Turpentine in having narrower leaflets and slightly hairy lf-stalks which are narrowly winged between the leaflets. It is of no commercial use.

OLEACEAE

Olive Family

A family of some 500 species of mostly temperate and semi-tropical trees, shrubs and a few climbers including a number of familiar native European or introduced ornamentals such as the Ashes, Privets, Lilac, Forsythia and Jasmines. Olive is of outstanding economic importance in Europe, but otherwise the family includes no food plants, with the marginal exception of Flowering Ash *Fraxinus ornus*. The sap of this tree hardens to a sweet gum called 'manna' which was for millennia a famine food in the Mediterranean. The tree, which may be distinguished from Common Ash *F. exelsior* by the conspicuous clusters of fragrant white fls which appear at the same time as the lvs (fls tiny and inconspicuous in Common and other ashes), is widely planted as an ornamental in central and southern Europe, and, it is said, is still cultivated for manna in S. Italy and Sicily. The foliage of Common Ash is sometimes harvested as cattle fodder in Scandinavia.

The family is distinguished by the structure of the fls, usually with only two stamens, a bell-shaped calyx, tubular corolla, and a superior, 2-celled ovary. The frts are of many types: compare Olive (a drupe) with the winged frts of Ash or the berries of Privet, etc.

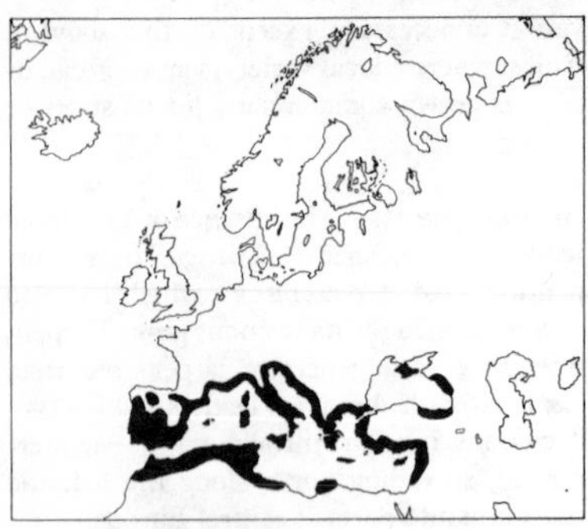

Natural distribution of Olive

Olea europea
OLIVE
(pp. 176, 213)

Description: The cultivated Olive is an evergreen tree, up to 15 m in height, with grey, closely-fissured bark on thick gnarled bowls on older specimens. Lvs narrow lanceolate, 2–8 cm long, dull green above, pale grey beneath, and covered in minute silvery scales. Fls small, creamy-white, in dense axillary clusters. Frt an ovoid drupe 1–4 cm long, pale green ripening through pink to black, rarely yellowish-white.

Many varieties exist, differing in frt size, flavour, oil content, etc.

Wild plants, sometimes referred to as var. *oleaster*, but not to be confused with the plant of that name belonging to the Eleagnaceae (p. 100), is usually smaller, bushier, more or less spiny, and often with small ovate lvs quite unlike the familiar cultivated varieties.

Names: Fr.: Olive; It.: Olivo; Sp.: Olivo, Acebuche; Ger.: Olive; Dtch.: Olijf; Dan.: Oliven; Gr.: Elia; Russ.: Olivkoye derevo; Yug.: Maslina.

Uses: Olives are cultivated for the frts which are first soaked in water to make them palatable, and preserved in brine or in oil, or else pressed for olive oil.

Green Olives are picked unripe in late summer. Red or pink Olives, rarely seen in northern Europe, are picked later, and black Olives when they are fully ripe, in late autumn.

The lack of enthusiasm for Olives often seen in northern Europe probably results from the poor quality tinned or bottled 'cocktail olives' which were almost the only kind available before Mediterranean grocers and delicatessens began importing a more interesting selection. Olives preserved in brine are rather dry and astringent. In any Mediterranean market a dozen or more different varieties, kept moist with olive oil and often partly crushed and spiced with different combinations of herbs, lemon rind, capsicums, anchovies, etc. show how important the Olive is in Mediterranean diet and cooking, and a taste of some of these should persuade any but the most prejudiced northerner of the excellence of this fruit. Olives are eaten on their own, or used to flavour salads, many kinds of cooked meat dishes, or vegetable dishes of tomatoes, eggplant, etc.

Olive oil varies as much in flavour and quality as do the frts. The best oil-producing varieties may be small and unpalatable, and good oil depends, like wine, on local conditions, soil, and years. The best quality of oil, called 'extra virgin' is pressed cold from fresh frt. Inferior qualities are from second pressings made under heat, and the worst are from bad olives, the oil of which is later treated chemically to remove the odour.

The discriminating European cook will keep one of the heavy, fruity varieties for certain salads, another, light and delicately flavoured one for mayonnaise, *brandade*, or for cooked dishes which call for olive oil, and a third, light, flavourless vegetable oil such as sunflower oil for other dishes.

Origin, distribution and cultivation: The noble Olive is more intimately associated with Mediterranean culture than any other plant. It originated in the eastern part of the basin, and was spread to the rest of the region in classical times. Olive is intolerant of frost or anything approaching tropical conditions, and outside the Mediterranean grows only in a few areas with a comparable climate: California, S. Africa and parts of Australia. So stringent are its climatic requirements that the natural distribution of the Olive tree (map, p. 114) is often used by botanists to define the precise limits of the Mediterranean Biogeographical Region.

Cultivation has declined in recent years in France and in parts of Italy in favour of less labour intensive crops, but is flourishing elsewhere. Hand-picking the fallen ripe frt from the ground has now disappeared in many places with the use of large plastic nets slung under the trees. Olives normally crop only every other year, but the use of certain fertilisers can often guarantee good annual crops.

Similar plants: Oleaster (p. 100).

Jasminum officinale
WHITE JASMINE
(p. 176)

Description: A scrambling plant with thin woody stems of older growth and long (reaching several m) green, ribbed and spirally-twisting current year's stems. These bear opposite lvs of 5–11 lanceolate, dull and green leaflets 1–8 cm long, the terminal leaflet longer than others. Fls in groups of 1–5 at ends of branches, with a small green calyx with awl-shaped teeth, and white tubular corolla expanding into 5 petal lobes, very fragrant. Frt a shiny black berry.

Names: Fr.: Jasmin; It.: Gelsomino; Sp.: Jazmin; Ger.: Jazmin; Dtch.: Jasmijn; Dan.: Jasmin; Gr.: Giasemí; Russ.: Zhasmin; Yug.: Jasmin.

Uses: Grown commercially for the perfume industry, for which the fls are hand-picked.

Origin, distribution and cultivation: *J. officinale* is a native of China, and is widely grown in European gardens for ornament. It is only included in this book because it is grown commercially on a field scale in a few places in south-east France.

Similar plants: *J. grandiflorum* is a similar plant, often with broader leaflets, and with larger fls, often with corolla tube and undersides of petals tinged with mauve. It is less frequent in gardens, but is cultivated in the same way as *J. officinalis* for the perfume industry in south-east France.

Several spp. of Jasmine are native to Europe, but have yellow fls. One of these, *J. odoratissimum*, a native of Madeira and the Canary Islands, has also been used in perfumery.

RUBIACEAE

Madder Family

This large (ca. 5000 spp.) family of mainly tropical trees and shrubs also includes several common European herbs. In the tropics it is represented by two genera of outstanding economic importance, the Coffee shrubs (*Coffea* spp.) and *Cinchona*, shrubs and trees whose bark yield the drug Quinine. *Gardenia*, *Ixora* and *Mussaenda*, widely grown for ornament, also belong to this family.

The Rubiaceae are only mentioned in passing for historical reasons, for one of its members, Madder *Rubia tinctorum* was extensively cultivated in Europe, especially in France, until the last war for a range of red to purple dyes obtained from the rhizome. The active substances, alizorine and others, have since been synthesised to produce infinitely more efficient industrial dyes. The plant is now grown on a very small scale for medicinal purposes.

PEDALIACEAE

Sesame Family

A small family of only 60 spp. of herbs from tropical Africa and Asia of which only one is of economic value.

Sesamum indicum
SESAME
(p. 176)

Description: An erect annual herb, 1–2 m tall, either bushy or unbranched, the whole plant slightly foetid. Stems square in section, furrowed, green, sometimes tinged with purple. Lvs on 3–6 cm stalks, variable, typically ovate, sometimes (especially basal lvs) coarsely toothed or even deeply palmately lobed, 5–15 cm long. Fls axillary on upper part of plant in groups of 1–3, with long green hairy calyx, and tubular corolla 3–4 cm long widening to 5 lobes, the middle lower one longest, white, pink or mauve, often mottled or striped inside with yellow or purple. Frt an oblong rectangular deeply-grooved capsule 2–3 cm long, ripening to brown or purple, borne erect and containing small (3 x 1.5 mm) ovate, usually creamy white, sometimes red, brown or black seeds.

Names: Fr.: Sesame; It.: Sesamo; Sp.: Sésamo; Ger.: Sesam; Dtch.: Sesam; Dan.: Sesam; Gr.: Soussami; Russ.: Kunzhut; Yug.: Sezam.

Madder

Uses: Sesame is cultivated for its seeds, the bulk of which are pressed for oil. The oil is a high-quality cooking and salad oil, which in Europe is also used in the manufacture of margarine and in industry (medicinal drugs, soaps, perfumery, lubricants, etc.). The seeds are used, especially in the Levant and in Eastern Europe, for flavouring pastries or bread, or amalgamated into blocks with honey as a sweetmeat. *Halva* may be made in many ways, but is typically based on sesame flour. Gastronomically the most noteworthy product is *Tahini*, a finely ground paste of the consistency of runny peanut butter used for flavouring *hummus* (see Chick Pea). The residual cake of seeds pressed for oil is a valuable cattle fodder.

Origin, distribution and cultivation: Sesame is often described as having originated in Africa, the home of its closest wild relations, but historical evidence points to India, where it has been in cultivation longer even than in Egypt, where it is first recorded about 1300 BC. It was grown by the Chaldeans, spread in ancient times to the

Mediterranean, and reached China during the Han dynasty. Today it is essentially a tropical crop, the main producers being India, China, Burma, the Sudan and Nigeria, but it is also grown on a substantial scale in the Middle East, and in Turkey, the Balkans, eastern Europe and the Soviet Union.

Similar plants: Field crops bear a vague resemblance to small-leaved Tobacco plants, especially to ones that have been stripped of their large basal lvs and allowed to stand for seed production, but the structures of fls, frt, etc. are unmistakable.

SCROPHULARIACEAE

Figwort Family

A family of many ornamental plants (*Verbascum*, *Antirrhinum* etc.), mostly herbs and shrubs with lvs that bear no stipules. Fls mainly symmetrical in one plant only, with parts in fives, and often a tubular or bell-shaped corolla. Apart from the medicinal spp. given below, none is of economic importance.

Digitalis purpurea
COMMON FOXGLOVE

Description: A tall downy biennial herb with an unbranched stem up to 1.5 m in height. Lvs alternate, ovate-lanceolate, softly hairy, bluntly toothed, 15–30 cm long, on short winged stalks. Fls in a long erect terminal raceme, the corolla tubular to narrow bell-shaped, 4–5 cm long, mauve with dark purple spots ringed with white inside tube; calyx short with pointed lobes. Frt an ovoid capsule.

Names: Fr.: Digitale pourprée; It.: Digitale; Sp.: Digital, Dedalera; Ger.: Fingerhut; Dtch.: Vingerhoedskruid; Dan.: Fingerbøl; Gr.: Khelidonokhorto; Russ.: Napertianka.

Uses: Digitalis, of which the active ingredients are glycosides (including digitoxin and gitoxin) is an important cardiac medicine, obtained from the lvs of second year plants of this and other spp. (see overleaf).

Woolly Foxglove (see overleaf)

Origin, distribution and cultivation: *D. purpurea* is a common plant, especially in woodlands, throughout Europe. Its showy inflorescence makes it a popular garden plant, and it is grown commercially as a field crop for the pharmaceutical industry in western, especially north-west, Europe, though only occasionally in Britain.

Similar plants: Woolly Foxglove *D. lanata*, easily distinguished from Common Foxglove by its narrower lanceolate lvs and broadly bell-shaped fls (with a large curving lower lip which are pale brown with darker mottling, the lip whitish) is a montane sp. ranging in the wild from Hungary to the mountains of the Middle East. It yields the same active ingredients, but in greater concentration, and has therefore largely replaced the common sp. in cultivation in Germany, Switzerland, Austria, and central Europe. Large Yellow Foxglove *D. grandiflora*, a sp. with pale ochre-yellow fls netted with brown inside corolla tubes, which grows wild on the Continent has also been grown for the same purpose.

VERBENACEAE

Vervain Family

A small family of herbs very similar to the Labiates, but differing in botanical details such as the style being terminal on frt. Two economic species are cultivated in Europe.

Verbena officinalis
VERVAIN
(p. 176)

Description: An erect hairy perennial herb 25–65 cm in height, with tough slender branching stems. Lvs opposite, narrow, pinnately lobed, bristly, 2–7.5 cm long. Inflorescences long (8–12 cm), leafless spikes bearing loosely spaced unstalked bluish-pink 5-petalled fls 4 mm in diameter, with long corolla tube and shorter calyx. Frt separating into 4 small nutlets.

Names: Fr.: Verveine; It.: Verbena; Sp.: Verbena; Ger.: Eisenkraut; Dtch.: Verbena; Dan.: Jaernurt; Gr.: Staurovótano; Russ.: Verbena aptechnaya.

Uses: Verbena is considered a purely medicinal plant, and is only included here because the popularity of Vervain infusion or 'tea' in France, Switzerland, etc, where the chopped dried flowering stems are available in packets or tea-bags from pharmacies, grocers or in cafés, has led to relatively large-scale cultivation in some places.

Origin, distribution and cultivation: Vervain occurs in the wild in most of Europe except the far north on waste land, scrub, often on chalky soils; it is cultivated, sometimes on a field scale, in France and in parts of central Europe.

Similar plants: Garden ornamentals belong to other *Verbena* spp. (*V. bonariensis*, *V.* x *hybrida*, etc.). They have much larger fls (5–7 cm across).

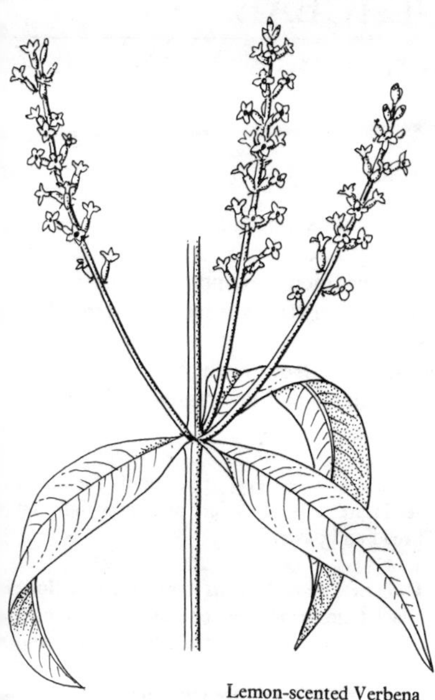

Lemon-scented Verbena

Lippia citriodora
LEMON-SCENTED VERBENA

Description: A shrub with a slender sparsely branching woody main stem standing 1–2 m in height and spreading to more than 1 m. Lvs large, narrowly lanceolate, on very short stalks, pale to mid-green, with a strong lemony scent when crushed. Fls tiny, mauve, in large loose panicles ca. 10 cm long.

Names: Sometimes called Spanish Thyme. Fr.: Verveine odorante, – citronelle; It.: Cedrina, Erba luisa; Sp.: Hierba luisa; Ger.: Punchpflanze; Russ.: Verbena limonnaya.

Uses: The commercial use of this plant, especially in France, as a herbal 'tea'. Much of the 'Verveine' available from French markets and chemists belongs to this sp. The essential oil is also used in perfumery and in toilet articles.

Origin, distribution and cultivation: This species is of Chilean origin. In the 16th and 17th centuries, many exotic plants were given the epithet 'Spanish' because they were first made known in Europe by early Spanish exploration. Spanish Thyme is cultivated on a commercial scale in south-east France and in a few places in Italy and Spain, for the perfume and pharmaceutical industries.

Similar plants: *Lippia* should not be confused with Lemon Thyme *T. citriodorus*, p. 296, nor should the French name *citronelle* cause it to be mistaken for Citronella *Cymbopogon nardus*, a tropical lemon-scented grass much used in S.E. Asian cooking.

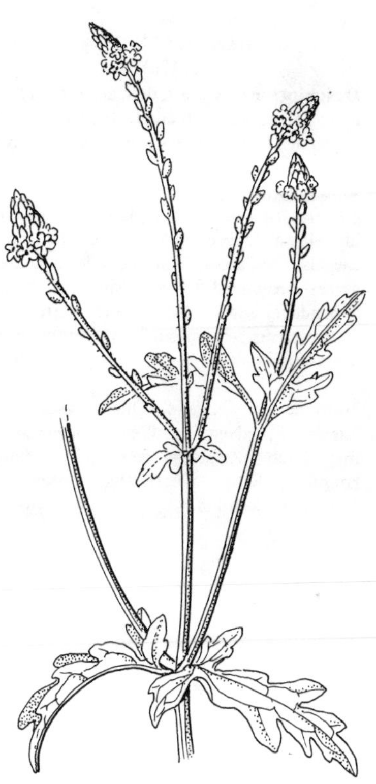

Vervain

RANUNCULACEAE

Buttercup Family

A family of mostly herbaceous and some woody plants that takes its name from the well-known buttercups (*Ranunculus* spp.). Only one member comes within the scope of this book, but many are grown for ornament, including Delphiniums, Anemones and Clematis. Many of the wild spp. are acrid or poisonous, and may be a threat to stock in pastures or hay meadows.

Fls are bisexual, with sepals and petals similar or with one or the other whorl lacking. The ovary is usually of many carpels, sometimes of a few many-seeded pods.

Nigella sativa BLACK CUMIN

(p. 176)

Description: A short, delicate annual herb up to 55 cm tall, with erect, slender, branching stems. Lvs pinnately divided into narrow linear segments, the lower ones stalked. Fls solitary, with 5 petal-like sepals, white with greenish tips or more or less flushed with blue. Frt a globose inflated ovoid capsule of 5 carpels fused along their entire length, their apices prolonged by a fleshy awl-shaped appendage; seeds black, ovoid, with wavy transverse ridges on surface, slightly bitter but aromatic.

Names: Fr.: Nigelle, Quatre-épices; It.: Nigella; Sp.: Neguilla; Ger.: Schwarzkümmel; Dtch.: Zwarte komijn; Gr.: Mauro koumino; Russ.: Chernoshka posevnaya; Yug.: Crna kumina.

Uses: The peppery, rather oddly flavoured seeds are a minor spice, used especially on bread and pastries.

Origin, distribution and cultivation: Black Cumin is widely cultivated, albeit on a small scale, in India, the Middle East and Egypt, where it is most used, but also to a small extent in Greece and Turkey.

Similar plants: *N. sativa* is often confused, even in some illustrated books, with the closely related common ornamental Love In A Mist, *N. damascena*. The latter has lvs much more finely divided, the segments thread-like, and the blue or white fls and frts are enveloped in a mass of thread-like bracts similar to the foliage.

PAPAVERACEAE

Poppy Family

A readily recognisable, homogenous family including a number of genera (*Papaver*, *Glaucium*, *Hypecoum*, etc.) widely distributed in the northern hemisphere. They are herbs with milky sap and lvs mostly divided and compound. Fls are large, showy, solitary, with 4 petals with a typically silky, creased appearance, often with 2 sepals which fall off after the bud opens, and numerous stamens. Frt is either a top-shaped capsule (*Papaver*) or a long pod. Only one species is an agricultural crop plant.

Papaver somniferum
OPIUM POPPY

(p. 176)

Description: A conspicuous annual, 60–150 cm high, glaucous, with branched stems which are sometimes slightly hairy. Lvs twisted, ovate-oblong, often slightly pinnately lobed, coarsely toothed; lower lvs on short stalks, upper lvs clasping. Fls large, 10–18 cm in diameter, with 4 petals in 2 whorls, and numerous stamens. Frt is a large swollen capsule.

The cultivated forms belong to 2 main subspecies:

ssp. *somniferum*, cultivated for opium, has white petals spotted with mauve to purple-black at base (sometimes unspotted), and a larger, ovoid capsule which does not split on ripening.

ssp. *hortense*, grown for seeds, has mauve petals always spotted with purple-black at base, and a smaller, rounder dehiscent capsule.

Names: Fr.: Pavot; It.: Papavero; Sp.: Adormidera; Ger.: Schlafmohn; Dtch.: Blauwmaanzaad, Witmaanzaad; Gr.: Aphioni; Russ.: Mak opiumni; Yug.: Urtni mak.

Uses: Opium Poppy is grown for opium, which is the coagulated sap which exudes from incisions made in the frt capsule, and for the seeds which are free of narcotic alkaloids, and are used as a flavouring, and pressed for oil.

Opium contains some 20 alkaloids, including codeine, and morphine, used as an anaesthetic, but increasingly replaced by synthetic non-addictive substances, and which is illegally refined to heroin on a large scale. The common use of raw opium, in pharmaceutical preparations in the 19th and early 20th centuries, has declined following the invention of synthetic sedatives and pain killers. Its use as a narcotic drug is largely confined to the areas of production, but its infinitely more dangerous and addictive derivative, heroin, is exported from Asia for illegal sale in Europe and N. America.

Poppy seeds are much used as a flavouring in confectioneries, pastry and baking, especially in eastern Europe and the Middle East, but the bulk of the crop is pressed cold to yield a clear edible oil, sometimes known as *olivette* in France; a second pressing under heat produces an inferior, coloured oil used in artist's paints and for industrial purposes.

Origin, distribution and cultivation: *P. somniferum* is a cultivated derivative of *P. setigerum*, a more hairy wild species, evolved in Asia Minor. It was used by the ancient Greeks, and spread in cultivation to India and China by the 18th century.

Cultivation for opium is centred in western Asia, from Turkey through Iran and Pakistan to the Himalaya, and in the highland area of N. Thailand, Burma and Laos known as the 'golden triangle'. Opium was also produced in the Balkans, and on a smaller, rigorously controlled scale in most of central Europe including France. The acreage of Poppy under cultivation has increased steadily in recent years, but this is of plants grown for the seeds, especially for oil. The Balkans, Eastern Europe and the Soviet Union are the largest producers, but substantial crops are grown in Germany, France and elsewhere. British crops are still experimental.

Similar plants: The variable common Corn Poppy *P. rhoeas*, distinguished together with several other wild European spp. from Opium Poppy by its smaller, scarlet fls, is a weed of cornfields which, owing to the widespread use of herbicides, is becoming uncommon in many areas. It was formerly cultivated in Europe both for the seeds, which have the same uses as Opium Poppy, and for the red petals, used medicinally.

BRASSICACEAE or CRUCIFERAE

Cabbage Family

A morpholgically homogenous family of about 3000 spp. of mainly herbaceous plants, mostly from temperate regions, including many native wild European spp. The crucifers are so called because their fls have 4 petals arranged in a cross in a single whorl. Sepals number 4 in 2 whorls; the stamens typically number 6, with the 2 outer filaments shorter than the 4 inner ones. Frt is a pod-like capsule called a siliqua when elongate, or silicula when no longer than broad. Lvs are usually alternate and simple, without stipules.

Although economically less important than the Leguminosae, the family is very much in evidence, for vast acreages are given over to the cultivation of a few of the spp. on all arable farms in Europe. A single sp., *Brassica oleracea*, provides several important vegetables, including Cabbage, as well as forage and fodder crops. Other spp. such as Turnip and Swede are important 'root' crops grown on a small scale as vegetables and very extensively for feeding livestock. Other forms of the same spp. and of others are grown for their seeds, used either as a source of oil or for the ground meal (mustard) used as a condiment.

Mustard – the condiment:
The seeds of several spp. of *Brassica* and *Sinapis* become pungent when crushed or milled and mixed with cold or tepid water. The pungency is due to an essential oil produced by an enzyme acting on a glucoside, and is not present in the living seed, in those subjected to the high temperatures of cooking, or in the vegetable oils expressed from the seeds. Three spp. are used in the manufacture of condiments: Black Mustard *Brassica nigra*, Brown Mustard *B. juncea* and White Mustard *Sinapis alba.* The colours refer to the seed coat of each sp.; the colour of the condiment is determined not by the sp. used, but by whether the seed coat of Black or Brown Mustards are removed. The flavour of the different types of commercial mustard is mainly determined by the method of manufacture and the other ingredients used. Although most people have a preference for one type, and use it universally, each is appropriate to different kinds of dishes. The major types of mustard are:

English mustard: Traditionally made from finely ground de-husked Black Mustard seed, the most pungent of the 3 spp., mixed with some White Mustard and a little wheat flour (a forbidden ingredient in other countries), and marketed as a yellow powder to be mixed with cold water shortly before use. For economic reasons Black Mustard seed has almost entirely been replaced with the less pungent Brown Mustard. English mustard has a sharp clean taste which enhances rather than masks the flavour of foods.

Dijon mustard: This is the most universally appreciated variety, accounting for more than 85% of the mustard produced in France. It is hot and pale like English mustard, but subtler, because the de-husked Black Mustard seeds (increasingly replaced by Brown Mustard) is unadulterated with White Mustard and is ground wet with verjuice (see Grape, p. 101) and sold as a paste. Dijon mustard also has a sharp clean taste, and has the widest range of uses, as an accompaniment to cold or hot meats, in cooking, dressings, etc.

Bordeaux mustard: This is the mild brown mustard commonly thought of as 'French' mustard in Britain, because it was introduced early, concurrently with the claret trade, but it accounts for less than 10% of the mustard used in France. It is dark because the seed husks are not removed, sweet and sour from the addition of sugar and vinegar, and heavily flavoured with tarragon and other spices.

German mustard: A similar dark, mild and sweetish mustard. Both this and Bordeaux mustard are suitable for well cooked cold meats, sausages, etc. and for some dressings, but are not 'clean', and quite unsuitable for more delicately flavoured dishes.

American mustard: The very mild, sweetish, bright yellow mustard used on hot dogs. Unlike the preceding types, this is made principally of the mild White Mustard seeds. Many other mixed or fancy mustards exist, some so dominated by other ingredients that they scarcely merit the appellation of mustard.

Mustard oil is one of the terms used for cooking oils obtained from the seeds of Rape (*Brassica napus*), Field Mustard (*B. campestris*) and Turnip Rape (*B. rapa*). Mustard seeds are also used in the kitchen, and the seedlings, in the cotyledon stage, of White Mustard and of Rape are used as a salad ingredient.

KEY TO THE MAIN CRUCIFEROUS CROP PLANTS

1	Fls white or tinged with purple=**2**	**(10)**
2	Aquatic plant=**Watercress**	**(3)**
3	Plant not aquatic=**4**	**(2)**
4	Frt as broad as long=**5**	**(7)**
5	A large perennial, with large (up to 60 cm) oblong unlobed lvs=**Horse-radish**	**(6)**
6	A delicate annual, with small pinnately lobed lvs=**Cress**	**(5)**
7	Frt longer than broad; lvs pinnately lobed=**8**	**(4)**
8	Roots tuberous; frt with a conical beak, not splitting open at maturity=**Radish**	**(9)**
9	Root not tuberous; frt with a flattened beak, splitting open at maturity=**Rocket**	**(8)**

KEY TO THE MAIN CRUCIFEROUS CROP PLANTS

10	Fls yellow=*Brassica* and *Sinapis* spp. – see keys below.	**(1)**

KEYS TO THE YELLOW-FLOWERED CRUCIFEROUS CROP PLANTS

(Although not a crop plant, Charlock is included as it is a very common weed which closely resembles some of the economic spp.)

Key 1 (using lvs and fls)

1	Lvs glaucous,* thick, hairless at maturity=**2**	**(8)**
2	Lvs totally hairless, even on young plants; bracts obovate, narrowed at base; inflorescence elongate and open when expanded, 10–25 cm long=*B. oleracea*	**(3)**
3	At least some lvs of young plants with a few hairs; inflorescence short when expanded, less than 10 cm long=**4**	**(2)**
4	Young lvs more or less hairy on nerves; upper lvs clasping; bracts lanceolate with broad clasping basal lobes; fls large, 1.2–1.5 cm long=*B. napus*	**(7)**
5	Roots slender, not tuberous=ssp. *oleifera*	**(6)**
6	Roots tuberous, globose=ssp. *napobrassica*	**(5)**
7	Young lvs slightly bristly-hairy; upper lvs not clasping, stalked; bracts linear-lanceolate, stalked; fls less than 1 cm long=*B. juncea*	**(4)**
8	Lvs grass-green, more or less hairy=**9**	**(1)**
9	Upper lvs unstalked=**10**	**(14)**
10	Lower lvs deeply lobed, the upper ones clasping the stem=**11**	**(13)**
11	Roots tuberous=*B. rapa*	**(12)**
12	Roots not tuberous=*B. campestris*	**(11)**
13	Lower lvs shallowly lobed, the upper ones not clasping=*S. arvensis*	**(10)**
14	Upper lvs stalked=**15**	**(9)**
15	Lvs not lobed=*B. chinensis*	**(16)**
16	Lvs lobed=**17**	**(15)**

KEY TO THE MAIN CRUCIFEROUS CROP PLANTS

17	Lower lvs pinnately lobed, the terminal lobe not large=*S. alba*	**(18)**
18	Lower lvs pinnately lobed, the terminal lobe much larger than others=**19**	**(17)**
19	Lvs at least slightly glaucous; basal lvs up to 20 cm long; fls pale yellow=*B. juncea*	**(20)**
20	Lvs grass-green; basal lvs up to 16 cm long; fls bright yellow=*B. nigra*	**(19)**
	* *B. juncea* which is only slightly glaucous is included in both sections of key.	
	Key 2 (using structure of pods (siliqua))	
1	Pods rough, each valve with 3 nerves (*Sinapis* spp.)=**2**	**(4)**
2	Beak as long as rest of frt, flattened; pods widely spreading from rachis=*S. alba*	**(3)**
3	Beak short, conical; pods less stiffly spreading from rachis=*S. arvensis*	**(2)**
4	Pods smooth, each valve with 1 nerve (*Brassica* spp.)=**5**	**(1)**
5	Pods short, 4-sided, erect, not spreading=*B. nigra*	**(6)**
6	Pods long, cylindrical, semi-erect or spreading widely from rachis=**7**	**(5)**
7	Pods semi-erect=*B. juncea*	**(8)**
8	Pods widely spreading=*B. napus, B. oleracea, B. rapa, B. campestris, B. chinensis*	**(7)**
	Key 3 (using colour and texture of testa, or outer covering of seed)	
1	Seed pale, buff or yellow=**2**	**(4)**
2	Seed large, 2–3 mm in diameter=*S. alba*	**(3)**

KEY TO THE MAIN CRUCIFEROUS CROP PLANTS		
3	Seed small, 1–2 mm in diameter = *B. juncea*	**(2)**
4	Seed dark = **5**	**(1)**
5	Seed dark purple-brown, ca. 2 mm in diameter = *B. napus*	**(6)**
6	Seed otherwise coloured = **7**	**(5)**
7	Seed brownish-grey, 2–4 mm in diameter = *B. oleracea*	**(8)**
8	Seed dark or lighter reddish-brown = **9**	**(7)**
9	Surface of seed minutely pitted, dark brown; seed 1–1.5 mm in diameter, with a sharp acrid flavour = *B. nigra*	**(10)**
10	Surface of seed not pitted = **11**	**(9)**
11	Flavour of seed mild = *B. rapa, B. campestris*	**(12)**
12	Flavour of seed sharp = *B. juncea, S. arvensis*	**(11)**

Brassica oleracea
CABBAGES
(p. 170)

Description: A polymorphic sp. including the familiar vegetables listed below. Although differing greatly in appearance due to enlargement of one or other parts of the plant in each type, these biennial cultivated forms scarcely differ from each other or from the wild form in the structure of root, frt and seeds, and cannot be distinguished as seedlings. The wild form is the perennial Sea Cabbage (not to be confused with Seakale, p. 233). The plant has branching, somewhat woody stems bearing pinnately lobed lvs. Lvs and herbaceous stem glaucous, entirely hairless. Fls large (2.5 cm long), the petals pale yellow, very occasionally white; sepals erect; filaments of outer stamens almost as long as inner ones; bracts stalkless, obovate, narrowed to base, not clasping. Frt 5–10 cm long, cylindrical, smooth, with short conical beak; seeds grey-brown, 2–4 mm across.

The cultivated forms belong to the following varieties or convars:

convar *acephala*: Marrow-stem Kale and 1000-headed Kale: Both these forms, together with the vegetable kales belonging to var. *laciniata* (below) are those closest to Wild Cabbage, particularly by virtue of their elongate, branching, leafy first-year stem. 1000-headed Kale has a slender woody stem growing to over 1 m in height, branching and leafy only in the upper part. Marrow-stem Kale is similar, but has a much thickened (edible) stem up to 10 cm in diameter.

convar. *acephala* subvar. *laciniata*: Borecoles (Winter Greens) and Curly Kale. These are similar to 1000-headed Kale but smaller. The latter has lvs curled and crisped in the manner of curled Parsley. Silvery, purple, or variegated varieties are grown for ornament.

var. *bullata* subvar. *gemmifera*: Brussels Sprouts. This plant also has an elongate first-year stem up to 1 m in height, but is readily recognisable by the numerous axillary buds which form the compact heads or 'sprouts' ca. 3 cm across along almost the whole length of the stem.

var. *gongylodes*: Kohlrabi. This is a curious form in which the base of the stem is thickened to form a white, green or purple spherical turnip-like swelling 5–12 cm in diameter. This edible portion is easily distinguished from turnips and similar 'roots' by the slender lf-stalks which arise from the upper half or even the whole surface.

convar. *botrytis* var. *botrytis*: Cauliflower and Broccoli. The former develops a large hemispherical white curd-like mass of tightly bunched abortive fls on thick branches, surrounded by lvs at the top of a short stem. Varieties with green or purple heads exist, but are rarely seen because the white form is preferred by consumers. Broccoli is similar in that it develops a hypertrophied mass of abortive fls, but these are purple, sometimes green, and do not form a compact mass, but a loose terminal cluster of heads on one or several branches.

convar. *botrytis* var. *italica*: Sprouting Broccoli or Calabrese. This form differs from Broccoli in that the bright green young inflorescences are not compacted at the tip, but are borne on axillary branches as well as on the terminal branches which are often fasciated, ie. partly fused in a bundle.

var. *capitata*: Head Cabbages. In these forms the stem is very short, the lvs forming a lettuce-like head, spherical and extremely compact in some forms, looser and more open in others. Cattle Cabbages are very large, usually with flattened heads. Many different forms are grown as vegetables; compact dark red varieties with white ribs are classed as form *rubra*, as distinct from the white or green varieties of form *alba*. Portugal Cabbage is a loose-headed form distinguished by the very broad midribs which fuse into a mass of side-veins, the whole occupying as much as half the surface of lf-blade.

var. *subauda*: Savoy Cabbage. This is similar in structure and size to the loose-headed cabbages, but the lvs are tightly crinkled. Because of its structure this variety has usually been considered to be a form of var. *capitata*, but in the EEC classification it is assimilated to var. *bullata*, Brussels Sprouts.

Names (Cabbage): Fr.: Chou; It.: Cavolo; Sp.: Col berza; Ger.: Kohl; Dtch.: Kool; Dan.: Kål; Gr.: Lachanon; Russ.: Kapusta; Yug.: Kapus.

Uses: Marrow-stem Kale, 1000-headed Kale and Cattle Cabbages are grown as winter forage and fodder crops for livestock. Borecoles, Curly Kales and all the other forms described above are winter vegetables. Sauerkraut (German *sauer*: acid, *Kraut*: herb, plant) is a sort of human silage extensively made and eaten from Alsace eastwards through Germany, Switzerland and central Europe to Russia. It is made of finely-shredded cabbage mixed with salt and compressed in its own liquid in tubs where it undergoes lactic fermentation, the acid produced acting as a preservative.

Origin, distribution and cultivation: Wild or Sea Cabbage (sometimes referred to a distinct sp., *B. sylvestris*) is a native of the Mediterranean and of S.W. Europe northward to southern England, where it occurs on seaside cliffs. This edible plant has been cultivated for at least 4000 years in the form of Kales. Head Cabbages were developed early on, the more extreme morphological forms later. Cauliflowers were introduced to Italy from the eastern Mediterranean during the Renaissance; Brussels Sprouts may be the latest major form to have been developed, since the earliest certain records are from Belgium in the 18th century. The cultivated forms are biennials picked for consumption at the end of the first year. Plants allowed to overwinter flower in the spring and die after fruiting. Forage forms are all grown as field crops, and some Head Cabbages are used as vegetables; other forms are grown mainly by market-gardeners.

Similar plants: Most cultivated forms of this sp. are unmistakeable. More primitive forms resemble *B. napus* (see keys p. 124–5 and description p. 225). A few primitive forms of *B. oleracea*, such as the Black Cabbage of Tuscany are still grown locally in parts of Europe. These are intermediate in structure between Kales and Head Cabbages, with short, sometimes branching stems, but the lvs do not form a tight head. *B. cretica*, a distinct sp. native to the eastern Mediterranean is similar to these, as is Abyssinian Cabbage *B. carinata*, which has been grown in Europe, and *B. perviridis*, usually called Spinach Mustard. The latter term has been used rather indiscriminately for any *Brassica* lvs, such as turnip tops, which are occasionally used as a boiled vegetable.

(continued on page 223)

ROSACEAE

1. Medlar *Mespilus germanica* p. 25
1a. Flower
1b. Twigs with leaves and fruit

2. Quince *Cydonia oblonga* p. 25
2a. Flower
2b. Twig with leaves and fruit
2c. Fruit in section

3. Rose *Rosa gallica medicinalis* p. 18
Flower

4. Azarole *Crataegus azarolus* p. 24
Twig with leaves and fruit

5. Service Tree *Sorbus domestica* p. 26
5a. Twigs with leaves and fruit
5b. Flower

6. Loquat *Eriobytra japonica* p. 26
Leaves and fruit

1a
1b
2a
2c
3
2b
4
5a
6
5b

ROSACEAE

1. Pear *Pyrus communis* p. 28
Blossom

2. 'Hazel' or 'Hessle' Pear p. 28
Fruit

3. 'Blakely' Perry Pear p. 28
Leaves and fruit

4. 'Williams Bon Chrétien' Pear p. 28
Leaves and fruit

5. 'Conference' Pear p. 28
5a. Leaves and fruit
5b. Section of fruit

6. Apple *Malus pumila* p. 27
Blossom

7. 'Spartan' Apple p. 27
Fruit

8. 'Golden Delicious' Apple p. 27
Leaves and fruit

9. 'Kingston Black' Cider Apple p. 27

10. 'Bramley' Cooking Apple p. 27
Fruit

11. 'Cox' Apple p. 27
11a. Fruit
11b. Section of fruit

1
2
3
5b
5a
7
4
6
11b
8
9
10
11a

ROSACEAE

1. Morello Cherry *Prunus cerasus* p. 34
Blossom and fruit

2. Sweet Cherry *Prunus avium* var. 'Stella' p. 33
Leaves and fruit

3. Peach *Prunus persica* p. 31
3a. Blossom
3b. Whole fruit
3c. Leaves and fruit in section

4. Nectarine var. *nectarina* p. 31
Fruit

5. Sweet Cherry *Prunus avium* var. 'Napoleon Bigarreau' p. 33
Fruits whole and in section, with leaves

6. Almond *Prunus communis* p. 32
6a. Leaves and fruit
6b. Fruit in section
6c. Blossom

7. Apricot *Prunus armeniaca* p. 31
7a. Twig with leaves and fruit
7b. Blossom

1
2
3a
3b
3c
4
5
6a
6b
6c
7a
7b

ROSACEAE

1. Sloe *Prunus spinosa* p. 35
Twig with leaves and fruit

2. 'Farleigh Damson' *Prunus damascena* p. 35
Twig with leaves and fruit

3. 'Prune Damson' *Prunus damascena* p. 35
Fruit whole and in section

4. Bullace *Prunus domestica* ssp. *insititia* p. 35
Twig with leaves and fruit

5. Mirabelle *Prunus cerasifera* × *Prunus domestica* p. 34
Leaves and fruit

6. Greengage *Prunus domestica* ssp. *italica* p. 36
Twig with leaves and fruit

7. Plum *Prunus domestica* p. 35
7a. Blossom
7b. 'Pershore'; whole fruit
7c. 'Coes Golden Drop'; whole fruit and section
7d. 'Quetsch'; whole fruit
7e. 'Prune d'Agen'; leaves and whole fruit; dried fruit
7f. 'Jefferson'; whole fruit
7g. 'Victoria'; whole fruit and section

1
2
3
4
6
7a
7b
7c
7d
7f
7g

ROSACEAE

1. Raspberry *Rubus idaeus* p. 20
1a. Flower and leaves
1b. Fruit

2. Strawberry *Fragaria* × *ananassa* p. 22
2a. Leaves and flower
2b. Fruit

3. Loganberry *Rubus loganobaccus* p. 21
3a. Flower
3b. Fruit

4. Alpine Strawberry *Fragaria vesca* p. 22
4a. Fruit
4b. Leaves and flowers

5. Wineberry *Rubus phoenicolasius* p. 21
Leaves and fruit

6. Wild Blackberry *Rubus ulmifolius* p. 19
6a. Leaf and flower
6b. Twig with leaves and fruit

7. Cut-leafed Blackberry var. 'Oregon Thornless' *Rubus laciniatus* p. 20
Fruit

8. Yellow Raspberry *Rubus idaeus* p. 20
Leaf and fruit

9. Cloudberry *Rubus chamaemorus* p. 22
Leaves and fruit

10. Dewberry *Rubus caesius* p. 20
Fruit

1a
1b
2a
2b
3a
3b
4a
4b
5
6a
6b
7
8
9
10

LEGUMINOSAE

1. Lima or Butter Bean *Phaseolus lunatus* p. 56
1a. Leaves and pods
1b. Flower
1c. Dried Butter Bean

2. Scarlet Runner Bean *Phaseolus coccineus* p. 56
2a. Part of vine with leaves and flower
2b. Pod
2c. Dried beans

3. Common Bean *Phaseolus vulgaris* p. 54
3a. Part of vine with leaves and pods of 'French' Bean
3b. Flowers of 'French' Bean
3c. Flowers and dried bean and pod of 'Mexican Black'
3d. Pod and dried beans of 'Pea' Bean
3e. Flowers, pod and dried bean of Purple-podded Bean
3f. Pod and dried bean of 'Deuil Fin Précoce'

4. Broad Bean *Vicia faba* p. 58
4a. Leaves and flowers
4b. Opened pod
4c. Dried beans

1a
1b
2a
2b
2c
3a
3b
3c
3d
3e
3f
4a
4b
4c

LEGUMINOSAE

1. Garden Pea *Pisum sativum sativum* p. 57
1a. Leaves, stipules, tendrils and flower
1b. Common Pea pod and seeds
1c. Pods of Mangetout
1d. Pod and seeds of Petit Pois

2. Field Pea *Pisum sativum arvense* p. 57
Flower and seeds

3. Asparagus pea *Lotus tetragonolubus* p. 48
3a. Flowering stem
3b. Pod

4. Lentil *Lens culinaris* p. 51
4a. Stem with flowers and green pods
4b. Mature pods
4c. Pod in section
Dried seeds of:
4d. Egyptian lentils
4e. Puy lentils
4f. German lentils

5. Chick Pea *Cicer arietinum* p. 51
5a. Flowering stem
5b. Stem with pods
5c. Fresh green pod and seed
5d. Dried seeds

6. Soya Bean *Glycine max* p. 52
6a. Stem with pods
6b. Flower
6c. Dried pod
6d. Various dried seeds

2
3a
1c
3b
1d
4a
1b
4c
4e
4f
4b
4d
5a
6a
6b
6c
5d
5b
6d

LEGUMINOSAE

1. Yellow Lupin *Lupinus luteus* p. 41
1a. Flowering stem
1b. Dried pod

2. Blue Lupin *Lupinus angustifolius* p. 41
2a. Flowering stem
2b. Dried pod

3. Yellow Trefoil *Medicago lupulina* p. 46
3a. Flowering stem
3b. Fruit

4. Sainfoin *Onobrychis sativa* p. 45
4a. Flowering stem
4b. Fruit

5. Lucerne *Medicago sativa* p. 44
5a. Flowering stem
5b. Fruit
5c. Flower of var. *falcata*, Sickle Medick

6. Bokhara Clover *Melilotus alba* p. 47
Flowering stem

7. Serradella *Ornithopus sativus* p. 45
7a. Flowering stem
7b. Dry Fruit

8. Common Vetch *Vicia sativa* p. 59
Flowering stem

1a
1b
2a
2b
3a
4a
4b
5a
5b
5c
6
7a
7b

LEGUMINOSAE

1. Carob Bean *Ceratonia siliqua* p. 42
1a. Mature dry pod
1b. Leaf
1c. Very young fruits

2. Red Clover *Trifolium pratense* p. 42
2a. Flowering stem
2b. Leaf

3. Kidney Vetch *Anthyllis vulneraria* p. 49
Flowering stem

4. Fenugreek *Trigonella foenum-graecum* p. 53
4a. Flowering stem
4b. Stem with fruit
4c. Dried seeds

5. Alsike Clover *Trifolium hybridum* p. 43
Flowering stem

6. White Clover *Trifolium repens* p. 44
Creeping stem with flowers and leaves

7. Liquorice *Glycyrrhiza glabra* p. 49
7a. Section of root
7b. Flowering stem

1a
1b
1c
2a
2b
4a
4b
4c
5
6
7a
7b

GROSSULARIACEAE, CORNACEAE, CAPRIFOLACIAE

1. Gooseberry *Ribes uva-crispa* p. 60
1a. Flowers
1b. Leaves
1c. Fruits of var. 'Careless'
1d. Fruit of var. 'Leveller'
1e. Fruit of var. 'Whinham's Industry'

2. Worcesterberry *Ribes divaricatum* p. 61
Twig with fruits

3. Black Currant *Ribes nigrum* p. 61
3a. Leaf and fruits
3b. Flowers

4. White Currant *Ribes sativum* p. 62
Fruits of var. 'White Versailles'

5. Red Currant *Ribes sativum* p. 62
5a. Flowers
5b. Leaves and fruit of var. 'Red Lake'

6. Cornelian Cherry *Cornus mas* p. 62
6a. Flowers
6b. Twig with leaves and fruit

7. Elder *Sambucus nigra* p. 63
7a. Leaves and flowers
7b. Fruit

1a
1b
1c
1d
1e
2
3a
3b
4
5a
5b
6a
6b
7a
7b

FAGACEAE, CORYLACEAE, JUGLANDACEAE

1. Sweet Chestnut *Castanea sativa* p. 65
1a. Leaves
1b. Male catkin and fruits
1c. Open fruit

2. Beech *Fagus sylvatica* p. 64
2a. Leaves and fruit
2b. Open fruit showing beech nuts

3. Cork Oak *Quercus suber* p. 65
3a. Leaves
3b. Acorn

4. Filbert *Corylus maxima* p. 67
4a. Leaf and fruit
4b. Nut

5. Hazel *Corylus avellana* p. 66
5a. Twig with leaves and fruit
5b. Male catkin
5c. Hazel nut

6. Turkish Hazel *Corylus colurna* p. 67
Fruit

7. Walnut *Juglans regia* p. 68
7a. Leaves and fruit
7b. Open fruit

8. Black Walnut *Juglans nigra* p. 69
8a. Leave
8b. Unopened fruit
8c. Fruit in section

1a
1b
1c
2a
2b
3b
3a
5a
4a
5b
4b
5c
6
8c
7a
8a
7b
8b

CANNABACEAE, MORACEAE, CAPPARACEAE

1. Black Mulberry *Morus nigra* p. 73
1a. Twig with leaves and fruit
1b. Flower

2. White Mulberry *Morus alba* p. 73
2a. Leaves
2b. Fruit

3. Caper *Capparis spinosa* p. 75
3a. Stem with buds
3b. Flower

4. Fig *Ficus carica* p. 74
4a. Leaf and fruit
4b. Fruit in section

5. Hemp *Cannabis sativa* p. 71
5a. Flowering stem of male plant
5b. Female flower
5c. Mature seeds

6. Hops *Humulus lupulus* p. 70
6a. Stems with leaves and fruits in burr stage
6b. Mature fruit

1a
2a
2b
3a
3b
4a
4b
6a
5a
6b
5c
5b

PASSIFLORACEAE, CURCURBITACEAE

1. Purple Passion Fruit *Passiflora edulis* p. 76
1a. Part of vine with leaf and fruit
1b. Flower
1c. Fruit in section

2. Cucumber *Cucumis sativus* p. 82
2a. Part of vine with leaf and fruit
2b. Male flower
2c. Female flower
2d. Fruit of Ridge Cucumber (right) and Gherkin *Cucumis sativus* (left)

3. West Indian Gherkin *Cucumis anguria* p. 83
Leaf

4. Melon *Cucumis melo* p. 81
4a. Fruit of Musk Melon
4b. Fruit of Canteloupe Melon
4c. Fruit of Honeydew Melon
4d. Fruit of Spanish Green Winter Melon

1a
1b
1c
2a
2b
2c
2d
4a
4b
4c
4d

CUCURBITACEAE

1. Water Melon *Citrullus lanatus* p. 83

1a. Fruit

1b. Leaf

1c. Female flower

2. *Cucurbita pepo* p. 79

2a. Marrow fruit

2b. Female flower

2c. Male flower in section

2d. Female flower in section

2e. Part of Courgette vine with whole leaf and young fruits

2f. Courgette fruit

2g. Fruits of Summer Crookneck

2h. Pumpkin

2i. Custard Marrow

3. Winter Squash *Cucurbita maxima* p. 80

3a. Part of vine and leaf

3b. Fruit of Turban Winter Squash

1b
2a
1c
2c
1a
2b
2d
2e
2f
2h
3b
2i

CACTACEAE, TILIACEAE, MALVACEAE, LINACEAE, ACTINIDIACEAE

1. Flax *Linum usitatissimum* p. 91
Upper part of stems with flowers and fruit

2. Cotton *Gossypium herbaceum* p. 89
2a. Part of stem of plant with leaves, flower and fruits
2b. Open boll

3. Lime *Tilia* x *europaea* p. 87
Leaf and fruits

4. Barbary Fig *Opuntia ficus-indica* p. 85
Fruit

5. Kiwi *Actinidia chinensis* p. 92
5a. Part of stem with leaf and fruits
5b. Fruit in section

6. Okra *Hibiscus esculentus* p. 88
6a. Stem with leaves and flower
6b. Fruits

1
2b
2a
4
3
5b
6b
5a
6a

ERICACEAE, VACCINIACEAE

1. Bilberry *Vaccinium myrtillus* p. 95
1a. Twig with leaves and fruits
1b. Flowers

2. Highbush Blueberry *Vaccinium corymbosum* p. 96
2a. Twig with leaves and fruits
2b. Flower

3. Cranberry *Vaccinium oxycoccus* p. 94
Stem with leaves and fruits

4. American Cranberry *Vaccinium macrocarpon* p. 94
4a. Stems with leaves and fruit
4b. Flowers

5. Strawberry Tree *Arbutus unedo* p. 96
Twig with fruits

6. Cowberry *Vaccinium vitis-idaea* p. 95
6a. Stem with leaves and fruits
6b. Flowers

b
1a
2b
2a
3
5
6a
6b
4a
4b

PUNICACEAE, MYRTACEAE, EBENACEAE

1. Pomegranate *Punica granatum* p. 98
1a. Twig with leaves, flower and fruit
1b. Fruit in section

2. Feijoa *Feijoa sellowiana* p. 97
Twig with leaves and fruit

3. Date-Plum *Diospyros lotus* p. 104
3a. Twig with leaves and fruit
3b. Flowers

4. Chinese Persimmon *Diospyros kaki* p. 103
4a. Twig with leaves and fruit
4b. Fruit in section

5. Oval Kumquat *Fortunella margarita* p. 110
5a. Twig with leaves and fruit
5b. Fruit in section

1b
1a
3b
2
3a
4b
5b
5a
4a

VITACEAE

1. Grapevine *Vitis vinifera* p. 101

1a. Part of vine with leaves and bunch of grapes of variety 'Black Hamburg'

1b. Chardonnay

1c. Seyval Blanc

1d. Cascade Seibel

1e. Cabernet Sauvignon

1f. Scherenber

1g. Riesling

1a
1b
1c
1d
1e
1f
1g

RUTACEAE

1. Seville Orange *Citrus aurantium* p. 107
1a. Twig with leaves and fruit
1b. Fruit in section

2. Sweet Orange *Citrus sinensis* p. 106
2a. Twig with leaves, flowers and fruit
2b. Section of Blood Orange
2c. Fruit of var. 'Washington Navel'

3. Bergamot Orange *Citrus bergamia* p. 107
Twig with leaves and fruit

4. Tangerine *Citrus reticulata* p. 107
4a. Twig with leaves and fruit
4b. Fruit in section

1a
2a
2c
1b
2b
3
4a
4b

RUTACEAE

1. Grapefruit *Citrus paradisi* p. 110
Twig with leaves and fruit

2. Lemon *Citrus limon* p. 108
2a. Twig with leaves and fruit
2b. Flower

3. Citron *Citrus medica* p. 109
3a. Twig with leaves and fruit
3b. Flower

4. Pomelo *Citrus grandis* p. 109
4a. Twig with leaves and fruit
4b. Fruit in section

2b
2a
1
4a
4b
3b

ANACARDIACEAE, LAURACEAE, ANONACEAE

1. Pistachio *Pistacia vera* p. 112
1a. Twig with leaves and fruit
1b. Dried fruit and kernels

2. Terebinth *Pistacia terebinthus* p. 113
2a. Twig with leaves and flowers
2b. Fruits

3. Lentisc *Pistacia lentiscus* p. 112
3a. Twig with leaves and flowers
3b. Twig with leaves and fruit

4. Cherimoya *Anona cherimolia* p. 15
4a. Twig with leaves and flowers
4b. Fruit

5. Sweet Bay *Laurus nobilis* p. 16
Terminal twig with flowers

6. Avocado Pear *Persea americana* p. 17
Leaves and fruit, with fruit in section

1a
2a
2b
3a
1b
3b
4b
4a
6
5

BRASSICACEAE

1. Black Mustard *Brassica nigra* p. 227
1a. Leaf
1b. Flowers
1c. Dry siliquas

2. Charlock *Sinapis arvensis* p. 229
2a. Leaf
2b. Siliquas

3. White Mustard *Sinapis alba* p. 228
3a. Leaf
3b. Inflorescences
3c. Dry siliquas
3d. Seedlings

4. Brown Mustard *Brassica juncea* p. 228
4a. Part of stem with inflorescences
4b. Leaf

5. *Brassica oleracea* p. 126
Leaf, inflorescence and dry siliquas

6. *Brassica napus* p. 225
6a. Leaf, inflorescence and dry siliquas of Oilseed Rape (ssp. oleifera)
6b. Root of swede root (ssp. napobrassica)

7. *Brassica rapa* p. 226
Turnip root

8. *Brassica campestris* p. 227
Leaf, inflorescence and dry siliquas

1a
1b
1c
2a
2b
3a
3b
3c
3d
4b
5
6a
6b
8

BRASSICACEAE

1. Watercress *Nasturtium officinale* p. 231
1a. Part of non-flowering plant
1b. Inflorescence with siliquas

2. Garden Cress *Lepidium sativum* p. 231
2a. Seedlings
2b. Flowering stem

3. Land Cress *Barbarea verna* p. 232
3a. Leaf
3b. Part of stem with inflorescences

4. Woad *Isatis tinctoria* p. 233
4a. Flowering stem
4b. Base stem and leaves
4c. Dried seed pods

5. Seakale *Crambe maritima* p. 233
Leaf of wild plant and blanched leaf-stalks

6. Rocket *Eruca sativa* p. 232
6a. Inflorescence
6b. Siliquas
6c. Leaf

1a
1b
2a
2b
3a
3b
4a
4b
4c
5
6a
6b
6c

BRASSICACEAE

1. Horse-radish *Armoracia rusticana* p. 230
1a. Root and leaves
1b. Inflorescence

2. Radish *Raphanus sativus* p. 229
2a. Siliquas
2b. Flower
2c. Whole young plant of salad radish
2d. Roots of 'French Breakfast'
2e. 'Black Spanish'
2f. Winter radish var. 'China Rose'

3. Gai Tsoi *Brassica juncea* p. 225
Leaf

4. Pak Choi *Brassica chinensis* p. 225
4a. Inflorescence
4b. Whole non-flowering plant

5. Pe Tsai *Brassica pekinensis* p. 225
5a. Inflorescence
5b. Leaf

2c
1b
2f
2e
1a
2a
2b
2d
4b
5b
5a
4a

PEDALIACEAE, VERBANACEAE, RANUNCULACEAE, PAPAVERACEAE, OLEACEAE

1. Olive *Olea europea* p. 114
1a. Twig with leaves and fruits
1b. Flowers

2. Sesame *Sesamum indicum* p. 116
2a. Upper part of stem with flowers
2b. Section of pod and seeds

3. Black Cumin *Nigella sativa* p. 120
3a. Stem with leaves, flower and fruit
3b. Seeds

4. Vervain *Verbena officinalis* p. 118
Part of stem with leaves and flowers

5. Opium Poppy *Papaver somniferum* p. 121
Stem with leaves, flower and capsule

6. White Jasmine *Jasminum officinale* p. 115
Flowering stem

1a
1b
2a
2b
3a
3b
4
5
6

AIZOACEAE, PORTULACACEAE, POLYGONACEAE

1. Rhubarb *Rheum rhabarbarum* p. 237
Stem with base of leaf

2. Round-leaved Sorrel *Rumex scutatus* p. 239
Parts of flowering stem

3. Garden Sorrel *Rumex acetosa* p. 238
Basal leaf

4. Buckwheat *Fagopyrum esculentum* p. 236
4a. Stem with leaves and flowers
4b. Achene

5. Fleawort *Plantago indica* p. 240
Flowering stem

6. Purslane *Portulacca oleracea* p. 235
Flowering stem

7. New Zealand Spinach *Tetragonia expansa* p. 234
Flowering stem

1
2
3
4a
4b
5
6
7

CHENOPODIACEAE

1. Beetroot *Beta vulgaris* p. 241
1a. Root with basal leaves of variety 'Globe'
1b. Section of root of variety 'Burpees Golden'
1c. Root of tankard-shaped mangel
1d. Root and leaf of Sugar Beet
1e. Leaf of Spinach Beet
1f. Leaf of Seakale Beet

2. Spinach *Spinacea oleracea* p. 244
Leaf

3. Fat Hen *Chenopodium album* p. 245
Flowering stem

4. Mercury *Chenopodium bonus-henricus* p. 245

5. Orache *Atriplex hortensis* p. 244
Non-flowering stem

1a
1b
1c
1d
1e
1f
2
3
4
5

APIACEAE

1. Parsnip *Pastinaca sativa* p. 253
1a. Inflorescence
1b. Root

2. Carrot *Daucus carota* p. 252
2a. Root and leaf bases
2b. Inflorescence

3. Chervil *Anthriscus cerefolium* p. 258
3a. Upper part of plant with inflorescences
3b. Seeds

4. Parsley *Petroselinum crispum* p. 257
4a. Leaves of Sheep's Parsley
4b. Curled Parsley
4c. Root and leaves of Hamburg Parsley
4d. Inflorescence of Curled Parsley
4e. Seeds of Curled Parsley

3b
2b
3a
2a
4a
b
4c
4d
4b
4e

APIACEAE

1. Celery *Apium graveolens* p. 253
  1a. Inflorescence
  1b. Leaf stalks
  1c. Stem and leaf of Celeriac

2. Dill *Anethum graveolens* p. 255
  2a. Leaves and inflorescence
  2b. Single seeds (enlarged)

3. Fennel *Foeniculum vulgare* p. 254
  3a. Leaf bases of Florence Fennel
  3b. Stem with leaves and inflorescences
  3c. Single seeds enlarged

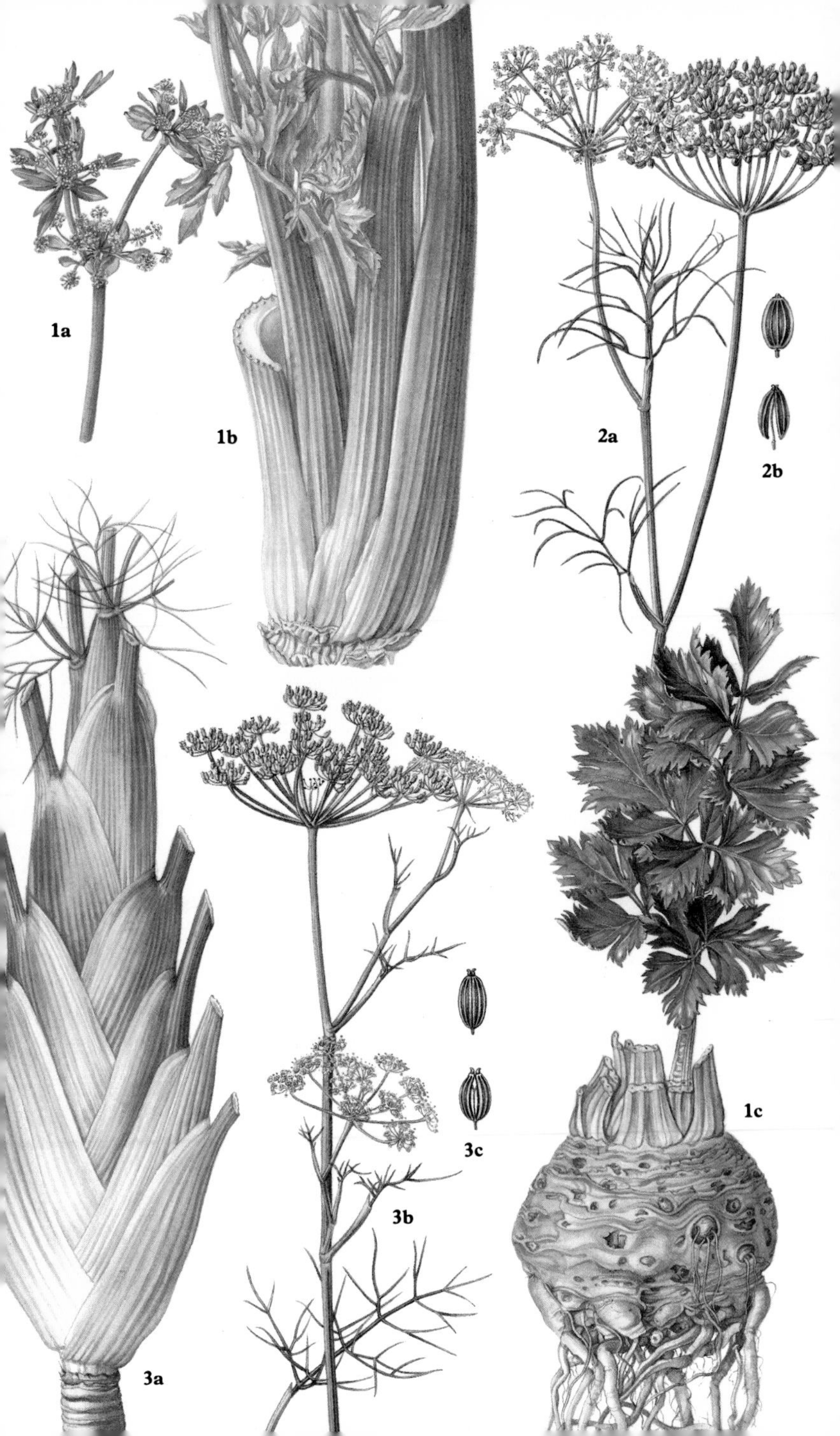

1a
1b
2a
2b
3a
3b
3c
1c

APIACEAE

1. Angelica *Angelica archangelica* p. 256
1a. Stalk with leaves and inflorescence
1b. Section of stalk

2. Caraway *Carum carvi* p. 260
2a. Flowering stem
2b. Stem with fruits
2c. Dried seed head

3. Anise *Pimpinella anisum* p. 261
3a. Flowering stem
3b. Stem with fruits
3c. Dried seed head

4. Cumin *Cuminum cyminum* p. 260
Flowering stem

5. Coriander *Coriandrum sativum* p. 259
5a. Leaf and flowering stem
5b. Dried fruits

6. Lovage *Levisticum officinale* p. 256
Leaf

7. Sweet Cicely *Myrrhis odorata* p. 257
7a. Leaf
7b. Inflorescence
7c. Seeds

1a
1b
2a
2b
2c
3a
3b
4
5a
5b
6
7a
7b
7c

VALERIANACEAE, ASTERACEAE

1. Cornsalad *Valerianella locusta* p. 263
Young plant and inflorescences

2. Lettuce *Lactuca sativa* p. 273
2a. Seedling
2b. Inflorescence and fruits

3. Chicory *Cichorium intybus* p. 274
3a. Flowering stem
3b. Leaves of *Cichorium intybus*
3c. Leaf of 'Radicchio di Treviso'
3d. Root of 'Soncino'

4. Dandelion *Taraxacum officinale* p. 273
Flowering plant

5. Salsify *Tragopogon porrifolius* p. 276
5a. Root
5b. Flower

6. Scorzonera *Scorzonera hispanica* p. 276
6a. Root and leaf
6b. Inflorescence

1
2a
2b
3a
3b
3c
3d
4
5a
5b
6a
6b

ASTERACEAE

1. Globe Artichoke *Cynara scolymus* p. 271

1a. Upper part of stem with inflorescences and immature head

1b. Cooked flower head in section

2. Sunflower *Helianthus annuus* p. 269

2a. Inflorescence

2b. Seeds

3. Jerusalem Artichoke *Helianthus tuberosus* p. 270

3a. Inflorescences

3b. Two tubers

4. Cardoon *Cynara cardunculus* p. 271

4a. Inflorescence

4b. Upper part of leaf

2a
1b
2b
3a
4a
4b
3b

ASTERACEAE

1. Pyrethrum *Chrysanthemum cinerarifolium* p. 267
Leaf and flowering stem

2. German Chamomile *Matricaria recutita* p. 267
Flowering stem

3. Roman Chamomile *Chamaemelum nobile* p. 266
Flowering stem

4. Tarragon *Artemisia dracunculus* p. 264
Flowering stem

5. Wormwood *Artemisia absinthium* p. 265
5a. Flowering stem
5b. Leaf

6. Southernwood *Artemisia abrotanum* p. 266
Upper part of flowering stem

7. Safflower *Carthamus tinctorius* p. 272
Flowering stem

1
3
2
4
7
5b
6

SOLANACEAE

1. Peppers *Capsicum annuum* p. 278
1a. Part of stem with leaves and fruit of Sweet Pepper
1b. Mature fruit of Sweet Pepper
1c. Flowering stem with fruit of Chili Pepper
1d. Single fruit of Chili Pepper

2. Bird Chili *Capsicum frutescens* p. 279
Stem with fruits

3. Deadly Nightshade *Atropa bella-donna* p. 277
Stem with flowers and fruit

4. Tomato *Lycopersicon esculentum* p. 282
4a. Stem with flowers and young fruit
4b. Single fruit of Round Tomato
4c. Plum Tomato
4d. 'Beef' Tomato

5. Garden Huckleberry *Solanum intrusum* p. 282
5a. Flowering stem
5b. Fruit

1a
1b
1c
1d
2
3
4a
4b
4c
4d
5a
5b

SOLANACEAE, CONVOLVULACEAE

1. Aubergine *Solanum melongena* p. 281
1a. Flowering stem
1b. Fruit

2. Winter Cherry *Physalis alkekengi* p. 285
2a. Stem with flower and unripe fruits
2b. (bottom left) Ripe fruit
(top left) Ripe fruit with husk cut open

2b. (top right) Tomatillo *Physalis ixocarpa* p. 285
Ripe fruit with husk cut open

3. Tobacco *Nicotiana tabacum* p. 280
3a. Single leaf
3b. Inflorescence

4. Potato *Solanum tuberosum* p. 281
4a. Upper leaf and inflorescence
4b. Single tuber of variety 'Desirée'
4c. Single tuber of variety 'King Edward'

5. Sweet Potato *Ipomoea batatas* p. 286
Part of vine with leaves and two tubers

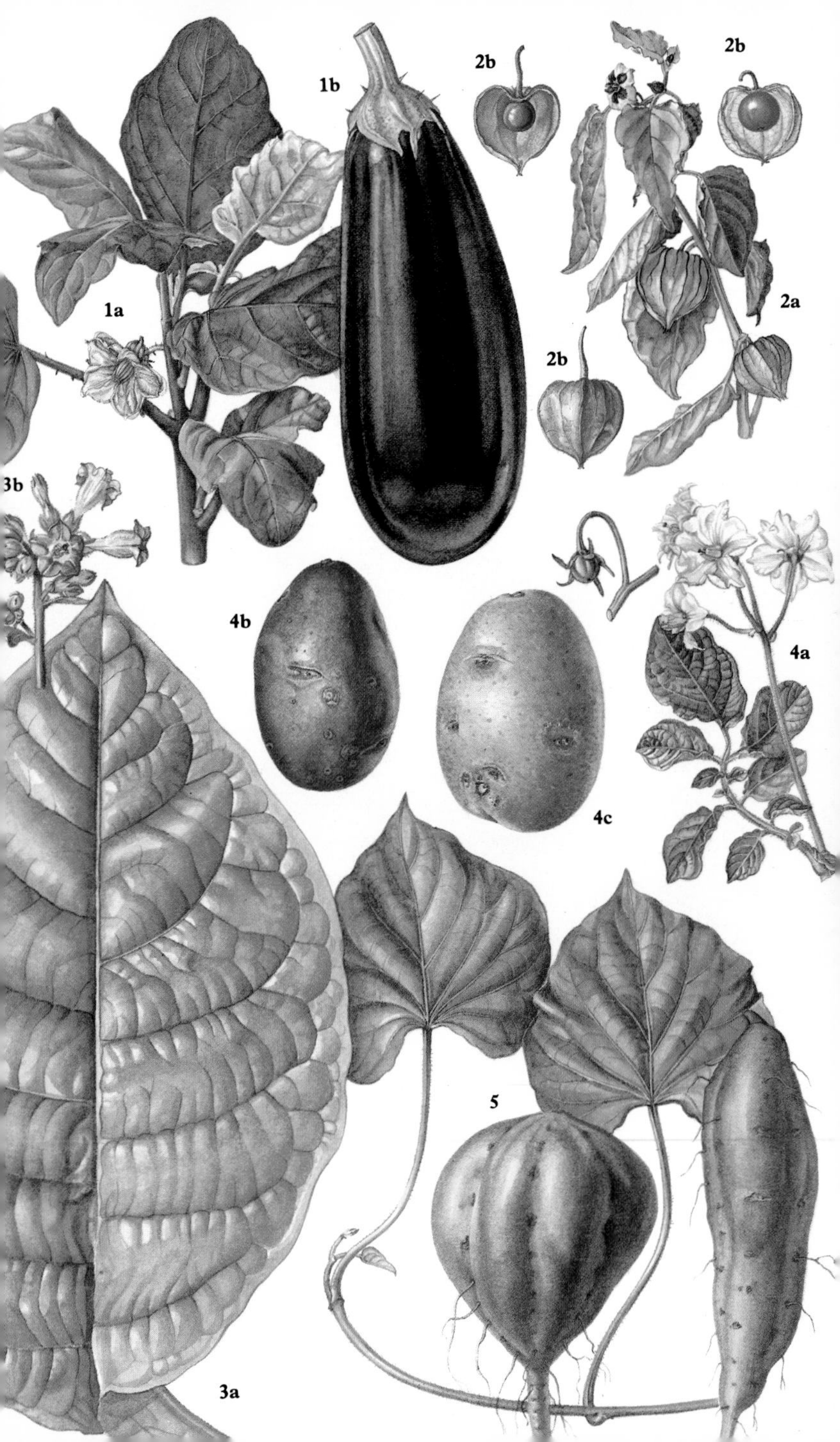

1a
1b
2b
2b
2a
2b
3b
4b
4a
4c
5
3a

HYDROPHYLLACEAE, BORAGINACEAE, LILIACEAE, IRIDACEAE

1. Russian Comfrey *Symphytum* × *uplandicum* p. 288
Flowering stem

2. Prickly Comfrey *Symphytum asperum* p. 289
Flowering stem

3. Phacelia *Phacelia tanacetifolia* p. 287
Flowering stem

4. Saffron *Crocus sativus* p. 303
Flower and stigmas

5. Asparagus *Asparagus officinalis* p. 312
Leaf and young shoots

1
2
3
4
5

LAMIACEAE

1. Rosemary *Rosmarinus officinalis* p. 292

2. Broad-leaved Lavender *Lavandula latifolia* p. 292

3. True Lavender *Lavandula officinalis* p. 291

4. Winter Savory *Satureja montana* p. 293

5. Summer Savory *Satureja hortensis* p. 294

6. Sage *Salvia officinalis* p. 295

7. Clary *Salvia sclarea* p. 296

8. Bush Basil *Ocimum minimum* p. 295

9. Basil *Ocimum basilicum* p. 294

1
2
3
4
5
6
7
8
9

LAMIACEAE

1. Garden Thyme *Thymus vulgaris* p. 296

2. Lemon Thyme *Thymus citriodorus* p. 296

3. Caraway Thyme *Thymus herba-barona* p. 297

4. Peppermint *Mentha* × *piperata* p. 298

5. Spearmint *Mentha spicata* p. 297

6. Pot Marjoram *Marjorana onites* p. 291

7. Sweet Marjoram *Marjorana hortensis* p. 290

8. Chinese Artichoke *Stachys affinis* p. 299
8a. Stem with leaves and flowers
8b. Three tubers

1
2
3
4
5
6
7
8a
8b

ALLIACEAE

1. Leek *Allium ampeloprasum* p. 308
  1a. Lower part of plant
  1b. Inflorescence

2. Garlic *Allium sativum* p. 306
  2a. Garlic bulb
  2b. Garlic inflorescence

3. Welsh Onion *Allium fistulosum* p. 311

4. Onion *Allium cepa* p. 309
  4a. Inflorescence of Common Onion
  4b. Inflorescence of Tree Onion
  4c. Shallot
  4d. Common Onion bulb
  4e. Spring Onion
  4f. Inflorescence of Shallot

5. Chives *Allium schoenoprasum* p. 310

6. Chinese Chives *Allium tuberosum* p. 306

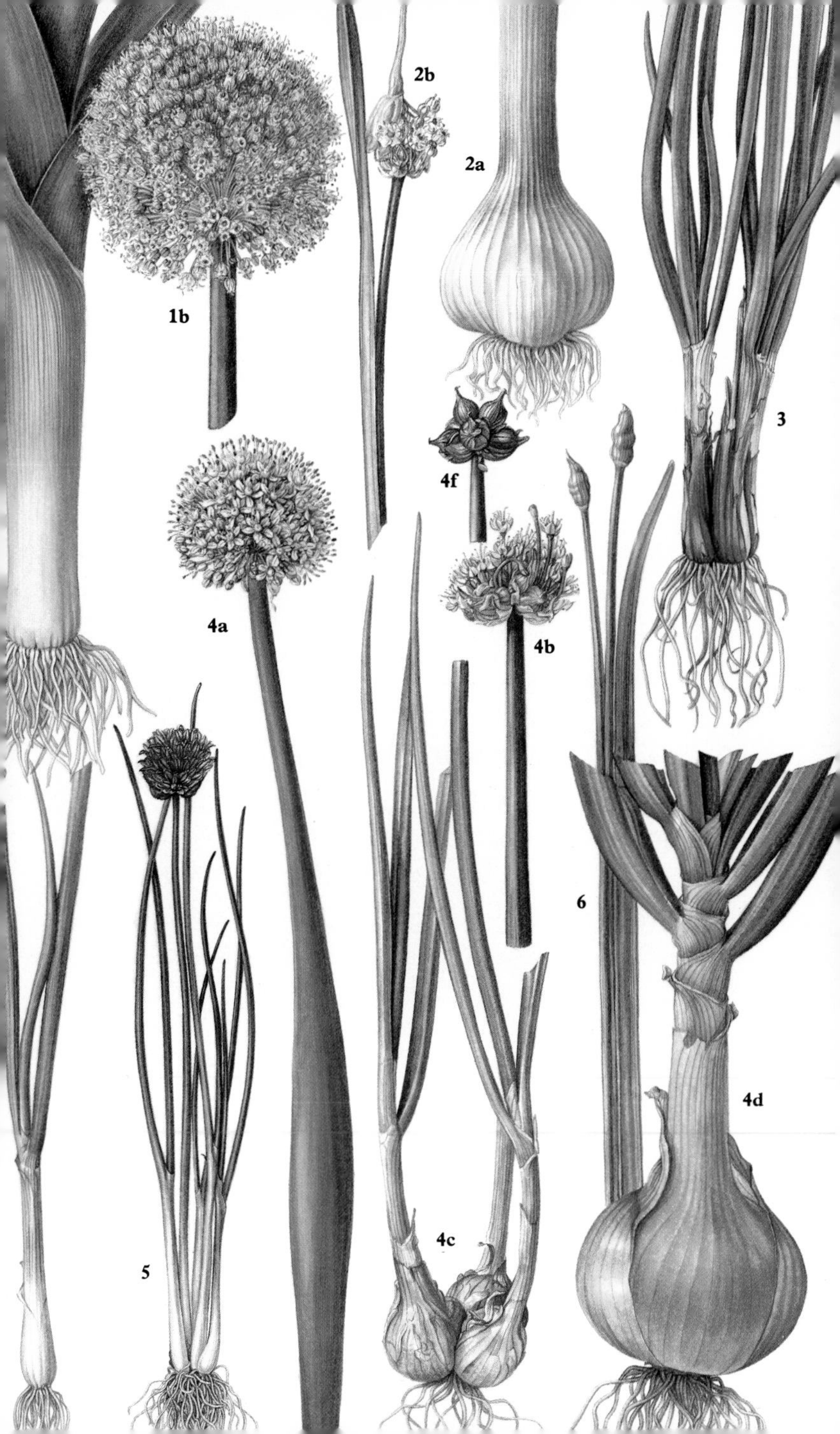
2b
2a
1b
3
4f
4a
4b
6
4d
4c
5

GRAMINAE

1. Wheat *Triticum* spp. p. 327
1a. Ear and grains of unawned Bread Wheat *Triticum aestivum* (*vulgare*)
1b. Ear of awned Bread Wheat
1c. Ear and grains of Durum Wheat *Triticum durum*
1d. Ear and grains of Emmer Wheat *Triticum dicoccum*
1e. Spikelet of Rivet Wheat *Triticum turgidum*

2. Rye *Secale cereale* p. 329
Ear and grains

3. Barley *Hordeum* spp. p. 325
3a. Ear of Two-rowed Barley *Hordeum distichum*
3b. Ear and grains of Six-rowed Barley *Hordeum polystichum*

4. Oats *Avena* spp. p. 324
4a. Panicle, spikelet and grains of Cultivated Oat *Avena sativa*
4b. Spikelet of Bristle Oat *Avena strigosa*

5. Rice *Oryza sativa* p. 323
Panicle and grains of unawned short-grain variety

6. Common Millet *Panicum miliaceum* p. 322
Panicle, spikelets and grain

1a
1b
1c
1d
1e
2
3a
3b
4a
5
6

GRAMINAE

1. Maize *Zea mays* p. 317
1a. Upper part of stem
1b. Cob and grains of Flint Maize

1c. Sorghum *Sorghum bicolor* p. 319

2. Japanese Millet *Echinochloa frumentacea* p. 322

3. Italian Millet *Setaria italica* p. 321

4. Bulrush Millet *Pennisetum typhoides* p. 320

1b
1c
1a
4
2
3

FUNGI

1. Parasol Mushroom *Lepiota procera* p. 336

2. Cultivated Mushroom *Psalliota bisporus* p. 337

3. Oyster Mushroom *Pleurotus ostreatus* p. 338

4. Shiitake Mushroom *Lentinus edodes* p. 338

5. Cep *Boletus edulis* p. 339

6. Chanterelle *Cantharellus cibarius* p. 339

7. Horn of Plenty *Craterellus cornucopioides* p. 339

8. Morel *Morchella esculenta* p. 340

9. Perigord Truffle *Tuber melanosporum* p. 340

10. Italian White Truffle *Tuber magnatum* p. 341

11. Saffron Milk Cap *Lactarius deliciosus* p. 338

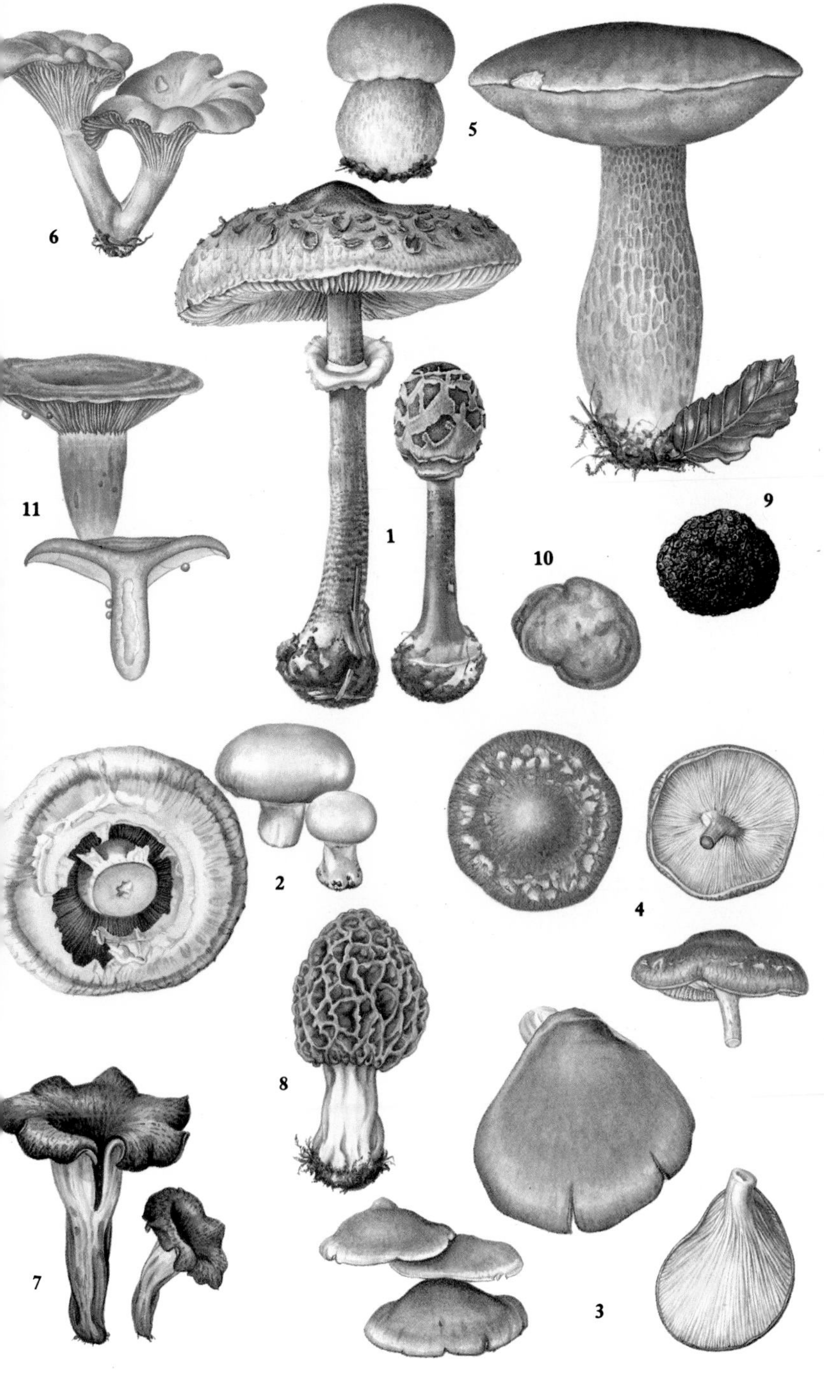

6
5
11
1
9
10
2
4
8
7
3

Common Jujube: The riper, red fruits will darken further, and shrivel when they dry. By the time they are marketed, they will somewhat resemble shiny, hard prunes (*G.M. de Rougemont*). See p. 99

Lemon trees in Alicante: Many such small groves, as well as extensive plantations are to be seen all over the hotter parts of southern Spain (*Spanish National Tourist Office*). See p. 108

Olive trees in Cordoba: The well tended and extensive groves demonstrate the importance of this industry in Spain (*Spanish National Tourist Office*). See p. 114

Sweet Potato: The resemblance to the closely related Bindweeds is striking, but stems always trail, never climb (*G.M. de Rougemont*). See p. 286

Sugar Beet growing in England: The front row of roots has been uncovered to display their quality. Normally only the tops show (*National Farmers' Union*). See p. 241

Harvesting Flax in Normandy: This specialised harvester uproots whole plants, which will be left to dry for several days before threshing (*G.M. de Rougemont*). See p. 91

Harvesting Two-rowed Barley in Normandy: A poor, weather-beaten crop destined for fodder (*G.M. de Rougemont*). See p. 326

Rice in Camargue: This 'paddy field' has only recently been established in a *Phragmites* marsh (*G.M. de Rougemont*). See p. 324

Grape-picking in Burgundy: These grapes, producing some of the finest wines in the world, are too valuable to risk any damage by mechanised harvesting (*Chastel, French Tourist Office*). See p. 101

Harvesting Lavender in Haute Provence: The flowering stems have been cut mechanically and tied in bundles before being forked into the trailer which will take them straight to the distillers (*Comité de Tourisme et des Loisirs des Alpes de Haute Provence*). See p. 292

Harvesting Plum Tomatoes in Provence: These are trailing plants. The rough method of harvesting damages some of the fruits, but this is unimportant, since they are destined for canning (*G.M. de Rougemont*). See p. 283

Banana plantation in Tenerife (*Mrs H.C. Phipps*). See p. 301

Cork Oaks in Spain: The freshly stripped pinkish under-bark will turn almost black before new bark begins to form (*G.M. de Rougemont*). See p. 65

Harvesting Pimientos in Murcia, Spain: This variety is destined to be dried and ground to be marketed as *pimentòn* (*Spanish National Tourist Office*). See p. 278

Peach Orchard, Provence: The fruits will be hand picked and packed on the site (*G.M. de Rougemont*). See p. 31

Sorting plums for drying in South West France (*French National Tourist Office*). See p. 35

Hop garden in Kent: The tall (2.5–3m) wire supports make this crop unmistakable, even from a distance (*National Farmers' Union*). See p. 70

Different varieties of Lettuce, Endive and Chicory

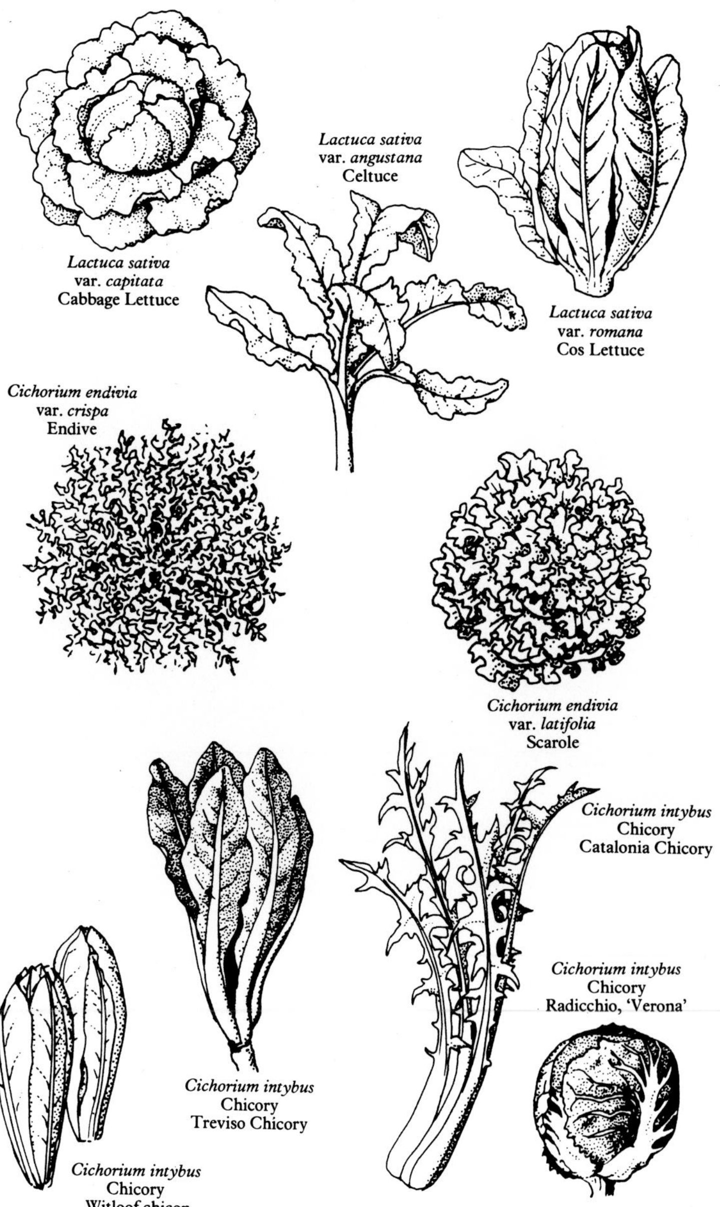

Different varieties of *Brassica oleracea*

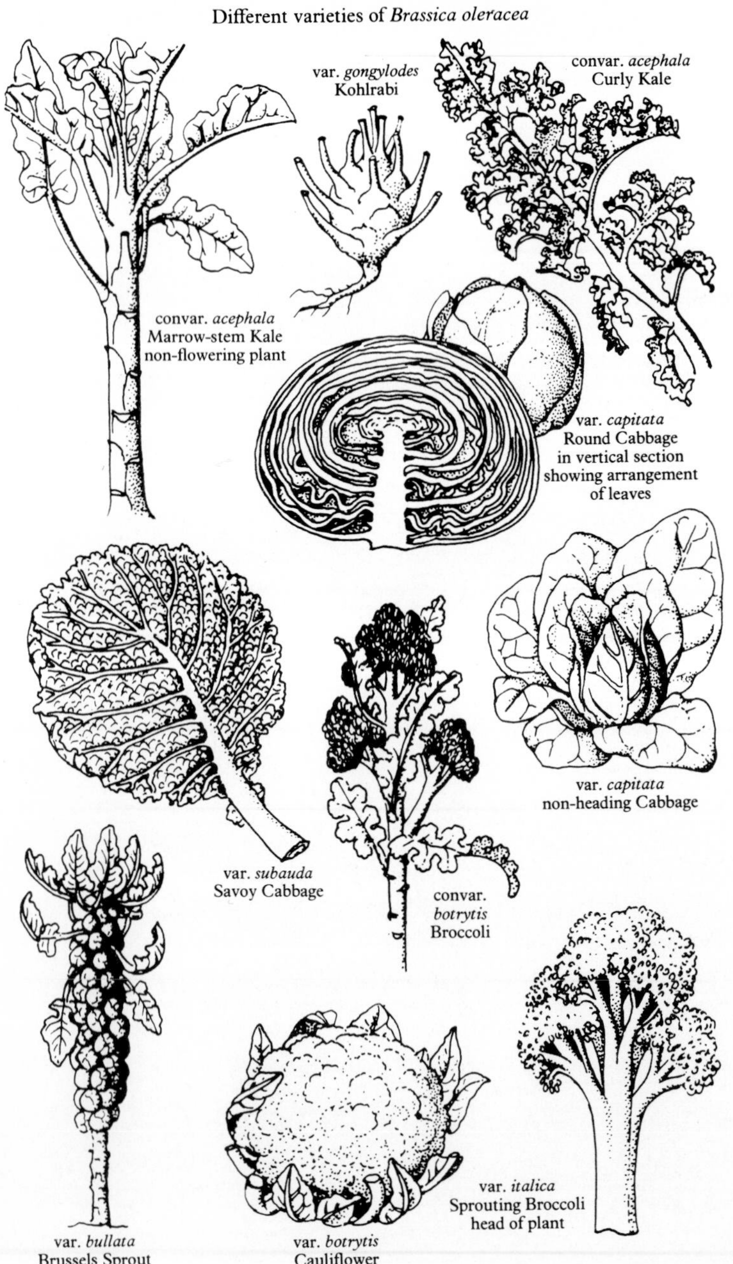

Brassica chinensis
PAK CHOI
(p. 174)

Description: A biennial 'green' grown as an annual with a very short stem giving rise to broad entire lvs with ovate blades 20–50 cm long and thickened, conspicuously white stalks, not forming a compact head. Lvs are dark dull green, but not glaucous. Fls pale yellow, ca. 1 cm long. Frts slender, 3–6 cm long, with a short conical beak.

Names: Fr.: Chou de Chine; It.: Cavolo sedano; Sp.: Col china; Ger.: Chinakohl; Dtch.: Chinese Kool; Dan.: Kinesisk Kål; Russ.: Kapusta kitayanska; Yug.: Kitajski kapus.
The names Pak Choi or Pak Tsoi and Pe Tsai, given to *B. pekinensis*, below, are specific only in European usage. The two names are approximations of the same Chinese words, meaning 'white vegetable' or 'white 'greens'', the former as pronounced in the Cantonese dialect, the latter in the Peking or Mandarin dialect. *B. pekinensis* is known to (Cantonese) Chinese grocers in Europe as Shu Tsoi or Wong nga Pak.

Uses: As a vegetable. In Chinese cooking this and other greens are usually merely blanched or fried and remain crisp, not boiled to a soft consistency as in Europe.

Origin, distribution and cultivation: This *Brassica* is a native of the Far East and is extensively cultivated in China, Japan, and all parts of S.E. Asia settled by Chinese. Imported plants are available from Chinese grocers in Europe, and cultivation has been taken up in parts of western Europe both by home- and market-gardeners, who now supply some of the commercial crop.

Similar plants: The fleshy white lf-stalks give this sp. a greater resemblance to Spinach Beet (p. 241) than to forms of *B. oleracea.*

Brassica pekinensis
PE TSAI
(p. 174)

Description: A biennial cabbage resembling Cos Lettuce, with unstalked lvs up to 30 cm long, more or less wrinkled, unlobed but with slightly toothed or wavy margins and a broad white midrib, the blade forming a jagged wing on either side. The lvs form a compact head, either barrel-shaped or narrow and cylindrical. Fls and frts similar to Pak Choi.

Names: Syns: *Brassica chinensis* var. *pekinensis.* Also known as Celeri Cabbage. In other European languages it is called Pe Tsai or, like Pak Choi, 'Chinese Cabbage'.

Uses: As a vegetable, like Pak Choi; in Europe sometimes in salads.

Origin, distribution and cultivation: This sp. is also widely cultivated in China and Japan. It is hardier than Pak Choi and is more extensively grown in northern China. Like Pak Choi it is available from Chinese grocers in Europe, and has been adopted in recent years by amateur and commercial growers in western Europe.

Similar plants: Cos Lettuce (p. 273). Another 'Chinese Leaf', Gai Tsoi, is a variety of *B. juncea* (p. 228) which has similarly shaped lf-blades but with more sharply and finely-toothed margins, and with narrow midribs.

Brassica napus
SWEDE, KALES, FORAGE RAPE and OIL RAPE or COLZA
(p. 170)

Description: The mature plant resembles the 'primitive' forms of *B. oleracea* (Wild Cabbage and Kales), being glaucous and hairless, but the young plants are slightly hairy, at least on the midribs of lvs. Lvs on inflorescence with heart-shaped base partly clasping the stem. Fls smaller than those of *B. oleracea*, the sepals slightly spreading; 2 outer stamens shorter and more curving; inflorescence more corymbose, ie. unopened buds are nearer or on the same level as open fls. Frt similar, but the seeds are purple-black, not brownish-grey.

The main forms fall into 2 main groups:

var. *napobrassica* (sometimes treated as a sp., *B. napobrassica*): Swede. In this form part of the stem and a small part of the root are enlarged, forming a large globose or ovoid 'root' with a distinct 'neck' beneath the basal lvs. The skin colour varies from white to yellowish with or without purple upper part; the colour of the flesh is related to that of fls, yellow-flowered varieties producing white-fleshed roots, while buff-flowered plants have yellow-fleshed roots.

ssp. *oleifera*: Oil Rapes, Rape-kale and Forage Rape. Winter and Summer Oil Rapes do not differ in structure, but are generally taller (ca. 1 m) than the forms grown for forage which range from short (50 cm) more spreading plants to taller ones up to 80 cm high. Other forms grown for forage or fodder with stouter stems and larger lvs are referred to as kales, for they closely resemble the *B. oleracea* Kales. Kale seen in late spring, by which time *B. oleracea* Kales have been consumed or have flowered, almost certainly belong to this sp. The two main forms are Hungry Gap Kale, with more slender and branching stems, and Sheep- or Rape Kale, with thick, little-branching stems. Asparagus Kale, formerly grown as a garden vegetable, also belongs to this sp.

Names: (Swede): Fr.: Rutabaga, Chounavet; It.: Navone, Rutabaga; Sp.: Colinabo; Ger.: Kohlrübe; Dtch.: Koolraap; Dan.: Kålrabi; Gr.: Gouli; Russ.: Bryukva; Yug.: Kavla.
(Oil Rape, Kale): Fr.: Colza; It.: Colza; Sp.: Nabo; Ger.: Raps; Dtch.: Koolzaad; Dan.: Raps; Gr.: Gouli; Russ.: Raps; Yug.: Ogršciča.

Uses: Swedes are mainly used for forage and fodder for livestock. They were formerly an important human food crop, but were largely abandoned with the introduction of Potato; they are now disdained as 'cattle fodder' by many Europeans, although they are still widely sold by grocers and eaten in Britain, northern Europe, and poorer areas elsewhere. Oil Rapes are grown for the oil expressed from the seeds, formerly used for burning and for lubrication, but which now has a wide range of uses in industry and as a cooking oil and for making margarine, especially in recent years when the high erucic acid content, associated with fatty deposits in the arteries, have been reduced in modern cvs. The other forms of *B. napus* are grown for forage. Although their yield is much lower than that of *B. oleracea* Kales, they are useful because they mature in late spring when few if any other forage crops are available. The 'mustard' of the 'Mustard and Cress' of commerce now more often consists of the seedlings of this sp. rather than of the traditional *S. alba*.

Origin, distribution and cultivation: *B. napus* is not known as a wild plant, and is assumed to be derived from *B. oleracea* and *B. rapa*. It is of ancient cultivation as a food plant in the Mediterranean, where not only the Swede root but also the lvs were used as a vegetable. Winter Oil Rape, sown in late August and harvested in July, and Summer Oil Rape, sown in spring for harvesting in late August, is extensively grown in many, especially western European countries, and has become one of the most familiar crops in Britain since the 1960s.

Similar plants: The very glaucous lvs of this sp. distinguishes it even from a distance from all the other cruciferous crops except *B. oleracea* (the Kales of the latter are rarely allowed to flower). The distinct 'neck' at the top of Swede roots distinguishes this vegetable from the generally smaller Turnip.

Brassica rapa
TURNIP

(p. 170)

Description: An annual or biennial herb up to 1 m in height, with the upper part of root and lower part of stem swollen to form a globose structure similar to Swede but without a distinct 'neck'. Flesh either white or yellow, the skin white or green, with the top reddish, bronze or purple. Lvs bright green; lower lvs lyre-shaped, pinnately lobed, bristly-hairy; upper stem lvs clasping, with broadly rounded basal lobes. Inflorescence rather flat-topped, with open fls above unopened buds; fls smaller than those of *B. napus*, with outer stamens shorter and curving. Frt similar to that of *B. oleracea* and *B. napus*, but seeds smaller and more variable in colour, with paler and redder seeds always mixed in samples with darker, purple-black ones.

Names: Syn.: *B. campestris* var. *rapifera.* Fr.: Navet, Rave; It.: Navone; Sp.: Nabo; Ger.: Weissrübe, Stoppelrübe; Dtch.: Knol, Stoppelknol; Dan.: Majroe, Turnips; Gr.: Rapa; Russ.: Turneps; Yug.: Repa.

Uses: Turnip is grown principally as a fodder and forage crop, both the 'root' and foliage being a valuable food, especially for sheep, but the root is also widely used as a vegetable.

Origin, distribution and cultivation: *B. rapa* arose from *B. campestris* (below) at a very early date, possibly through human selection. Turnips have been cultivated in Europe for at least 4000 years. They had considerable importance as a food crop until the introduction of the Potato, and were introduced to all the other continents. Turnips are still extensively grown all over Europe, principally as an agricultural field crop, but also in market-gardens.

Similar plants: See key to Brassicas p. 123. The tuberous root distinguishes Turnip from other forms of *B. campestris* (below).

Brassica campestris
FIELD MUSTARD or TURNIP RAPE

(p. 170)

Description: The structure of lvs, fls and frts is the same as that of *B. rapa* (above) and for this reason *B. campestris* is treated by botanists as a non-tuberous rooted form of *B. rapa*, just as two main forms are recognised of *B. napus*, but following EEC classification, it is listed as a distinct species here.

B. campestris includes Wild Turnip, an annual charlock-like weed, and a biennial form especially common on river banks; also the following cultivated types:

ssp. *oleifera*: Oil Rapes. Winter and Summer Turnip Oil Rapes which are equivalent to the *B. napus* oil rapes but have a lower oil content in the seeds.

Forage Rapes: These were developed in the 1970s by crossing a European form of *B. campestris* with a Far Eastern market-garden subspecies, *nipposinica*. They are usually recognisable by their more finely divided lvs than those of Turnip Oil Rapes or Turnips.

Names: Syns.: *Brassica rapa* var. *campestris*; *B. rapa* var. *sylvestris.* Also known in English as Indian Colza or Indian Rape, and in other European languages simply as Colza or Rape, like the preceding sp.

Uses: Turnip Oil Rapes are hardier than *B. napus*, and because of their lower yield are only grown in areas too hot or cold or dry, or with too short a growing season, for the latter. The oil is used in the same way.

Origin, distribution and cultivation: *B. campestris* is a native of central and southern Europe, and occurs in the wild in several forms over a greater range covering most of the sub-continent, including Britain. As an oil seed crop *B. campestris* is important in India. It is never cultivated in Britain or in western Europe, where true Colza can be grown, but is grown in Rumania and in other parts of eastern Europe, the Soviet Union and parts of Scandinavia.

Similar plants: See keys to Brassica crops (p. 123).

Brassica nigra
BLACK MUSTARD

(p. 170)

Description: An annual branched herb 1 m or more in height. Lvs bright green, all stalked, the lower ones lyre-shaped, pinnately lobed and bristly-hairy, the upper ones undivided, elliptical, narrowed at base, hairless and slightly glaucous. Fls bright yellow, ca. 8 mm long, with spreading sepals, in elongate racemes. Frt short, ca. 2 cm long, smooth, more or less 4-sided, with very short beak, borne erect, almost parallel to rachis; seeds small, ca. 1–1.3 mm in diameter, dark brown, the surface conspicuously, minutely pitted.

Names: Fr.: Moutarde noire, Sénevé; It.: Senape nera; Sp.: Mostaza negra; Ger.: Schwarzer Senf; Dtch.: Zwarte mosterd; Dan.: Sort sennep; Gr.: Mauri moustarda; Russ.: Gorchitsa chornaya; Yug.: Orna gorjušica.

Uses: Black Mustard is the original basis of the condiment mustard all over Europe. The seeds are the most pungent of all the mustards, and the best-suited to the purpose, but because many pods open and shed their seeds before harvesting and the yield is therefore low, it has largely been abandoned in favour of the slightly less pungent Brown Mustard (below). The foliage is unpalatable, and therefore useless as a forage crop.

Origin, distribution and cultivation: Black Mustard is a native of Eurasia and has been cultivated in the Mediterranean at least since classical times. It is still grown to a small extent in areas where it can be harvested by hand, especially in Mediterranean countries, but was abandoned in the 1950s in Britain and on most of the continent.

Similar plants: See keys to Brassicas, (p. 123). The short erect 4-sided pods and pitted seeds provide the best distinguishing characters. See also *Barbarea* spp., (p. 232).

Brassica juncea
BROWN MUSTARD
(p. 170)

Description: A branched annual up to 1 m in height. Lvs usually slightly glaucous, slightly hairy when young, the basal ones stalked, pinnately lobed, with very large ovate terminal lobes, the upper also stalked, entire, narrow, not clasping. Inflorescence and fls similar to *B. rapa* but with stalked, linear-lanceolate bracts not clasping stem. Fls pale yellow, 7–9 mm long. Frts borne semi-erect, cylindrical, 3–5 cm long. Seeds small, light to reddish-brown, with a sharp biting flavour, the testa not pitted.

Names: The name 'Black' Mustard is often transferred to this sp. which is also known as Chinese or Indian Mustard.
Fr.: Moutarde brune, – de Chine; It.: Senape Indiana; Sp.: Mostaza de Indias; Ger.: Rutensenf, Sareptasenf; Dtch.: Krulmosterd; Dan.: Sareptasennep; Gr.: Indikí moustárda; Russ.: Gorchitsa sareptskaya; Yug.: Sarepta, Rjava gorjušca.

Uses: This sp. has become the principal source of seed for the production of the condiment mustard in Europe, having entirely replaced Black Mustard in Britain and on most of the continent, because it is a better agricultural crop, more compact and uniform, does not shed its seed prematurely, and is suitable to mechanised harvesting. In Asia it is grown mainly for oil seed, and the seeds are used whole as a flavouring in cooking.

Origin, distribution and cultivation: *B. juncea* is either of African or Oriental origin. It is an important oil seed crop in India, where it has been cultivated for thousands of years. It is also of ancient cultivation in eastern Europe, but is a recent introduction to Britain and western Europe, having replaced *B. nigra* in the 1950s. It is grown locally near centres of mustard production such as East Anglia, Dijon and Düsseldorf, but much of the mustard produced in these places is now made from seeds imported from North America, where, together with White Mustard, it is grown on a vast scale.

Similar plants: See keys to Brassicas (p. 123) and Black Mustard, above.

Sinapis alba
WHITE MUSTARD
(p. 170)

Description: An annual, up to 80 cm in height, with bright grass green foliage. Lvs hairy, all stalked and pinnately lobed, the terminal lobe of lower lvs not conspicuously large. Fls similar in size to those of *B. napus*. Frt stiffly hairy, 2.5–4 cm long, each valve with 3 veins and beak flattened, sword-like, as long or longer than valves. Seeds pale yellow, large: 2.5 mm across.

Names: Syns.: *Brassica alba*, *B. hirta*. Also known as Yellow Mustard.
Fr.: Moutarde blanche; It.: Senape bianca; Sp.: Mostaza blanca; Ger.: Weisser Senf; Dtch.: Witte mosterd; Dan.: Gul sennep; Gr.: Léuki sinápi, Leuki moustarda; Russ.: Gorchitsa belaya; Yug.: Bela gorjušca.

Uses: White Mustard seed is the basis of American mustard, and an additive to English and some continental condiments, but not of Dijon mustard. The seedlings of 'Mustard and Cress' are traditionally those of this sp., but for economic reasons, mainly because they are hardier, seedlings of Rape *B. napus* are now used in most commercial mixtures. White Mustard is a fast growing crop producing a greater amount of foliage than other mustards, and is often sown in Britain and on the Continent as a break crop, for forage or to be ploughed in as green manure in the flowering stage. Other crops are grown for seed, particularly around the mustard producing centres such as East Anglia.

Origin, distribution and cultivation: White Mustard is a native of the Mediterranean and occurs in other parts of Europe, including Britain, as an escape from cultivation. Fields of yellow-flowered crucifers seen in Britain and W. Europe in mid or late summer, after the flowering of Winter and Summer Oil-seed Rape are likely to be of this sp.

Similar plants: Charlock, below, has simple, stalkless upper lvs, and the beak of frt is little more than half as long as the valves.

Sinapis arvensis
CHARLOCK
(p. 170)

Description: A roughly hairy annual similar to White Mustard, but generally smaller, under 60 cm in height, with stalked, shallowly lobed, lyre-shaped lower lvs and stalkless, simple upper lvs not clasping the stem. Fls similar to *B. alba.* Frt hairy, 2.5–4 cm long, spreading, the beak little more than half the length of the 3-veined valves. Seeds small, dark reddish-brown, similar to those of *B. rapa* but more pungent.

Names: Syn.: *Brassica alba.*
Fr.: Sanve; It.: Senape; Sp.: Sinapo; Ger.: Akersenf; Dtch.: Herik; Dan.: Ager sennep; Gr.: Sinápi; Russ.: Gorchitsa polevaya.

Uses: Charlock is a common weed of arable land, often infesting crops of similar crucifers. It was formerly used as a vegetable in the poorer parts of Europe.

Origin, distribution and cultivation: Charlock occurs throughout Europe on arable and waste land.

Similar plants: White Mustard, above.

Raphanus sativus
RADISH
(p. 174)

Description: An annual bristly-hairy herb 20–100 cm in height, with a swollen white-fleshed tap root. Lvs pinnately lobed, lyre-shaped, usually with a very large terminal lobe and 1 or 2 pairs of small narrow lateral lobes. Fls white or violet, small. Frt swollen, not splitting open at maturity, 3–7 cm long and 0.5–1.5 cm across, with a conical beak. Seeds 6–12 in each frt, ca. 3 mm in diameter, irregular, greyish-pink.

Very many cvs of this sp. exist, particularly in China and Japan, including the large white radishes or Daikon, and others with roots up to 20 kg in weight. In Europe the cvs fall into the following groups based on use:

Salad Radishes These are cvs with white, white and red, or red roots which may be globose, intermediate, or cylindrical, which are picked when small and immature for use as a salad vegetable.

Winter Radishes Varieties of oriental origin which have solid, firm-fleshed roots which unlike the salad varieties do not become pithy and hollow in the centre when mature, and may be harvested later and stored for winter use. The roots, which are much larger, of the size of large Carrots or of Beetroots, are variable, white or red, usually cylindrical; one variety, Black Spanish Radish, has turnip-shaped roots with a patchy-brown skin quite different in appearance from other Radishes.

Fodder Radish These are large forms, some with large whitish roots, whilst in others they are scarcely swollen. These cvs are classed as var. *oleifera* by EEC convention, although strictly speaking this category applies only to forms without swollen tap roots grown in Russia and in Asia as an oil seed crop.

Names: Fr.: Radis; It.: Ravanello; Sp.: Rabano; Ger.: Rettisch, Radies; Dtch.: Radijs; Dan.: Radis, Raeddike; Gr.: Rapáni; Russ.: Rediska; Yug.: Redkev.

Uses: Salad Radishes are eaten raw; the best, pungent varieties deserve to be eaten on their own, as an appetiser, with salt, bread and butter; the relatively insipid ones common in commerce, especially in Britain, are usually included in mixed salads. Winter Radishes can be grated and used as a garnish, or pickled, or treated as a vegetable. Fodder Radishes provide autumn and winter forage for cattle and sheep.

Origin, distribution and cultivation: Radish probably originated in western Asia. It was cultivated 4500 years ago in Egypt, in Assyria, and in Greece and Rome, and spread at least 2000 years ago to China. Many cvs were developed here at an early date, including ones grown for the oil from seeds, as well as for the lvs and roots. Radishes are cultivated in all European countries. Salad Radishes are grown in market- and home-gardens, Winter Radishes in market-gardens and as a field crop, Forage Radish only on mixed farms. Salad Radishes require very rapid growth to be crisp and succulent, and are harvested when very immature.

Similar plants: Young Forage Radish, seen in the field before the flowering stem is produced, might be mistaken for one of the bristly-hairy Brassicas. In Radish all the first lvs arise from the root, whereas in Brassicas they are borne on the stem, which rapidly elongates. The distinction becomes difficult in the case of *Raphanobrassicas*, recently developed fertile hybrids of *R. sativus* and *Brassica oleracea*, which are being tried in some countries as a fodder crop.

Wild Radish, a very common weed of waste land in Britain and on the continent is a different sp., *R. raphanistrum*, with white, violet, or yellow fls and without a tuberous root. This plant is very similar to Charlock (p. 229), but has long-beaked frts, each valve being up to 5 times the length as the top joint of frt.

Armoracia rusticana
HORSE-RADISH

(p. 174)

Description: A tall hairless perennial herb with a long irregular transversely striate tap root with whitish flesh and skin. Root lvs long-stalked, 30–60 cm long, ovate or oblong, shiny dark green, with coarsely toothed margins. Stem up to 1.25 m, not always produced, bearing panicles of small white fls 8–9 mm across. Frt an ovoid silicula with few seeds.

Names: Syns.: *Cochlearia armoracia*, *Radicula armoracia*, *Armoracia lapathifolia*.
Fr.: Raifort, Cranson; It.: Rafano; Sp.: Rabano rusticano; Ger.: Meerettisch, Kren; Dtch.: Meerikswortel; Dan.: Peberrod; Gr.: Alogorádiko; Russ.: Khren.

Uses: The grated roots of Horse-radish are used as a condiment. The flesh, especially the outer layers, are exceedingly pungent due to a volatile oil similar to those of mustards, which affects the nose and makes the process of grating very unpleasant. The pungency vanishes with cooking and decreases rapidly after the roots are grated unless they are dried in suitable conditions. Good commercial dried root, especially from Sweden and Germany, is the best substitute for fresh root; the sweetish (usually very mild even when advertised as hot) ready-made bottled horse-radish sauces of commerce are hardly worth using. In Britain Horse-radish sauce is used to accompany roast beef, but on the Continent many different sauces, a number designed to go with fish, are made. Germany and north-east Europe are the main producers and consumers; Horse-radish is little-known in the Mediterranean countries.

Origin, distribution and cultivation: Horse-radish is a native of south-east Europe, but exists in the wild as an introduced sp. in most of western Europe including Britain. It is most extensively cultivated in Germany, Scandinavia and north-east Europe, but also in Britain, Alsace and many parts of central Europe. It is rarely grown in the Mediterranean, except in northern Italy and parts of the Balkans. It is a field- or large market-garden crop.

Similar plants: The large dock-like lvs are unique among cruciferous crop plants.

Nasturtium officinale
WATERCRESS
(p. 172)

Description: An aquatic hairless perennial with hollow angular stems 10–60 cm long, trailing, with fine white roots at lower nodes, then ascending. Lvs dark green, shiny, pinnate, with 3–9 leaflets including a larger terminal one, persistent in winter. Fls white, small, 4–6 mm across, with pale stamens. Frts 13–18 mm long, 2 mm wide, curved, with seeds visible in 2 rows inside.

Two forms of Watercress are cultivated: The one described above, often called Green Watercress; and Brown, or Winter Watercress, a nearly sterile hybrid of *N. officinale* and of another sp., One-rowed Watercress *N. microphyllum*, whose lvs, like those of the hybrid, turn purplish-brown in autumn. *N. microphyllum* has only a single row of seeds in each pod.

Names: Syn.: *Rorippa nasturtium-aquaticum.*
Fr.: Cresson de fontaine; It.: Crescione; Sp.: Crenchos, Berro de Agua; Ger.: Brunnenkresse; Dtch.: Waterkers; Dan.: Brondkarse; Gr.: Nerokárdamo; Russ.: Kress volyamoi.

Uses: Watercress has a distinctive, pleasant, fresh and slightly pungent flavour. The tips of the leafy stems make an excellent salad or garnish for steaks. They may also be cooked as a vegetable, and make a particularly good soup when thickened with potato and cream.

Origin, distribution and cultivation: Watercress and One-rowed Watercress is a common plant of streams with a wide distribution, from Britain through central and southern Europe to western Asia. It has probably been gathered in the wild since ancient times; commercial cultivation only began in the 19th century, but it is now grown in most European countries where beds can be established in clean, clear running water. It has been introduced to many other parts of the world, and has become a pest weed in New Zealand.

The hybrid Brown Watercress has the advantage of being relatively frost-hardy, and can therefore be produced throughout the winter. A bed of watercress will yield up to 10 crops a year.

Similar plants: Fool's Watercress *Apium nodiflorum* belongs to a different family, the Apiaceae, and consequently is easily distinguished by the structure of the inflorescence (an umbel) and the 5-petalled fls. The lvs of this plant are a brighter, lighter green; the easiest way to tell the plants apart is by biting a leaflet: although not poisonous, Fool's Watercress has an unpleasant flavour.

Lepidium sativum
GARDEN CRESS
(p. 172)

Description: A delicate annual 15–30 cm tall with a single or branched stem. The plant in the vegetative stage resembles Parsley. Basal lvs on long stalks, lyre-shaped, with obovate toothed lobes; stem lvs once or twice pinnate; in some varieties the lvs are crisped and curled in the manner of curled Parsley; lvs near tip of stem stalkless, linear, undivided. Fls minute, white. Frt a flattened elliptical silicula notched at apex, ca. 5.5 x 3.5 mm.

Names: Fr.: Cresson alénois; It.: Agretto; Sp.: Lepido; Ger.: Gartenkresse; Dtch.: Tuinkers; Dan.: Havekarse; Gr.: Kárdamo kípou; Russ.: Kress-salat; Yug.: Urtna kresa.

Uses: In Britain this plant is mainly used in its cotyledon stage as the cress of 'Mustard and Cress' for salads, garnishes, in sandwiches, etc., but on the Continent it is more often grown to near-maturity for use as a salad or soup vegetable, in the same way as Watercress.

Origin, distribution and cultivation: Cress is a native of the Near East and also occurs in the wild in Ethiopia. It has been used as a salad or pot-herb since classical times, and is now cultivated all over the world. On the European continent it is grown in market- and home-gardens, but in Britain commercial production is almost entirely of seedlings, sold in the plastic punnets or trays in which they are sown, often mixed with Mustard. Cress takes several days longer to germinate, and so must be sown before the Mustard in these mixtures.

Similar plants: The deeply 3-lobed cotyledons make the seedlings easy to recognise. Plants in the vegetative stage resemble the umbellifers Parsley and Chervil, but the structure of inflorescences and the flavour of each sp. is quite distinctive.

Barbarea verna
LAND CRESS

(p. 172)

Description: A biennial usually grown as an annual, not dissimilar to Watercress in appearance, but bright green. Flowering stem up to 1 m in height. All lvs deeply pinnately lobed, with 6–10 pairs of narrow lateral lobes and a slightly larger ovate terminal lobes. Fls yellow, small, 7–9 mm across, in dense racemes at ends of several branches. Frts 3–6 cm long, curving upward.

Names: Also called Spring-, American- or Belle Isle Cress, Mustard Greens, Scurvy Grass and Winter Cress, though the latter name should be restricted to *B. vulgaris* (see similar plants, below).
Fr.: Barbarée, Roquette des jardins; It.: Barbarea; Sp.: Berro-mastuerzo; Ger.: Winterkresse; Dtch.: Landkers, Winterkers; Dan.: Landkarse; Gr.: Kardamo edaphous; Russ.: Surepka vesennaya.

Uses: Lvs picked in winter may be used like spinach. The young shoots and lvs in early spring make a fine salad at a time when few other salad plants are available in the kitchen garden, but because imported salad plants now are available throughout the year from grocers, this useful plant is little-grown, and no longer enters commerce.

Origin, distribution and cultivation: This sp. is a native of central Europe but is widely naturalised in other parts of the Subcontinent and in North America. It was formerly widely cultivated in kitchen gardens, but is now rarely grown except by smallholders on the continent, who may offer the plant for sale in country markets.

Similar plants: The very common wild *Barbarea vulgaris*, Yellow Rocket or Winter Cress, which is used, though less often, in the same way, has much larger terminal lobes of lvs and only 2–4 pairs of lateral lobes, and much smaller, straight pods. Other wild *Barbarea* spp. also occur all over Europe.

B. verna has not been included in the keys to the yellow-flowered crucifers, because it is not a field crop, and would have complicated the keys unnecessarily.

Eruca sativa
ROCKET

(p. 172)

Description: An annual with an erect, little-branching flowering stem up to 60 cm tall. Lvs pinnately lobed with about 3–4 pairs of often assymetrical narrow lateral lobes and a larger, ovate terminal lobe, rather similar to Radish. The wild plant is smaller, with yellowish fls; the cultivated varieties have fls creamy white often veined or flushed with violet or dark red. Fls relatively large, few, in small terminal racemes. Frt a cylindrical siliqua about 3 times as long as broad with a flattened beak, borne erect, parallel to rachis.

Names: Syn.: *Eruca vesicaria* ssp. *sativa.* In order to distinguish this plant from other rockets it is sometimes called Roman Rocket, Salad Rocket, or Rocket-gentle.
Fr.: Roquette; It.: Rucola, Ruchetta; Sp.: Oruga; Ger.: Ruke; Gr.: Roketa; Russ.: Eruka posevnaya.

Uses: Rocket is now little-known in Britain, but is an important plant used for flavouring salads in southern France, Italy, Yugoslavia, Greece and the Near East. It has a rather pungent, distinctive flavour which is admirably suited to salads served with grilled meat.

Origin, distribution and cultivation: Rocket is a native of southern Europe and western Asia, where it has been cultivated since classical times. It does not enter commerce in Britain or northern Europe, but is widely grown in kitchen- and market-gardens in the Mediterranean countries, where it is available on country markets and sometimes from grocers.

Similar plants: Several other crucifers, mostly with yellow fls, are called 'rocket' and are sometimes used as salad plants, but none of them are economic spp. See *Barbarea vulgaris*, above.

Crambe maritima
SEAKALE
(p. 172)

Description: A large cabbage-like perennial 40–60 cm tall and up to 1 m across, with large bluish-grey basal lvs on long fleshy stalks. Lf-blades broad, ovate, with lobed or wavy margins. Fls white, 10–16 mm across, borne in large, flat-topped dense heads up to 30 cm across. Frts ca. 13 x 8 mm, with a narrow lower joint and a pear-shaped upper joint which does not split open at maturity.

For uses as a food the young plants are blanched in winter or early spring, either by burying them under a pile of shingle, or, more effectively, by covering the crown with a pot or box under fermenting manure. This produces thick white lf-stalks with only a tiny fringe of lf-blade at their apices.

Names: Fr.: Chou marin; It.: Cavolo marino; Sp.: Col de mar; Ger.: Meerkohl; Dtch.: Zeekool; Dan.: Strandkål; Gr.: Krámvi i Parálios; Russ.: Katran.

Uses: The blanched lf-stalks, which have a pleasant but rather bitter flavour, are eaten as a boiled vegetable with white or cheese sauces.

Origin, distribution and cultivation: Seakale occurs on shingle and sandy coasts of the Baltic, Atlantic and parts of the Mediterranean. In Britain it is locally abundant, but absent from Scotland. The plant was formerly cultivated on a commercial scale, either in the open or in hothouses, but now is only grown by amateur gardeners. It is occasionally available locally in East Anglia, Holland, etc., sometimes from wild plants blanched with shingle.

Similar plants: This plant is often confused with Seakale Beet (p. 241). The blanched stems are similar, but in Seakale they are picked when only about 15 cm long; the lf-blade in Seakale is reduced to a tiny crinkled terminal fringe which is glaucous, and often purplish, whereas in Seakale Beet it is much larger, and even if blanched, retains a much larger, green lf-blade. The name 'Sea Cabbage' in most other languages should not cause *Crambe* to be confused with the wild form of *Brassica oleracea* (p. 126).

Isatis tinctoria
WOAD
(p. 172)

Description: A medium to tall, more or less hairless biennial or perennial herb with basal rosettes of stalked, long lanceolate, downy lvs; upper lvs conspicuously arrow-shaped, hairless, and clasping the stem. The large branching inflorescences bear numerous yellow fls ca. 4 mm in diameter. Frts obovate, 1–2 cm long, drooping on thin stalks, ripening to purplish-brown.

Names: Fr.: Pastel, Guède; It.: Guado; Sp.: Hierba pastel, Gualda; Ger.: Waid; Dtch.: Wede; Dan.: Farvevajd; Gr.: Pastél; Russ.: Vaida; Yug.: Sač.

Uses: Formerly one of the most important European dye plants, yielding a range of blues from the lvs.

Origin, distribution and cultivation: Woad is included in this book because it may be of interest to identify a plant which was of considerable economic importance in the past. A native of southern and central Europe, it occurs as a relict escape from cultivation in many other areas, including Britain, for it was widely cultivated from prehistoric times until the present century.

Britons may remember Woad only in terms of Latin and schooldays; Caesar's colonising armies were confronted by their barbarian ancestors painted in woad, but in France the plant has more important associations. The expression Land of Cockaigne (*cocagne*), meaning a land of ease and plenty, alludes to the great prosperity brought by the woad industry to large parts of southern France in the Middle Ages, *'coques'* being the earthenware 'shells' or cups in which the dye, in the form of a paste, was marketed.

AIZOACEAE

Ice-plant Family

A small family of herbs and shrubs, usually with succulent lvs with or without stipules, bisexual fls with numerous calyx and corolla segments, and the frt a capsule. The family is concentrated in parts of the southern hemisphere, with the greatest number of spp. in South Africa. It contains only one economic species.

Tetragonia expansa
NEW ZEALAND SPINACH

(p. 178)

Description: A fast-growing annual herb with sprawling, rather fleshy stems 35–50 cm long. Lvs alternate, fleshy, 5–12 cm long with margins 3- or 5-angled, otherwise entire, on short narrowly-winged stalks. Fls small, solitary, yellowish, in lf-axils. Frt a green top-shaped capsule ca. 8 mm long crowned with 4 small thorns.

Names: Fr.: Tetragone; It.: Spinacio della Nuova Zelanda; Sp.: Espinaca de Nueva Zelandia; Ger.: Neuseeländischer Spinat; Dtch.: Nieuwzeelandse spinazie; Dan.: Nyzeelandsk spinat; Gr.: Spanaki Neas Zilandias; Russ.: Novozelandski shpinat; Yug.: Novozelanska shpinat.

Uses: The lvs are eaten like Spinach, which they rival in quality, although the flavour is different. Lvs may be picked from the growing plant throughout the summer.

Origin, distribution and cultivation: *T. expansa*, a native of New Zealand, has been in cultivation in Europe since the 19th century. It is little-known in Britain because it is less hardy than spinach and other spinach substitutes, but is popular and widely cultivated on the Continent, particularly in France, both in cottage gardens and by large market-gardeners, and it is generally available from greengrocers and markets throughout the summer.

Similar plants: The lvs are smaller than those of Spinach, and of a different shape. They resemble those of some other Spinach substitutes (Amaranths, etc.) rarely if ever used in Europe, and also *Chenopodium* and *Atriplex* spp. (pp. 244 and 245), but are rather fleshier. The plant's sprawling habit, and fl and frt structure are distinctive.

PORTULACACEAE

Purslane Family

A small family of herbs with entire, unlobed lvs usually opposite in equal pairs. It is very similar to the large campion family (Caryophyllaceae) but with a calyx of only 2 sepals and a 3-seeded frt capsule. They are mostly New World species, including a few (*Montia* spp.) which are naturalised in Europe. Only two are of economic use.

Portulacca oleracea
PURSLANE

(p. 178)

Description: A fleshy annual plant with sprawling stems up to 35 cm long, bearing numerous erect branches. Stems and branches usually red, or flushed with red or pink. Lvs nearly opposite, 1–3 cm long, obovate, glossy dark green, crowded in upper parts of stems and branches. Fls terminal or in axils in groups of 1–3, ca. 1 cm in diameter, with 4–6 yellow petals and up to 15 stamens. Frt a green capsule ca. 6 mm across.

Cultivated Purslane is sometimes treated as a distinct form, var. *sativa.*

Names: Fr.: Pourpier; It.: Porcellana; Sp.: Verdolaga; Ger.: Portulak; Dtch.: Postelein; Dan.: Portulak; Gr.: Glistrida; Russ.: Portulak ogorodni.

Uses: The rather spicy, peppery flavour of Purslane lvs and tender shoots is generally considered too strong for it to be used on its own like Spinach. It is more often used in soups, or as an ingredient of salads, and as a herb to mix with olives, capers, etc. or in sauces.

Origin, distribution and cultivation: Purslane occurs in most of Europe, including Britain, often as an escape. It is a non-hardy summer vegetable which is often grown under glass, both by amateur and market gardeners. France is the biggest producer and consumer, but it is available in many other European countries, though rarely in Britain.

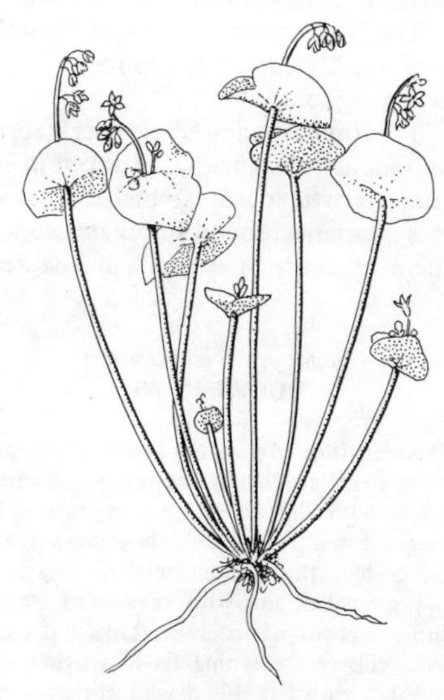

Winter Purslane

Similar plants: Winter Purslane *Claytonia perfoliata* belongs to the same family but is quite different in appearance (above). It is hardy and usually grown as a winter vegetable, but is less frequent than *P. oleracea* and rarely seen in commerce. It is naturalised in many parts of Europe, including Britain.

POLYGONACEAE

Dock Family

A family of many species of herbs distributed all over the northern hemisphere. Lvs are alternate, simple. Small, often pink or white fls are borne in racemes or in axillary clusters. Frt, usually referred to as an achene, is a 3-cornered nutlet with a leathery skin. The best distinguishing character is the *ochrea*, a tubular sheath formed by the fusion of 2 sepals which encloses the stem at each lf axil.

The family includes one agricultural crop and a number of horticultural spp., but is of much greater importance to farmers for the number of weeds, such as docks, belonging to it.

The Rhubarbs and edible docks (sorrels) described below all contain oxalic acid, a poisonous substance when taken in large doses, but which give these plants the characteristic sourness which can be useful to balance flavours in cooked dishes. It is this substance, found in greater concentration in some other docks which make them a menace to livestock in pastures.

Fagopyrum esculentum
BUCKWHEAT
(p. 178)

Description: An annual herb with slender erect stems swollen at the nodes and often tinged with pink or red, growing to 1 m in height. Lvs alternate, broadly arrow-shaped, 3–7 cm long, the lower ones on long stalks, the upper smaller and with very short stalks. Inflorescences in clusters on stalks in lf axils, each cluster containing fls of varying age together with frts. Fls devoid of petals but with 5 petal-like pinkish-white sepals. Frt a top-shaped green nutlet ca. 6 mm long with 3 sharp angles or wings often coloured red, the whole ripening to pale grey-brown to dark brown according to cv.

Names: Both the generic name (from *Fagus*=Beech and *Pyrum*=Cereal) and the English name (derived from the German *Buch*=Beech) refer to the frt's resemblance to a tiny beech nut. The name Saracen, common to several European languages, dates from the Middle Ages when novelties introduced from the East were generally attributed to the Arabs.
Fr.: Sarrasin, Blé noir; It.: Grano saraceno; Sp.: Trigo sarraceno, Alforfón; Ger.: Buchweizen; Dtch.: Boekweit; Dan.: Boghvede; Gr.: Fagopyron; Russ.: Grechikha; Yug.: Navadna ajda.

Uses: Buckwheat is usually cultivated for the achenes which are milled to produce a coarse flour. This can be baked, or made into gruel, or used for feeding stock. In Poland and the Soviet Union the whole achenes are lightly roasted and then boiled in water or stock to make *kasha*, and in parts of northern Italy the flour is used in the same way as maize flour to make *polenta.*

On some farms crops may be grown to provide cover and food for game birds, or simply as a green manure.

Origin, distribution and cultivation: Buckwheat originated in Eastern Siberia, in the area between Lake Baikal and Manchuria, and spread westward with successive migrations of central Asian peoples, reaching Europe probably with the Mongols in the 13th century. It was soon taken into cultivation all over Europe, for it had certain advantages over the native cereals: Buckwheat is fast growing, easy to cultivate, and tolerant of poor, even very acid soils, thus providing many regions with a home-grown supply of flour, where previously the poorer inhabitants could not afford it.

The disadvantages of Buckwheat, which have led to its disappearance in Western Europe in recent times, are that the husk content of flour is very high, and the crop is unsuited to modern harvesting methods. In the true cereals all the grain matures at the same time when the plants are dry. With Buckwheat the frts mature irregularly, and unopened buds, fls and ripe and unripe frt are on the plant at the same time. Thus much potential 'grain' is lost, the yield is relatively low (up to 2 tons per hectare), and since the plants are still actively growing at the time of harvest, the cut plants must be dried before threshing.

Buckwheat is now an obsolete crop in Britain, France, the Low Countries, etc., but is still grown to a small extent in Germany, parts of Scandinavia and northern Italy, and on a large scale in eastern Europe, especially Poland and the Soviet Union.

Similar plants: Tartarian Buckwheat *F. tataricum* is generally taller and less red, with fewer and smaller fls and frts with rounded, not keeled angles. It occurs through contamination of seed as a weed in Buckwheat crops, and is cultivated in Soviet Asia on soils too poor for *F. esculentum.*

Rheum rhabarbarum
RHUBARB

(p. 178)

Description: A large perennial with short rhizomes cultured into a thick rootstock which gives rise in spring to potentially very large lvs (stalk and blade more than 1 m long). Stalks are slightly ribbed, deeply concave on inner face, red or reddish in forced plants. Lf-blades more or less heart-shaped or triangular, rather crinkled, smaller and incompletely formed on forced shoots. Inflorescence a large panicle growing to 2 m in height, with numerous small white fls. Frt a small green 3-sided nutlet.

Names: Syns.: *R. rhaponticum*, *R. undulatum.* Fr.: Rhubarbe; It.: Rabarbarbo; Sp.: Ruibarbo; Ger.: Rhabarber; Dtch.: Rabarber; Dan.: Rabarber; Gr.: Raventi, Rion; Russ.: Reven; Yug.: Rabarbara.

Uses: The lf-stalks are used as a fruit substitute, especially in winter and spring. They are acid, so must be cooked with large amounts of sugar to make them palatable and achieve the right fruit-like balance of tartness and sweetness. They are eaten as a compote, or in tarts, crumbles, etc.

Origin, distribution and cultivation: The genus *Rheum* includes about 20 spp. distributed from the mountains of the Lebanon to those of central China, their large dormant rhyzomatous rootstocks and rapid spring growth being well adapted to the harsh climate of those regions. *R. rhabarbarum* occurs in the wild in south-east Russia eastwards through the Tien Shan to western China. With several other spp. (see below) it has been cultivated by the Chinese as a medicinal plant for at least 2000 years. Although it was first introduced to western Europe in the 16th century, it was only used medicinally and occasionally as a vegetable. Its use as a fruit substitute only began in the 19th century, after which new, superior edible varieties were imported as part of the developing China trade. Rhubarb is now grown in all European countries. The best eating stalks are produced by unearthing the rootstocks and exposing them to winter frosts, before planting them in warm, dark conditions in early spring to break winter dormancy and induce the rapid growth of etiolated shoots.

Similar plants: *R. officinalis* and *R. palmatum*, the latter recognisable by its deeply-lobed lvs, are widely cultivated in China, and to a small extent in Europe for the drug rhubarb (anthaquinones and other substances) used in pharmaceutics. The stalks of these species are not edible. European Wild Rhubarb *R. alpinum* which occurs in the mountains of central and southern Europe has duller, more crinkled lvs which are sometimes used in the Alps for wrapping fresh cheeses; the rhizomes may be gathered for pig food.

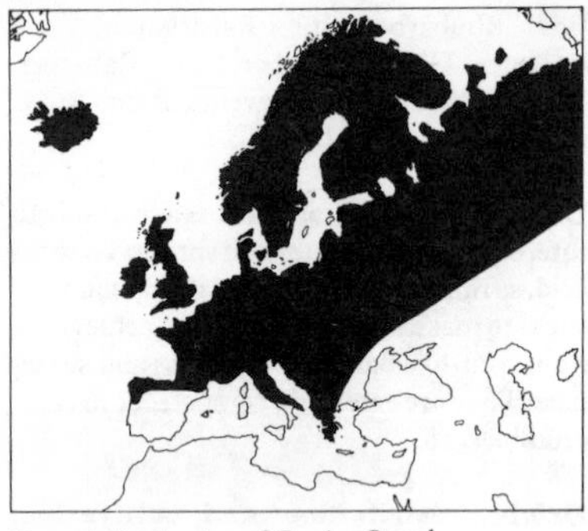
Natural distribution of Garden Sorrel

Rumex acetosa
GARDEN SORREL
(p. 178)

Description: A perennial herb, variable in height from 30–100 cm. Lvs shiny, arrow-shaped, up to 15 cm long, 2–6 times as long as broad, with conspicuous backward-pointing acute basal lobes; basal lvs on long stalks, the upper almost stalkless, their lobes clasping the stems. Inflorescence little-branched, rather loose; fls small, green often turning red, in whorls; sepals in 2 whorls of 3, the inner ones becoming the 'valves' of the 3-sided nutlet.

Cultivated plants, which are larger than the wild form, with generally broader lvs than those illustrated, are usually seen growing in clumps of large basal lvs. These are picked at the stage before the longer stems bearing upper lvs and inflorescences appear.

Names: Fr.: Oseille de Belleville; It.: Acetosa maggiore; Sp.: Acedera; Ger.: Grosser Sauerampfer; Dtch.: Zuring; Dan.: Syre; Gr.: Lapathon, Thinitha; Russ.: Shavel ogorodni; Yug.: Navadna kislica.

Uses: *R. acetosa*, like the other cultivated sorrels described below, is an edible dock. The lvs are too sour and acid to make them pleasant to eat in a large quantity like Spinach, yet this sourness is the plant's particular virtue, and in small quantities is invaluable in counterbalancing the bland or oily nature of some foods. The classic uses are in sorrel soups thickened with egg and cream, and as a purée made by melting the finely chopped lvs in butter for a few minutes and used to accompany white meat and fish or in omelettes. The raw chopped lvs may also be added to salads.

The lvs must be chopped only with a stainless steel knife, for iron oxidises quickly on contact with the acid, and turns the lvs black and unpalatable. The lvs are rarely seen in commerce, except sometimes in the morning on country markets, for they must be consumed as fresh as possible.

Origin, distribution and cultivation: Common Sorrel, from which Garden Sorrel is derived, is a very common wild plant of grasslands and open woods throughout Europe, including Britain, although not in southern Spain or Turkey. The larger cultivated varieties have been evolved through centuries of selection, the best known being that developed in the 19th century, in the market gardens of Belleville in Paris. Sorrel was used in ancient Egypt, and by the Romans, and has been cultivated in most of Europe ever since. It is mainly a cottage garden or allotment crop, where small quantities of lvs can be picked from the growing clumps according to need, but it is also grown in large market gardens for the restaurant trade and for grocers, particularly in France. The productive life of plants is extended by preventing the development of flowering shoots.

Similar plants: *R. acetosa* is typically distinguished from other sorrels by the long, acute basal lobes of its arrow-shaped lvs. From other plants with similarly shaped lvs it can be recognised by the long tubular, often reddish sheaths or *ochreae* (which are characteristic of the family). Many of the cvs attributed to this sp., especially those known as 'Belleville', have much less pronounced basal lobes than the typical form, often approaching those of the Round-leaved Sorrels, possibly as the result of ancient hybridisations.

The wild Sheeps Sorrel *R. acetosella* is a smaller plant with the basal lobes of lvs spreading laterally or even pointing forward.

The true Sorrels (*Rumex* spp.) should not be confused with Wood Sorrel *Oxalis acetosella*, a common small herb of dry woodland with clover-like trifoliate lvs and 5-petalled white fls. This plant, which belongs to a different family, the Oxalidaceae, is so called because it also contains oxalic acid and is sometimes used in the same way as Sorrel, although not cultivated for the purpose except perhaps by amateur gardeners.

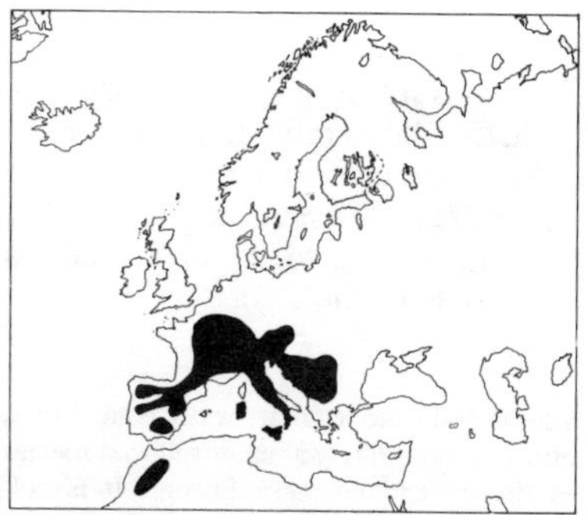

Natural distribution of Round-leaved Sorrel

Rumex scutatus
ROUND-LEAVED SORREL
(p. 178)

Description: *R. scutatus* is similar to *R. acetosa*, but is shorter, with much broader lvs (often as broad as long) which are duller and have less acute or obsolete basal lobes.

Names: Also known as French Sorrel. Fr.: Oseille à feuilles rondes; It.: Acetosa romana; Sp.: Acedera con hojas redondas; Ger.: Rundblättriger ampfer; Gr.: Gallikí thinítha; Russ.: Shavel shitkovitni.

Uses: As Garden Sorrel. The lvs are slightly less acid, and may be used more liberally in the same recipes.

Origin, distribution and cultivation: *R. scutatus* occurs in the wild throughout Europe, and in Britain as an introduced species. It is cultivated in the same way as *R. acetosus*, and is more widely available in commerce.

Similar plants: Cvs. of French or Round-leaved Sorrel are often listed as belonging to other species: *R. rugosus*, *R. montanus*, etc. There seems to be some confusion in the taxonomy of the cultivated forms of these sorrels, possibly as a result of hybridisations.

Rumex patientia
HERB PATIENCE or **SORREL-DOCK**

Description: A much taller plant (up to 1.6 m) than the sorrels, with thick, conspicuously grooved stems and many erect branches. Lvs narrow, 30–100 cm long, 4–5 times as long as broad. Inflorescence large, branching.

Names: Fr.: Oseille-épinard, Epinard perpetuel; It.: Romice domestica, Erba pazienza; Sp.: Romaza; Ger.: Englischer Spinat, Gartenampfer; Dtch.: Patientie; Dan.: Engelsk spinat; Gr.: Thinítha; Russ.: Shavel vorobini.

Uses: The lvs of this plant, being somewhat less acid than those of the sorrels, are used more as a vegetable than as a flavouring.

Origin, distribution and cultivation: This sp. is a native of S.E. Europe. It was widely spread in cultivation in the Middle Ages, but is now rarely seen except in some cottage gardens or in the wild (including Britain), as an ancient escape from cultivation. It is not produced commercially.

Similar plants: The large size distinguishes this sp. from other edible *Rumex* spp. It resembles Water Dock *R. hydrolopathum*, a wild riverside plant, but the wings of frts are rounder, and frequently have only one swollen; they are triangular and all swollen in Water Dock.

PLANTAGINACEAE

Plantain Family

A widespread family of herbs with leaves usually all in a basal rosette, often with parallel veins like those of monocotyledons. Plantains are recognisable by their type of inflorescence, a dense spike of tiny fls with chaffy 4-lobed calyx and corolla and 4 long conspicuous stamens. The frts are capsules. The most familiar member of the family is the exceedingly common weed Ribwort *Plantago lanceolata*.

This family is of no agricultural use. It has nothing to do with Bananas (Musaceae) which are known in some countries as 'plantains'.

Plantago indica
FLEAWORT
(p. 178)

Description: An annual, 8–40 cm tall. Stems erect and spreading, branched, leafy and hairy. Lvs opposite, 2.5–10 cm long, linear, entire or with minute teeth, the lower ones frequently with axillary branches. Fls 3–4 mm across, arranged in dense ovoid spikes ca. 1 cm long.

Names: Syns.: *P. psyllum*, *P. ramosa*, etc. Also known as Branched Plantain.

Uses: The highly mucilaginous seeds which have gentle purgative properties are used in a number of proprietary medicines.

Origin, distribution and cultivation: Fleawort occurs throughout most of southern and central Europe on dry waste land, dunes, etc., and more rarely as an introduced species in Britain and northern Europe. It is cultivated to a small extent as a field crop, especially in southern France, for the pharmaceutical industry.

Similar plants: Fleawort is distinguished from other plantains by its branching stems.

The very elongate mature spikes of Giant Plantain *P. major* are sometimes sold on southern European markets as food for cage birds. *P. coronopus*, variously known as Buck's-horn Plantain, Star of the Earth, Crow's-foot Plantain, Capuchin's Beard (but see also Chicory, p. 274) was once widely used as a salad plant, but is now rarely seen. It differs from other plantains in having deeply pinnatifid lvs, not unlike some forms of Dandelion.

CHENOPODIACEAE

Goosefoot Family

A small family of worldwide distribution composed of herbs and small shrubs, many of them adapted to living by the sea, in salt marshes, etc. The lvs are simple and alternate, often 'mealy', ie. with an irregular cover of short recumbent swollen hairs. The fls are small, inconspicuous, borne in branched cymes.

One species, cultivated mainly for its tap-root, is of considerable economic importance. Other European members have edible lvs, and in Peru a species is cultivated for its frt, used for flour at altitudes too high for maize to grow. The family takes its name from the genus *Chenopodium* meaning the foot of a goose, alluding to the shape of the lvs of some species. The following key may help to identify the less familiar European plants sometimes used as Spinach substitutes.

KEY TO GOOSEFOOT FAMILY		
1	Fls bisexual, with both stamens and style; sepals 5, more or less equal; lvs always green=**2**	**(6)**
2	Calyx lobes swollen at base and adhering in clusters in frt; lower lvs untoothed=**Wild Sea Beet**	**(3)**
3	Calyx lobes not swollen at base, not adhering in clusters in frt; all lvs more or less lobed or toothed=**4**	**(2)**
4	Tufted perennial; lvs sharply triangular; long stigmas projecting from fls=**Mercury**	**(5)**
5	Annual; lvs lanceolate to diamond-shaped, bluntly-toothed; stigmas short=**Fat Hen**	**(4)**
6	Fls unisexual, male fls with 5 sepals and 5 stamens, female with 2 pointed sepal-like bracts; lvs pale green or dark maroon to purple=**Orache**	**(1)**

Beta vulgaris

BEETROOT, SUGAR BEET, FODDER BEETS, MANGELS, SPINACH BEET and **SEAKALE BEET**

(pp. 180, 214)

Description: Wild Sea Beet, from which the cultivated forms are believed to derive, is a usually perennial plant with a woody tap-root giving rise to branching, often red-striped stems up to 1 m long. The lvs are rather small, angular, heart-shaped or diamond-shaped to oblong (on upper part of stem), always untoothed, and dark glossy green. Fls resemble those of *Chenopodium* in having 5 equal sepals, but these are fleshy, more conspicuous, and swollen in frt. Frts adhere by their swollen sepals in globose clusters in the axils of bracts on the long branching flowering stems.

The cultivated forms of *B. vulgaris* are biennials which are harvested at the end of the first year unless they are grown for seed. During the second year the swollen tap root sends up a stout-ridged, branching, flowering stem up to 2 m in height and often a number of secondary stems. In the first-year plants, the stem is so short as to be quite inconspicuous, forming the crown at the top of the root from which a number of large, ovate, fleshy, long-stalked basal lvs arise. The different forms belong to 3 main varieties, as follows:

var. *maritima*	Wild Sea Beet
var. *cicla* (leaf beets)	Spinach Beet
	Seakale Beet
var. *esculenta* (root beets)	Beetroot
	Mangels
	Fodder Beets
	Sugar Beet

The cultivated forms all differ from Wild Sea Beet in the much larger basal lvs and, in those belonging to var. *esculenta*, in the large swollen 'root' (in fact formed by the root, the hypocotle and the stem base).

Spinach beet resembles Beetroot plants but does not have a large swollen root. Lf-stalks are usually green, but red in one variety.

Seakale beet is readily recognisable by the hypertrophied white lf-stalks, and often greatly reduced lf-blades. The roots are not swollen.

Beetroot has globose or slightly flattened roots with dark red skin and flesh in all the commercial varieties, but bright yellow- and white-fleshed varieties also exist.

Mangels have variably shaped roots, always with yellowish flesh. Globe Mangels are round, reddish in upper half, yellowish-white beneath; 'long' and 'tankard' roots are very large, elongate, the former more gradually tapering, the latter cylindrical.

Fodder Beets are similar in size and shape to *Sugar Beet* (below) but often less conical.

Sugar Beet is conical in shape, whitish, similar to most fodder beets but with a much higher (up to 20%) sugar content.

These types can be identified in the field by the depth at which they sit in the ground (see illustration, p. 242). This is directly related to the ratio of water to food content in each type: those with the high concentrations of dry matter are more deeply-buried than the more watery roots.

Shape and depth in the soil of the principal types of *Beta* roots.

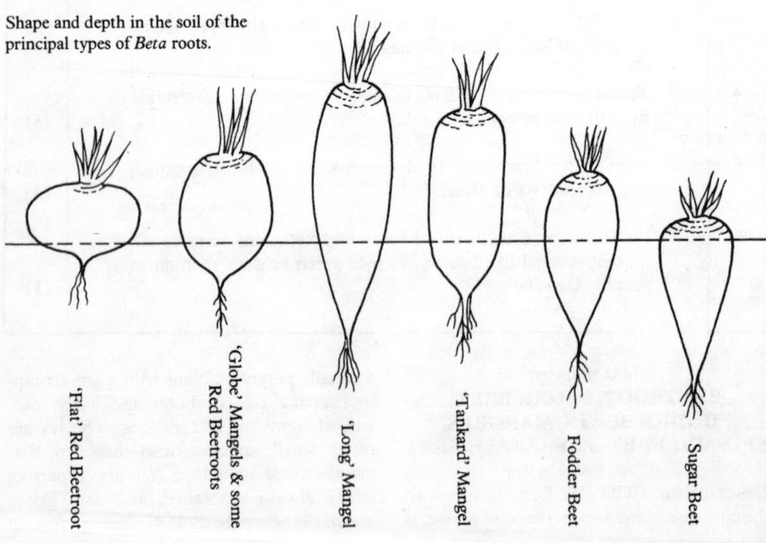

Names: Mangel is also known as Mangelwurzel, or spelled Mangold. Spinach Beet, together with some other plants, is often called Perpetual Spinach. Seakale Beet is just as often called Swiss Chard, a name which usefully avoids confusion with *Crambe* (p. 233).

Fr.: Betterave, Bette, Poirée; It.: Barbetiola, Bieta; Sp.: Remolacha, Acelga; Ger.: Rübe, Beisskohl; Dtch.: Biet, Kroot; Dan.: Bede, Bladbete; Gr.: Pantsári; Russ.: Svekla stolovaya, Svekla; Yug.: Pesa.

Uses:

Spinach Beet the lf-blades only are used as a Spinach substitute.

Seakale Beet is also grown for the lvs, but it is the fleshy lf-stalk which is used, as a boiled vegetable, in the same way as true Seakale.

Beetroot is cultivated for the swollen root which is boiled and eaten as a vegetable, usually cold, in salads, etc., sometimes hot, alone or in composite dishes, or pickled in vinegar. It is the basis of *Borshch*, the beetroot soups of Russia and Poland.

Sugar Beet is by far the most important economic variety. The crops are harvested by a machine which slices off the tops of the plants before lifting the roots. These are shredded in the factory, and the juice extracted, refined and reduced to crystallised white sugar. The residual pulp, compressed into pellets, is a valuable high-energy animal food. Molasses, also used as stock food and for making industrial alcohol is another by-product; the filter cake, the residue left from the filtered juice, is used as a manure.

Mangels are grown for lifting and feeding to stock. The fresh roots are mildly toxic, and must be stored in a clamp for two months or more before they can be used. They have the advantage over Swedes in that they do not taint the milk of dairy cows, and in favourable climates they yield a larger crop.

Fodder Beets are also grown for stock-feeding. They are more useful than Mangels in that they can be fed fresh, and have a higher food content, but the roots are buried more deeply in the soil, and are consequently more difficult to lift. This is done without 'topping' them like Sugar Beets, for mutilated roots would quickly rot in storage.

Origin, distribution and cultivation: Wild Sea Beet, a common seashore plant of all the coasts of Europe and Western Asia, is perhaps a complex of closely-related species. Primitive 'superior' forms of this plant have been used as a leaf vegetable since prehistoric times, and Root Beets, the ancestors of modern varieties, have been cultivated since the first century of our era.

Leaf Beets and Beetroot are grown throughout Europe, mainly in market-gardens, the latter sometimes on a field scale.

Sugar Beet was developed at the end of the 18th century from White Silesian Beet, then used for fodder. In the past, Europeans had had no commercial source of sugar – the traditional sweetening agent for food or drinks was honey – but by the 17th century demand had been created by the import of cane sugar (see p. 318) from European colonies in the tropics. When France and her continental dependencies found themselves deprived of this commodity by the Royal Navy's continental blockade at the beginning of the 19th century, Sugar Beet was rapidly developed to provide an alternative source. Britain, continuing to rely on imports of cane sugar, as it still does to a large extent today, only began to cultivate Sugar Beet in the 1920s, as part of the price guarantee scheme to alleviate the economic depression.

Today Sugar Beet supplies most of Europe's needs, and accounts for about one-third of the world's total production. Sugar Beet is grown extensively in France, Belgium, the Netherlands, Germany and Denmark eastwards through central Europe to Russia, always as an agricultural field crop, and usually within easy reach of a processing factory, as the weight of the roots makes transport expensive.

Mangels, which have been cultivated at least since the Middle Ages, and Fodder Beets, developed mainly in Denmark and Holland between the two world wars, are now falling out of favour, at least in western Europe: the labour costs involved in harvesting and storage makes them an uneconomical alternative to modern silages, cheap grain fodders and processed cattle foods.

Similar plants: Turnips and Swedes (pp. 226 and 225) which resemble some forms of

Mangels, have deeply-lobed lvs. Other root crops, such as those of the carrot family are likewise distinguished by their quite different lvs, fls and frts.

Seakale Beet is often confused with true Seakale (*Crambe*, p. 233). Spinach Beet has much larger lvs than Spinach.

Spinacea oleracea
SPINACH
(p. 180)

Description: An annual herb with broad, dark green, often very crinkled lvs forming a rosette in the young plant. 'Bolting' plants produce an erect leafy stem up to 60 cm high; the upper lvs are smaller, narrower, with usually pronounced, acute, laterally spreading basal lobes. Fls are borne in clusters in the axils of these lvs; they are unisexual, the male fls with 4–5 green sepals and stamens, the female with 2–4 toothed sepal-like bracts around the 1-seeded ovary, with 4–5 short styles.

Two main forms of spinach are cultivated: **Round,** or **Summer Spinach** so called because the 'seed', actually the frt, is almost globose, has the habit described above. It is usually sown in spring or summer.
Prickly, or **Winter Spinach** has frts with 2–3 projecting prickles which are the spreading calyx teeth; the plant has a more spreading, branching habit, and the lvs are less rounded, broadly triangular. It is hardier, and can be sown in autumn for overwintering. Both forms, but particularly Prickly Spinach, are prone to rapid bolting in warm weather with long days, and therefore have a short productive period.

Names: Fr.: Epinard; It.: Spinaci; Sp.: Espinaca; Ger.: Spinat; Dtch.: Spinazie; Dan.: Spinat; Gr.: Spanaki; Russ.: Shpinat; Yug.: Špinača.

Uses: Spinach is the best and most nutritious of all the leaf vegetables. The whole lvs may be blanched in boiling water, or better, the whole or chopped lvs melted in their own juice, without the addition of water, and drained. This basic preparation may be eaten after adding butter, or used in a great variety of recipes, usually combined with dairy products, in tarts as a filling, or for flavouring soufflés, green pastas, etc.

Large quantities are canned or frozen after blanching.

Origin, distribution and cultivation: Spinach, a native of Iran, has been known in Europe since the Arabs introduced it to Spain in the 11th century, but intensive and widespread cultivation only began in the 18th century, particularly in France, the Netherlands and in England, later spreading to the rest of Europe. It is now grown on a large scale in market-gardens all over Europe.

Similar plants: See New Zealand Spinach (p. 234), and spinach substitutes of the goosefoot family (below). Young plants resemble some forms of Lettuce and of the leaf vegetables of the cabbage family, but are a darker green than any of these.

Atriplex hortensis
ORACHE
(p. 180)

Description: A tall annual herb growing to 2 m in height, either pale green, yellow, or dark red, according to variety. Lvs are triangular, shallowly toothed, 8–12 cm long, exceptionally up to 20 cm. Male and female fls on same plant, the male fls with 5 sepals and 5 stamens, most female fls with 2 large triangular sepal-like bracts and a minute ovary, some with a perianth as in male fls.

Names: Sometimes known as Mountain Spinach.
Fr.: Arroche; It.: Atriplice; Sp.: Armuelle; Ger.: Gartenmelde; Dtch.: Melde; Dan.: Hacemelde; Russ.: Lebeda ogorodnaya.

Uses: As Spinach. Only the young lvs are eaten, before the plant sets seed.

Origin, distribution and cultivation: Orache is a native of western Asia and southeast Europe, where it has been cultivated since ancient times. It was introduced to western Europe in the Middle Ages, and was widely grown in kitchen gardens until the 18th century. It is still grown for food to a small extent in France and in central Europe, but not on a commercial scale. The red and yellow forms are often grown as ornamentals.

Similar plants: The dark red form of this plant is unmistakeable, only resembling some of the exotic red amaranths. The green form may be confused with a number of wild European *Atriplex* spp. which are not used for food.

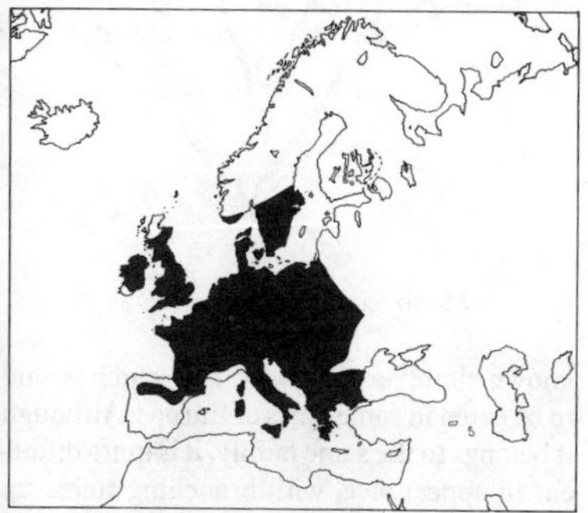

Natural distribution of Mercury

Chenopodium bonus-henricus
MERCURY or **GOOD KING HENRY**
(p. 180)

Description: A perennial herb, 30–50 cm tall. Lvs broadly triangular, with acute basal lobes and wavy margins, up to 10 cm long and 8 cm broad at base, mealy at first, becoming smooth and green later. Fls small, with 5 sepals and stamens, and 2–3 stigmas, borne in erect, almost leafless spikes.

Names: Fr.: Anserine bon-henri, Epinard sauvage; It.: Spinacio selvatico; Sp.: Pie de ánade; Ger.: Bingelkraut; Dtch.: Brave Hendrik; Dan.: Stol Hendriks-gåsefod; Russ.: Mar dobrogo teirikha.

Uses: As Spinach.

Origin, distribution and cultivation: Mercury is sometimes locally abundant on waste ground, road sides, etc. as an ancient escape from cultivation in most of Europe. It may have been introduced from the eastern Mediterranean in the Middle Ages. Like Orache, it was formerly widely cultivated in kitchen gardens, but is rarely seen today, and is never grown commercially.

Similar plants: Mercury differs from Fat Hen (below) and all the many wild spp. of *Chenopodium* in that it is perennial, and in the sharply triangular lvs.

Chenopodium album
FAT HEN
(p. 180)

Description: An annual herb 30–100 cm tall. Lvs greyish-green, more or less covered in a grey 'meal', variable in shape, lanceolate to diamond-shaped, toothed. Fls ca. 2 mm across, with 5 sepals, borne in erect, dense, greyish spikes bearing small lvs almost to tip.

Names: Fr.: Chénopode blanc; It.: Chenopodi bianco; Sp.: Cenizo, Yuyo; Ger.: Rutenmelde; Dtch.; Melganzevoet; Dan.: Hvdmelet; Russ.: Mar belia.

Uses: As Spinach.

Origin, distribution and cultivation: Fat Hen is a very common weed of arable land and gardens in the whole of Europe, including Britain. Its economic importance is therefore a negative one, and it is never cultivated. Its use as a spinach or pot-herb was once widespread, but confined today to only the poorest country people of southern Europe and a few back-to-nature enthusiasts.

Similar plants: The combination of lf shape and their 'mealy' texture distinguish Fat Hen from other wild goosefoots.

Salicornia europaea
MARSH SAMPHIRE

Description: This plant is so odd in its structure that kinship with the species described above is far from obvious. It is a small erect green herb with succulent stems and short opposite branches ca. 3–5 mm thick which are jointed into swollen segments; each segment bears a pair of opposite, triangular adpressed lobes which represent the lvs.

Natural distribution of Marsh Samphire

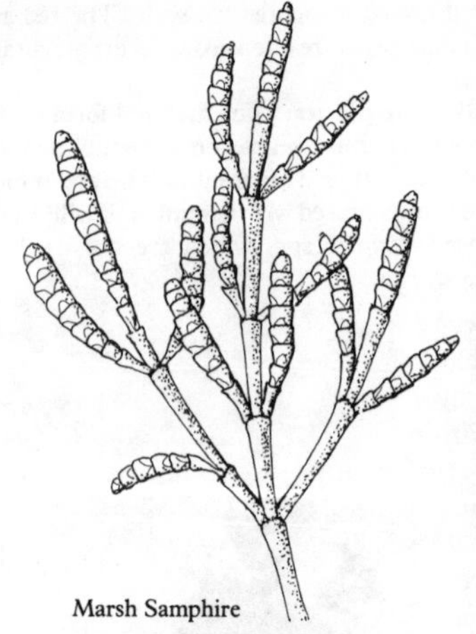

Marsh Samphire

Small fls consist of a fleshy disc from which a single anther emerges from a central pore, and are borne in 1–3s in the axils of lf lobes.

Names: Also known, together with other plants, as Saltwort or Glasswort, or, incorrectly, simply as Samphire.
Fr.: Salicorne; It.: Salicornia; Sp.: Sosa de las salinas; Ger.: Echtes Glassmaltz; Dtch.: Zeekrael, Loogkruid; Dan.: Salturt.

Uses: The tender branching shoots are eaten as a seasonal delicacy, either steamed or boiled, and served like other delicate greens with melted butter, hollandaise sauce, etc.

Origin, distribution and cultivation: Marsh Samphire occurs on the muddy parts of salt marshes on the coasts of western Europe, including Britain. It is gathered in these places in late spring and summer for sale on local markets, and is sometimes retailed by fishmongers in the large inland towns. In Russia and in Central Asia the plant occurs inland, near salt lakes, etc.

Similar plants: Many other spp. of *Salicornia* occur in Europe, some occupying subtly different biotopes of salt marshes. They are for the most part difficult to differentiate, and do not bear specific common names. Some are too woody to be eaten, but others are gathered, and the Marsh Samphire of commerce may belong to different spp. according to the locality.

Marsh Samphire should not be confused with Prickly Saltwort *Salsola kali*, also known simply as Saltwort, and which is said to be eaten in some parts of Europe. Although it belongs to the same family, it is quite different in appearance, with branching stems up to 40 cm long, bearing small (1–4 cm long) succulent lvs tapered into a spine at the tip.

True Samphire is an umbellifer (see p. 262). Another samphire is Golden Samphire, an inedible member of the daisy family. The name samphire is derived from the French *herbe de Saint Pierre*, and was given to a number of different edible or medicinal plants associated with the seashore.

GENTIANACEAE

Gentian Family

This family of familiar mostly blue- or pink-flowered herbs is mentioned briefly because it contains one member which has been brought into cultivation (for other than purely medicinal purposes) since the rapidly diminishing wild plants can no longer supply commercial needs. Yellow Gentian *Gentiana lutea* is a perennial plant with a thick rootstock with a basal rosette of large elliptical lvs which produces a tall flowering shoot only after at least 4 years' growth. The yellow fls are borne in dense clusters in the axils of paired unstalked lvs along the length of the stem.

The plant occurs naturally in the mountains of central and southern Europe, from the Alps eastwards to western Turkey, and is grown commercially in central and eastern Europe. The part used is the rootstock. This yields an aromatic drug with a flavour that is initially sweet and then exceedingly bitter, used in medicine. The fermented root is used to flavour many apéritifs such as *Suze* in France, and *enzian* in Austria.

This family also includes Common Centaury *Centaurium erythraea*, a common wild flower of Europe, including Britain, which has similar properties to Gentian, and is grown commercially for the pharmaceutical industry in central and eastern Europe.

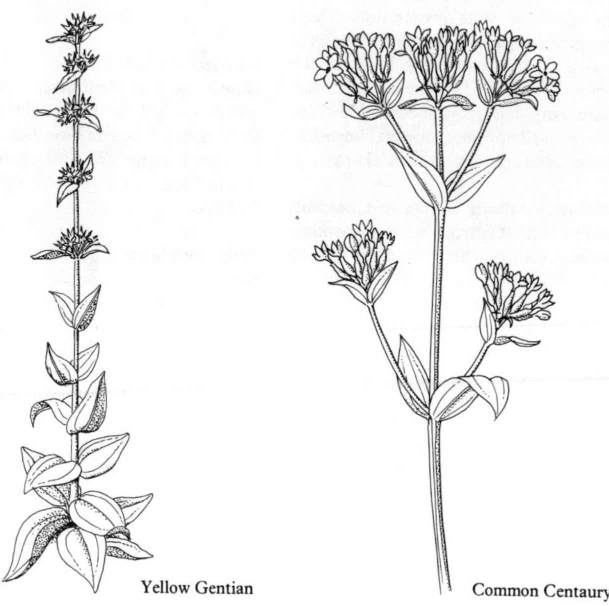

Yellow Gentian

Common Centaury

ONAGRACEAE

Willowherb Family

A family of herbs with lvs in opposite pairs and fl parts in 2s or 4s, and frts which are either capsules or spiny nuts. It is familiar through the many European species of pink-flowered willowherbs (*Epilobium* spp.) and the yellow-flowered Evening primroses (*Oenanthera*), but the edible species described below bears no resemblance to these.

Trapa natans
CALTROPS

Description: A perennial aquatic plant composed of long stems anchored to the bottoms of ponds and rising to the surface where they bear a dense crown of partly-submerged brownish-green, diamond-shaped lvs with finely-toothed front margins, borne on long stalks which are swollen and hollow in their centre, providing the plant's buoyancy. Below this the stem bears a pair of much-branched feathery roots at each node (these are sometimes described as modified lvs). Fls small, with 4 white petals. Frts, borne on the upper part of stem amid and below the crown of lvs, are hard, dark grey, obconical, 3–5 cm across, bearing 2 opposite, unequal horn-like projections, and contain a whitish kernel.

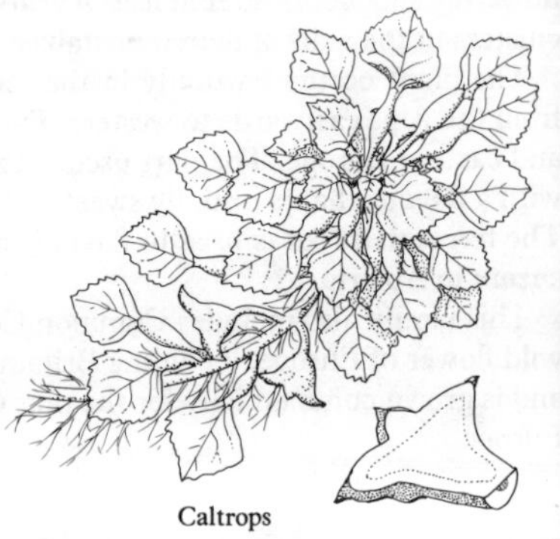
Caltrops

Names: Also known as Water Chestnut, Jesuit's Nut, etc. (Caltrops were four-spiked iron balls strewn on the ground by Roman armies to maim enemy cavalry).
Syn.: *T. quadrispinosa.*
Fr.: Macre; It.: Tribolo aquatico; Sp.: Castaña de agua; Ger.: Jesuitennüss; Dtch.: Kalketrip; Gr.: Nerokastaniá; Russ.: Vodianoy orekh plavayushi.

Uses: The kernels, which have a similar texture and flavour to roasted chestnuts, are boiled and eaten in some parts of Europe.

Origin, distribution and cultivation: Caltrops has a discontinuous natural distribution in Eurasia, from the Loire Valley through central Europe to Thailand and Cambodia. The plant occurs mainly in lakes and ponds, but also in the calm backwaters of large rivers. The frts have been gathered for food since prehistoric times, and are still used in a few places such as the Loire and Danube Valleys.

Similar plants: In Europe: none. At least two related spp., both distinguished from *T. natans* by the frts which have only 2 horns and thus recall a bull's head, are semi-cultivated in Asia. Singhara Nut *T. bispinosa* is harvested in great quantities from all the lakes of the Vale of Kashmir and in many other parts of India, and Ling Kok *T. bicornis* are available in the shops of S. China, Thailand, Malaysia, etc.

The common epithet 'water chestnut' should not cause this plant to be confused with *Eleocharis dulcis* or with Chufa, both members of the sedge family (see p. 330), with quite differently shaped 'nuts'.

APIACEAE (UMBELLIFERAE)

Carrot Family

A family of between 2000 and 3000 species including many common European herbs. With the exception of a few genera, the family is readily identifiable, at least when in flower or fruit, but many of the wild species are very similar and difficult to identify. The small fls have 5 separate petals, 5 or no sepals, 5 stamens and 2 stigmas, and an inferior ovary with 2 carpels which form the variously flattened, ridged or winged casing of the frt. The fls are arranged in flat-topped umbels which may themselves be grouped in umbels to form a very large inflorescence. In the great majority of spp. the lvs are pinnately lobed, pinnate, or trifoliate, the stems hollow or pithy and more or less furrowed.

Nearly all the useful plants of this family are natives of temperate Eurasia. A few are grown for their swollen roots, used as vegetables or for feeding stock. Many others contain specifically distinct, strongly scented resin-like substances and are therefore cultivated for the stems, lvs or frts, used as cooking herbs or spices. One such, which does not enter the geographical range of this book, is asafoetida. The product, widely used as a spice in India, especially in Kashmir where it is a flavouring substitute for the alliums forbidden to local Hindus, and available from Indian grocers in Europe, is the dried sap of a large *Ferula*, closely allied to Giant Fennel. Under the name laserpitium, or silphium, asafoetida was a favourite spice in ancient Rome, at first obtained from a native European sp. which, it is thought, was exploited to extinction, later imported from Asia.

Another umbelliferous food plant is Pignut *Conopodium majus*, a wild sp. of England and western France which produces a pleasantly flavoured knobbly white-fleshed tuber. It has never been cultivated, and is only gathered in the wild by a few connoisseurs, but is mentioned here because its alternative name, Earth Nut, might cause confusion with Chufa (p. 330).

KEY TO THE CULTIVATED UMBELLIFERS

1	Lower lvs simple, more or less lobed and coarsely toothed; fls white=**Anise**	**(2)**
2	Lower lvs pinnate=**3**	**(1)**
3	Lower lvs once-pinnate=**4**	**(10)**
4	Plant more or less hairy; leaflets ovate, coarsely toothed; fls yellow=**Parsnip**	**(5)**

KEY TO THE CULTIVATED UMBELLIFERS

5	Plants hairless; leaflets deeply lobed and toothed; fls greenish-white or pink=**6**	**(4)**
6	Robust plant, up to 1 m, with stems grooved and jointed; all leaflets more or less lobed and coarsely toothed; fls greenish-white=**7**	**(9)**
7	Lf-stalks much thicker, deeply concave on inner side, only slightly thickened at base=**Celery**	**(8)**
8	Lf-stalks much more slender, arising from a large globose, mostly underground base resembling a wrinkled Turnip=**Celeriac**	**(7)**
9	Smaller, much more slender plant, with stems not grooved or jointed; lower leaflets broad, deeply lobed, upper leaflet pinnately lobed, very narrow, linear; fls white or pink=**Coriander**	**(6)**
10	Lower lvs 2- or 3-pinnate=**11**	**(3)**
11	Leaflets crisply curled at edges=**12**	**(14)**
12	Lvs ternately pinnate; leaflets more tightly curled, more deeply lobed; scent characteristic; fls yellow=(curled) **Parsley**	**(13)**
13	Lvs 3-pinnate; leaflets less tightly curled, scarcely lobed; scent somewhat like parsley but with a trace of anise or liquorice=(curled) **Chervil**	**(12)**
14	Lvs not curled at edges, flat or linear=**15**	**(11)**
15	All lvs pinnately divided into thread-like or very narrow feathery leaflets, narrower than those of Carrot=**16**	**(22)**
16	Larger plants (over 60 cm) with thread-like leaflets; fls yellow=**17**	**(19)**
17	Stem solid; frts oblong-ovoid, only slightly flattened, greenish, greyish or yellowish-brown with yellow ridges; all parts of plant smell strongly of Aniseed=**Fennel**	**(18)**
18	Stem hollow; frts broader, more flattened, with ridges and lateral wings; frts taste of Caraway, scent of seeds distinctive, unlike Aniseed=**Dill**	**(17)**
19	Smaller plants, under 60 cm, with leaflets very narrow, but distinctly broader than thick; fls white or mauve=**20**	**(16)**

KEY TO THE CULTIVATED UMBELLIFERS

20	Larger plant, up to 60 cm, erect, with stouter stems, more numerous lvs; fls white, numerous, in large umbels; frt distinctively scented=**Caraway**	**(21)**
21	Smaller plant, under 30 cm, with slender weak stems and fewer lvs; fls white or mauve, few, in small umbels; frts with strong distinctive scent=**Cumin**	**(20)**
22	All leaflets at least as broad as Carrot, or only upper lvs very narrow (Coriander)=**23**	**(15)**
23	Lvs ternately pinnate; leaflets broad, more or less 3-lobed, bluntly toothed at apices; fls yellow; strong Parsley scent in garden varieties=**'Continental'** and **Sheep's Parsley**	**(24)**
24	Lvs 2 or 3-pinnate=**25**	**(23)**
25	All lvs feathery, the leaflets finely divided; bracts subtending umbel large, conspicuously pinnate or 3-forked; large white or orange tap-root present=**Carrot**	**(26)**
26	Lower lvs not finely divided into very narrow lobes; bracts absent or otherwise shaped=**27**	**(25)**
27	Small plants, under 60 cm=**28**	**(32)**
28	Root tuberous, 12–15 cm long, dark grey with yellowish flesh; foliage similar to Chervil, but leaflets usually more deeply lobed; fls white=**Turnip-rooted Chervil**	**(29)**
29	Roots not tuberous=**30**	**(28)**
30	Lower lvs 1–2-pinnate; upper lvs very narrow, pinnately lobed; fls white or pink; scent characteristic, of bed- or shield-bugs=**Coriander**	**(31)**
31	All lvs 3-pinnate, broad; fls white; scent characteristic=**Chervil**	**(30)**
32	Larger plants, over 60 cm tall=**33**	**(27)**
33	Lvs 2–3-pinnate, large, fern-like, with leaflets finely toothed; fls white; stems hollow; scent characteristic, between Aniseed and Liquorice=**Sweet Cicely**	**(34)**
34	Lvs 2–3-pinnate, but not fern-like, less finely toothed=**35**	**(33)**
35	Fls yellow; leaflets glossy, divided into coarse teeth or lobes in apical half; scent characteristic=**Lovage**	**(36)**

KEY TO THE CULTIVATED UMBELLIFERS

36	Fls greenish-white; lvs more finely toothed almost to base=**37**	**(35)**
37	Very large (up to 2 m) plant with hollow aromatic stalks which are not conspicuously jointed; leaflets oblong-ovate, sharply toothed, not lobed=**Angelica**	**(38)**
38	Smaller plant, with jointed stems deeply concave on inner side, strongly ribbed on outerside; leaflets deeply lobed and toothed=**Celery** (see also **Celeriac**)	**(37)**

Daucus carota

CARROT

(p. 182)

Description: An erect branched, roughly hairy biennial (a few plants may bolt and die after the first year). First year consists of a rosette of 3-pinnate lvs, rather feathery in appearance, with small, narrowly lanceolate pointed leaflets 5–10 mm long. Second-year stem is up to 1 m in height, leafy, bearing flat-topped or slightly convex, compound, umbels 3–15 cm in diameter, composed of many bristly rays and many large leafy bracts forming a radiating collar below the umbel. Fls 2–3 mm in diameter, white, but the central fl usually dark red. Frt characteristic, 3–5 mm long, oval, downy, with 4 sharp ridges bearing a fringe of flattened spines on each carpel. The tap-root is woody, purplish-brown to white in the wild form, thick and succulent in the cultivated varieties; these are variable in size and shape according to cv, either almost globose, cylindrical or conical, pointed or blunt-tipped. European varieties grown for food have orange skins and flesh; larger yellowish or white roots are 'Belgian' fodder carrots; in parts of Asia garden varieties may be white, yellow, orange or dark red to purple.

Most botanists treat the cultivated forms as a distinct ssp. *sativus*, and recognise several other sspp. among wild Carrots, for instance ssp. *gummifer*, Sea Carrot, which differs from the nominate form by its fleshier, shorter leaflets, the frt spines which are joined by broad webs, and by its habitat on the coasts of western Europe.

Names: Fr.: Carotte; It.: Carota; Sp.: Zanahoria; Ger.: Karotte, Möhre; Dtch.: Peen, Wortel; Dan.: Karot, Gulerod; Gr.: Karoto; Russ.: Morkov; Yug.: Korenje.

Uses: Carrot is rich in carotene (source of vitamin A) and sugar, and is the most valuable root crop grown for food in Europe. Most roots, which should be lifted young, are sold fresh. They may be eaten raw, grated with salad dressing, cooked as a vegetable, or purěed for infant or invalid foods. From a culinary point of view their greatest value is as a flavouring (for this purpose they should never be peeled or scraped, for most of the aromatic quality resides in the skin). Carrot is an essential ingredient of many soups and stews, of marinades for fish and many other dishes. It should always be used in carefully measured quantities, for the distinctive sweetish flavour otherwise dominates most other ingredients, turning what should be subtle meat or vegetable dishes into carrot stews. Large quantities of roots are also canned or dehydrated; carrot juice is used, usually for blending with citrus in 'mixed fruit juices', and carotene is extracted for the production of concentrates. On farms, the roots and tops may be fed to livestock. The frts contain an essential oil which has a limited industrial use in flavouring and perfumery.

Origin, distribution and cultivation: Wild Carrots occur in the whole of Europe, a large part of Asia and in North Africa. Cultivated forms have been used for food in all these areas at least since classical times. Carrots are tolerant of a wide range of temperatures and are grown in suitable light, well-drained soils in all but the most northerly parts of Europe and in most of the world, including the tropics. They are grown by home-gardeners, extensively in market-garden strips, and as a field crop, usually in beds separated by tractor wheelings. Fodder carrots have fallen out of favour in recent years because the cost of harvesting and storing the roots makes them uneconomical.

Similar plants: See key (p. 249). The dark red central fl of the umbel and the spiny frt distinguish carrot plants from many similar wild plants belonging to other genera.

Pastinaca sativa
PARSNIP
(p. 182)

Description: An erect downy branching biennial with stems angled, hollow and deeply furrowed. Lvs rough, once-pinnate, with ovate toothed leaflets arising in a rosette from tap-root; second-year plants produce a tall (1 m or more) much-branched stem bearing numerous rather loose umbels 5–10 cm in diameter composed of 5–15 rays. Fls yellow, 1.5–2 mm across. Frt ovate, much flattened 6–7 mm long, with winged edges and 3 ridges on each carpel. The yellowish white tap-root is small and rather woody in the wild form, large and succulent in cultivated plants, usually conical with a transversely wrinkled surface and characteristic scent.

Names: Fr.: Panais; It.: Pastinaca; Sp.: Pastinace; Ger.: Pastinak; Dtch.: Pastinaak; Dan.: Pastinak; Gr.: Elaphovoskon; Russ.: Pasternak; Yug.: Pastinak, Navadni rebrinek.

Uses: Grown for the swollen tap-root used as animal fodder or as a cooked vegetable. The eating quality of the root is improved by prolonged exposure to frost, which increases the quantity of starch converted to sugar. Parsnip 'wine' is sometimes made in Britain.

Origin, distribution and cultivation: Wild Parsnip, sometimes classed as ssp. *sylvestris*, is a common plant of roadsides, waste lands, etc., especially on calcareous soils throughout southern and central Europe, and occurs as an introduced species in the same situations in Britain and northern Europe. It has been cultivated for food at least since Roman times, but superior forms were probably only developed after the Middle Ages.

Although Parsnip has a higher nutritive value than most other fodder roots, cultivation for that purpose has likewise declined because of the cost of harvesting and storage. It is still grown throughout Europe, in home-gardens, market-gardens and as a field crop, but principally as a winter vegetable of minor importance. The roots are widely available from British grocers and in northern Europe, but are much less popular in France and in southern Europe.

Similar plants: See key (p. 249 and ff.). The characteristic scent distinguishes the root from other white roots such as fodder Carrots, Hamburg Parsley, etc.

Apium graveolens
CELERY and CELERIAC
(p. 184)

Description: Wild Celery is a hairless biennial 40–60 cm tall with hollow, grooved stems and characteristic celery scent. Lvs long-stalked, once or twice pinnate, shiny, yellow-green, with large coarsely-toothed leaflets; second-year plants with tall branching stems bearing numerous short-stalked terminal and axillary umbels. Fls greenish-white. Frt 1.5 mm long, ovoid, each carpel (including edges) with 5 entire longitudinal ridges, with celery scent.

The cultivated forms belong to two distinct subspecies:

var. *dulce*, cultivated **Celery**, is basically similar to wild Celery but is a larger plant with greatly enlarged lf-stalks thickened at base, semi-circular in section and conspicuously ridged on outer face, and blanched. A number of different cvs exist which can be grouped into two main categories: Winter Celery, which provides the bulk of the commercial crop, requires blanching by earthing up the lf-stalks in the latter part of growth. Without this, the stalks become green and bitter. The stalks are usually white, but in some cvs are tinged with red or pink. Self-blanching Celery includes several cvs which do not require earthing-up to produce good-flavoured stalks; a few cvs of American origin have stalks which turn green without becoming bitter. Var. *dulce* also includes forms commonly sold in the Mediterranean countries which are green, thin-stalked and in some ways intermediate between the wild form and those commonly available in northern Europe.

var. *rapaceum*, **Celeriac**, is a very different form, not grown for the lf-stalks, which remain narrow and green, but as a root vegetable. The short stem and upper part of the root are greatly swollen, forming a globose structure ca. 8–12 cm in diameter with a gnarled or transversely wrinkled brown surface above, and giving rise to a tangle of rootlets on the lower, buried half. The flesh is white, in consistency like a soft Carrot.

Names: Wild Celery was formerly known as Smallage. Celeriac is sometimes referred to as Turnip-rooted Celery.
(**Celery**): Fr.: Céleri; It.: Sedano; Sp.: Apio; Ger.: Sellerie; Dtch.: Sederij; Dan.: Sellerie; Gr.: Sélino; Russ.: Selderei; Yug.: Celer.
(**Celeriac**): Fr.: Céleri-rave; It.: Sedano rapa; Sp.: Apio nabo; Ger.: Knollensellerie; Dtch.: Knolselderij; Dan.: Knoldesellerie; Gr.: Rapanosélino.

Uses: Wild Celery or Smallage has been used since classical times as a pot-herb, but it is mildly poisonous unless cooked, and is too strong in flavour to be used as a vegetable. Cultivated Celery is sometimes eaten raw as a salad plant but is rather indigestible. Its principal culinary value is as a flavouring in soup, stews, or in braised meat or vegetable dishes. In Britain and northern Europe only the large, blander 'salad' types are available, but in the Mediterranean countries smaller green and bitter plants are often used.

Celeriac is best eaten as a salad, grated and dressed with mayonnaise, but may also be boiled, as a vegetable on its own or in stews, soups, etc.

Celery seeds may also be used as a flavouring agent, and dehydrated salt flavoured with celery is a common commercial condiment.

Origin, distribution and cultivation: Wild Celery occurs in most of Europe including the British Isles in brackish marshes, by tidal waters and near the sea. Cultivated Celery, obtained by selecting types with fleshier, less bitter stalks, was first developed in Italy and reached France in the 17th century, but remained almost unknown in Britain until the 19th century. Though thought to have been developed later, Celeriac has long been a popular winter vegetable on the continent, but has only become widely available in Britain in recent years.

Commercial cultivation of Celery is largely confined to areas such as fenlands where the soil is suitably rich and moist. Winter Celery is planted in trenches which are later earthed up around the growing stalks; in home-gardens paper or other materials may be wrapped around the stalks to blanch them. Even Self-blanching Celery requires some protection from light; this is usually achieved by planting densely, and screening the peripheral plants with boards. Celeriac is grown in similar soils, but in the open.

Similar plants: See key (p. 249 and ff.).

Foeniculum vulgare
FENNEL
(p. 184)

Description: An erect hardy perennial-grown as an annual or biennial. Four forms of this species, falling into 3 varieties, are cultivated in Europe.
Wild Fennel A large hairless plant with solid stems growing up to 2 m in height. Lvs repeatedly pinnate, the segments 1–5 cm long, thread-like, waxy, dark green, not in the same plane; fls bright yellow, 1–2 mm across, in fairly numerous terminal and axillary many-rayed umbels 4–10 cm wide, without bracts or bracteoles. Frt ca. 4 mm long, oblong-ovate, flattened, greenish or greyish, often darker between the prominent ridges, without lateral wings, rather bitter to the taste.
Sweet Fennel (var. *dulce*): The form of this plant that is grown for seed has the same structure as Wild Fennel but the frts are generally larger. It is easily distinguished from Wild Fennel by the aniseed scent of both lvs

and frts. Sweet Fennel contains the essential oil, anethol, which is lacking in the latter, and the frt is not bitter.

Florence Fennel also belongs to var. *dulce.* It has shorter basal lvs which are greatly swollen at bases, forming a sort of false bulb the size of a large Apple, which is blanched by earthing up.

Carosella (var. *piperatum*) is a larger plant than Wild or Sweet Fennel, with very long lf sheaths which envelop the flowering stalks.

Names: Fr.: Fenouil; It.: Finocchio; Sp.: Hinojo; Ger.: Fenchel; Dtch.: Venkel; Dan.: Fennikel; Gr.: Máratho; Russ.: Fenkhel; Yug.: Komorač.

Uses: Both Wild and the standard form of Sweet Fennel are cultivated primarily for the 'seeds' (frts) which have a wide use as a culinary flavouring, but in Europe they are particularly associated with fish dishes, in marinades, court-bouillons, sauces or stuffings. The frts (of Sweet Fennel) are offered after meals in Indian restaurants to be chewed as a digestive and breath freshener. Fennel stems and lvs, fresh or dried, are also used as a herb for flavouring dishes, and Fennel is used in the preparation of various liqueurs.

The delicate aniseed-flavoured leaf-base 'bulb' of Florence Fennel is used as a vegetable to be eaten raw in salads or cooked, au gratin, braised, or otherwise. Carosella, also called Cartucci is rarely seen outside central and southern Italy. The tender flowering stems, naturally blanched by the enveloping sheaths, are usually served as an hors d'oeuvre.

Origin, distribution and cultivation: Wild Fennel is a native of the Mediterranean region where it has been harvested in the wild and cultivated since very early times, and spread and became naturalised in most of Europe. In Britain it is common on the coasts of England and Wales, and inland on bare waste ground. Wild Fennel is the form mainly cultivated in central and eastern Europe, while Sweet Fennel is grown on a large scale in France, Italy, Greece and Turkey. Much of the seed of European commerce comes from India, which exports up to 2000 tons annually. Both these forms are grown as a field crop. The development of Sweet Fennel and of the vegetable forms is due entirely to the Italians. Florence Fennel, which demands careful husbandry, is now produced by market-gardeners in France, Holland, etc., but the bulk of the crop still comes from Italy. Although Carosella is much easier to cultivate than Florence Fennel, production is mostly confined to Italy, particularly Naples.

Similar plants: Florence Fennel and Carosella are distinctive. The standard forms of Fennel closely resemble Dill (see key p. 249 and ff. and descriptions), but are a paler, yellowish green.

Anethum graveolens
DILL

(p. 184)

Description: Very similar in appearance and structure to Fennel (above), but Dill is an annual plant. When mature usually smaller than Fennel, 60–100 cm high, with hollow stems and darker, blue-green foliage. The frts are more flattened, broader because the edges are winged, and the scent of each is distinctive.

Names: Dill is sometimes known as Russian Fennel.

Fr.: Aneth, Fenouil bâtard; It.: Aneto; Sp.: Eneldo; Ger.: Dill; Dtch.: Dille; Dan.: Dild; Gr.: Anithon; Russ.: Ukrop ogorodni; Yug.: Koper.

Uses: Both the lvs and the frt, which have quite different properties, are used as flavourings. In Britain the best known use is in pickled cucumbers, but both have many other uses as a culinary herb. Although the plant is widespread in the Mediterranean, it is made little use of there, except in Greece, but it is very popular in Scandinavia, where it is used especially with fish, and in Germany, eastern Europe and in the Soviet Union. The frts or 'seeds' are rather bitter, reminiscent of Caraway because they contain a certain amount or the same essential oil, carvone, and are used as a condiment in the same way, in bread, etc., especially in central and eastern Europe.

Origin, distribution and cultivation: Dill, a native of southern Europe and western Asia where it is a frequent weed of arable and waste land, has spread as an escape from cultivation to most of the rest of Europe, including Britain and Scandinavia, probably in medieval times. Today it is cultivated on a commercial scale in the countries in which it is most used (see above), but only infrequently in Britain, France and south-west Europe.

Similar plants: Fennel (see above).

Levisticum officinale
LOVAGE
(p. 186)

Description: A stout strongly aromatic perennial with a rosette of lvs growing to 1 m or more and a flowering stem to over 2 m. Stems hollow, grooved, with scale-like remains of lf-stalks at base. Lvs twice, sometimes 3-pinnate, with diamond-shaped leaflets deeply toothed in upper half, entire at base, shiny. Umbels dense, compound, of 12–20 stout rays, with numerous reflexed bracts and many bracteoles. Fls yellowish. Frt 5–7 mm long, broadly elliptic, with all 10 ridges narrowly winged. Cultivated plants do not differ from the wild form.

Names: Syn.: *Ligusticum officinale.* Fr.: Livèche; It.: Levistico; Sp.: Apio de montana; Ger.: Liebstökel, Badekraut; Dtch.: Lavas; Dan.: Løvstikke; Gr.: Lóva; Russ.: Lyubistik.

Uses: Lovage is an old pot-herb with a strong celery-like flavour which may be either boiled or braised like Celery, or used in soups and stews. It can also be used, in moderation, to flavour salads. The young stems are sometimes candied, like those of Angelica.

Origin, distribution and cultivation: Lovage is a mountain plant which grows in moist meadows at medium altitudes. It is native to S.W. Asia and perhaps also in the Mediterranean, and has spread to most of the mountain ranges of south and central Europe, northwards to the Vosges, Germany and Scandinavia, but not Britain. It was formerly widely cultivated in kitchen gardens in Britain and throughout its range, but is now rarely seen, although fresh plants grown on allotments are still sometimes offered for sale on markets in central and southern Europe.

Similar plants: See key (p. 249 and ff.). Black Lovage is a different species, Alexanders *Smyrnium olusatrum.* Scot's Lovage *Ligusticum scoticum* is a maritime plant of the North Sea and north Atlantic coasts which was formerly gathered in the wild and cultivated in kitchen gardens in those areas as a vegetable. It is a medium to tall plant with celery-scented stems rather swollen at bases and often flushed with pink or purple, twice trifoliate lvs with broad glossy toothed leaflets and white fls.

Natural distribution of Angelica

Angelica archangelica
ANGELICA
(p. 186)

Description: A large almost hairless annual, biennial or triennial herb growing to 2 m in height. Stems very stout, hollow, finely ribbed, downy only near base, green. Lvs 30–70 cm long, 2- or 3-pinnate, the leaflets 3–10 cm long, ovate, sharply toothed, on broad, hollow lf-stalks which are deeply furrowed on upper side, with broad inflated sheathing bases; upper lvs forming simple sheaths around umbels: umbels terminal and axillary, 4–15 cm in diameter, with many stout rays. Fls ca. 2 mm in diameter, greenish or yellowish white, with sepals and petals. Frt

5–7 mm long, ovate, much flattened, with corky lateral wings.

Names: Fr.: Angélique; It.: Angelica; Sp.: Angelica; Ger.: Englewurz, Brustwurz; Dtch.: Engelwortel; Dan.: Kvan; Gr.: Aggeliki; Russ.: Dudnik.

Uses: The best known use of Angelica is in the form of the candied green stems used as a sweetmeat and for decorating cakes and confectionery. The lvs are used to a small extent for flavouring fish and stews, the young fresh stems may be used for flavouring marmalade or acid frt desserts, or blanched and added to salads. In Scandinavia, Finland and the Faroe Islands the whole plant is eaten as a cooked vegetable. The roots are used in the distillation of some gins, and the seeds in certain liqueurs.

Origin, distribution and cultivation: Angelica has the typical boreo-alpine distribution of species which ranged over the whole of Europe during the last glacial age and is now confined to the colder parts. Angelica occurs from Iceland through Scandinavia, including Lapland, to central Russia, and further south in the mountain ranges, from the Pyrennees eastwards to Syria. It is also found as an old escape from cultivation in many other parts, including Britain. Angelica was probably gathered in the wild in Scandinavia, Russia, etc. since prehistoric times, but does not seem to have been cultivated until the Renaissance. Despite its range of uses it is of slight economic importance and is only cultivated in a few places, mainly in France and Germany.

Similar plants: See key (p. 249 and ff.). Wild Angelica *A. sylvestris*, a much commoner plant in Britain, is less robust, has stems tinged with purple, fls without a calyx, and is much less aromatic.

Myrrhis odorata
SWEET CICELY
(p. 186)

Description: A perennial herb growing to 1 m or more, rather bushy in habit, with hollow, more or less downy stems and lvs. Lvs 2- to 3-pinnate, fern-like, up to 30 cm long, often blotched with white at base. Fls white, in loose umbels with ca. 8–12 long rays. Frt spindle-shaped, very large (25 x 8–10 mm), sharply ridged, with a terminal beak.

Names: Fr.: Cerfeuil d'Espagne; It.: Mirride odorosa; Sp.: Perifollo; Ger.: Englischer (Spanischer) Kerble; Dtch.: Roomse kervel; Dan.: Sodskaerm.

Uses: An old-fashioned herb with a characteristic scent of aniseed/liquorice used mainly in sweet dishes and for flavouring liqueurs. The roots are sometimes eaten after boiling, as a salad ingredient.

Origin, distribution and cultivation: Sweet Cicely is probably a native of mountain areas of central and southern Europe, but it is well naturalised in lowland areas of most of central and northern Europe. In Britain it is commonest in northern England and southern Scotland. It was formerly widely cultivated in kitchen gardens but is now obsolete.

Similar plants: See key (p. 249 and ff.). Sweet Cicely is similar to the very common Cow Parsley *Anthriscus sylvestris*, from which it is easily distinguished by the aromatic scent when lvs are crushed; it is a bushier plant than Cow Parsley, has hollow stems, and quite different frt (short and covered with spines in Cow Parsley).

Petroselinum crispum
PARSLEY
(p. 182)

Description: The standard plant is an erect hairless biennial or short-lived perennial 30–70 cm tall with a thick tap-root and a rosette of long 3-pinnate lvs. Lvs triangular in outline, the leaflets 1–2 cm long, roughly diamond-shaped, coarsely toothed at apex, more or less tightly crisped and curled in 'curled' varieties. Fls 2 mm across, yellowish, in flat-topped umbels (2–5 cm in diameter) of many rays and bracts and bracteoles. Frt 2.5 mm long, ovate, slightly flattened, finely ridged. All parts with familiar Parsley scent.

Three main forms of Parsley are cultivated:

Curled Parsley the commonest, is a more compact plant with shorter lf-stalks and smaller leaflets.

Uncurled Parsley Larger plants with longer lf-stalks and larger, broad leaflets. Sheep's Parsley is the name given in Britain to a form which is feebly aromatic and therefore unsuitable as a culinary herb, but useful as a fodder or forage plant. Continental Parsley is the English name given to plants of similar structure which are often more aromatic than curled forms, and common on the continent. Naples Parsley is a particularly large variety of Uncurled Parsley.

Hamburg Parsley is a distinct form (var. *tuberosum*), similar in structure to the Uncurled Parsleys, but with a large swollen taproot resembling a small turnip.

Names: Syns.: *P. hortense*, *P. sativum*, *Carum petroselinum.* Hamburg Parsley is also known as Turnip-rooted Parsley or Thell.
Fr.: Persil; It.: Prezzemolo; Sp.: Perejil; Ger.: Persil; Dtch.: Petersilie; Dan.: Krupersille, Persille; Gr.: Maïdanos; Russ.: Petrushka; Yug.: Petersilj.

Uses: Parsley is the most important kitchen herb grown in Europe, with uses too many to mention. Used as a fresh herb the lvs should be finely chopped, or the whole lvs added to stews, etc. during cooking. They are usually combined with other herbs in a *bouquet garni.* Curled Parsley is often used merely as a garnish, in the same way that butchers landscape their displays of raw meat with hedgerows and copses of the herb. It is often assumed that uncurled varieties are superior in flavour to the curled cvs; this is certainly often true in Britain when imported Continental Parsleys, grown in more favourable climates, are compared with locally-grown crisped cvs selected more for appearance than for taste; but the flavour depends more on strains, climate and soils than on lf shape.

Hamburg Parsley is a garden root vegetable which is boiled or included in stews. Sheep's Parsley is sometimes included in seed mixtures for fodder and forage leys.

Origin, distribution and cultivation: Parsley is a native of southern Europe. It was used by the ancient Greeks and Romans, and is now naturalised in the whole of Europe and in most temperate countries of other continents. It is widely grown in home- and market-gardens throughout its range. Hamburg Parsley has been known since the 16th century but is now only grown to a small extent as a garden plant. It is occasionally offered for sale in central European markets.

Similar plants: Chervil (see key p. 249 and ff. and descriptions).

Anthriscus cerefolium
CHERVIL

(p. 182)

Description: An annual herb with hollow stems 40–70 cm tall which are finely hairy above the nodes. Lvs 3-pinnate, the leaflets pinnatifid, neatly spreading in the same plane, curly in some varieties, hairy on lower surface. Umbels compound, 2.5–5 cm in diameter, on short hairy stalks opposite lvs, without bracts; bracteoles linear, hairy. Fls ca. 2 mm across, on very short stalks, whitish. Frt 1 cm long, oblong-ovoid, smooth, with a long slender beak.

Names: Fr.: Cerfeuil; It.: Cerfoglio; Sp.: Perifolio; Ger.: Kerbel; Dtch.: Kervel; Dan.: Kørvel; Gr.: Kharéfillo; Russ.: Kupr.

Uses: A culinary herb. The flavour is less robust than that of Parsley, with a hint of aniseed and liquorice. Although little-known in Britain and many other parts of Europe, it is an important herb in France, where it is a standard ingredient of many recipes such as *sauce ravigote*, *fines herbes* for omelettes, and has all the usual uses in salads. It is not suitable for long cooking, but is chopped and added to soups and other dishes just before serving.

Origin, distribution and cultivation: Chervil is a native of south Russia, the Caucasus and Asia Minor. It was spread in Europe by the Romans who used it extensively and is now naturalised in most of Europe, including Britain. Commercial cultivation is rare outside France and to a lesser extent Belgium, the Netherlands and Switzerland. Elsewhere it is an infrequent kitchen-garden plant.

Similar plants: Garden Chervil should not be confused with several wild spp. also called 'Chervils'. It is similar to Cow Parsley *A. sylvestris*, but is a smaller plant with umbels opposite lvs, less elongate leaflets, narrower, long-beaked frts and quite different scent. See also Sweet Cicely (p. 257) which has a much stronger aniseed scent, and Parsley and Turnip-rooted Chervil (pp. 257 and 258).

Chaerophyllum bulbosum
TURNIP-ROOTED CHERVIL

Description: A biennial, similar in appearance to Chervil but with lvs usually more deeply toothed, terminal umbels which are larger and looser, and frts 6 mm long, spindle-shaped, ridged and unbeaked. It is immediately recognisable by the large (12–15 cm long) grey to almost black tuberous root with yellowish flesh.

Names: Fr.: Cerfeuil bulbeux; It.: Cerfoglio bulboso; Sp.: Perifolio tuberoso; Ger.: Kerbelrübe; Dan.: Rod-kørvel; Gr.: Goggúlio kharefillo; Russ.: Buten lukovichi.

Uses: Grown only for the succulent root which is used as a cooked vegetable.

Origin, distribution and cultivation: Turnip-rooted Chervil is a native of southern Europe which spread in cultivation, probably in the Middle Ages, and has become naturalised in much of central and northern Europe, including Britain. It is only cultivated to a very small extent by home-gardeners, and the roots are not to be found in commerce.

Similar plants: Chervil (above). *C. bulbosum* more closely resembles Wild or Rough Chervil *C. temulentum*.

Coriandrum sativum
CORIANDER
(p. 186)

Description: A rather weak-stemmed hairless annual growing to about 60 cm in height. All parts of the plant with a strong foetid scent reminiscent of bed- or shield-bugs when crushed. Lvs of 2 types: the lower with broad leaflets similar to those of Uncurled Parsley, the upper divided into narrow linear segments. Fls small, white or pink, in small loose umbels, the inner fls smaller, sterile, the outer with longer petals and are fertile. Frts globose, ca. 3 mm in diameter, ribbed, yellowish-brown, containing 2 seeds.

Names: The name Coriandrum, used by Pliny, is derived from the Greek for a bug, and refers to the foetid odour described above.
Fr.: Coriandre; It.: Coriandorlo; Sp.: Coriandro; Ger.: Koriander; Dtch.: Koriander; Dan.: Koriander; Gr.: Koriandros; Russ.: Kishnets posevnoy.

Uses: Coriander is cultivated for two distinct products.

In Europe, with the exception of the Balkans, it has been grown almost exclusively for the frts ('seeds') which when dried lose the plant's characteristic odour, leaving a mild, sweet aromatic flavour with a hint of orange peel. They are ground and used as a spice in curries, meat dishes, in most 'à la grecque' dishes, and in bread, especially in Eastern Europe and the Balkans. In Britain and Western Europe Coriander is little-used except as a pickling spice, but it is indispensable for anyone interested in Indian or Levantine cooking. Coriander seeds are also used for the production of the essential oil, obtained by steam distillation and used in the manufacture of condiments, in liqueurs, vermouths and in baking.

The leaves, with their strong bug-like scent, are used as a fresh culinary herb in all 'eastern' cooking, from Morocco through the Middle East (by extension including Greece, Turkey, etc.) and southern Asia to China and Japan, perhaps even more widely than is Parsley in Europe. Western Europeans, with the exception of converts to Asian cooking, remain prejudiced against this herb, and some genuinely dislike its distinct, rather metallic flavour, but fresh plants, usually imported, are increasingly available from luxury and foreign grocers, even in Britain.

They are used either to flavour dishes during cooking, or coarsely chopped and sprinkled over salads, soups and many other dishes before serving.

Origin, distribution and cultivation: Coriander is probably a native of the eastern Mediterranean, where it was used by the ancient Greeks. It spread to India and from there to China in early times. The Romans, who cultivated it extensively, are probably responsible for its introduction to north-west Europe, including Britain, where it was commonly used until the 16th century and still occurs in the wild. Though the plant is hardy and easy to grow it is rarely cultivated in western Europe except by a few amateurs, but it may be seen in large market-garden plots and even on a field scale in North Africa, Hungary, the Balkans and Russia.

Similar plants: Plants picked before the upper feathery foliage develops resemble Uncurled Parsley, but the respective scent of each is distinct. The (more usual) presence of both types of lf on the stalks, and sometimes of the small pinkish fls make Coriander unmistakeable.

Carum carvi
CARAWAY
(p. 186)

Description: A biennial much-branched herb 30–80 cm in height, with narrow, finely grooved leafy stems. Lvs usually 2- but up to 5-pinnate, the leaflets linear-lanceolate to linear, 5–25 mm long. Umbels compound, 2–4 cm in diameter, with 5–16 unequal rays 5–30 mm long; bracts and bracteoles 1 or absent. Fls 2–3 mm across, the outer ones larger than inner ones, white. Frts 3–6 mm long, oblong, light brown with pale ridges and characteristic strong when rubbed.

Names: Fr.: Carvi; It.: Carvi; Sp.: Alcaravea; Ger.: Kümmel; Dtch.: Karwij; Dan.: Kommen; Gr.: Karos; Russ.: Tmin; Yug.: Kumina.

Uses: Caraway is cultivated for the frts used as a flavouring and spice. It is particularly associated with Germany, Austria and neighbouring central European countries, where it is used to flavour bread, biscuits, cakes, cheese, etc., and as a spice in meat dishes, sausages and sauerkraut. It is also the basic flavour of the liqueur *kümmel.*

The young lvs may be used in salads, and the thick tap-root eaten as a vegetable, like parsnips.

The seeds should not be used as a substitute for Cumin. 'Caraway' in many recipes in Indian and Middle Eastern dishes is nearly always a mistranslation for Cumin, and the latter should be used in such cases.

Origin, distribution and cultivation: Caraway occurs in the wild throughout northern and central Europe (but only as a naturalised sp. in Britain), eastwards to central Asia, and in the south reaching the Mediterranean. Although it grows in Morocco where it was probably introduced by the Romans, it is absent from southern Italy and Greece. It has been cultivated since classical times, and today is mainly grown in the Netherlands, Germany, Hungary, Czechoslovakia and the Soviet Union, and to a lesser extent in Scandinavia and the rest of Europe excluding the Mediterranean countries.

Similar plants: Cumin (see descriptions and key p. 251) is often confused with Caraway. The respective flavours are distinct, and the geographical ranges of each scarcely overlap in Europe.

Cuminum cyminum
CUMIN
(p. 186)

Description: Similar to Caraway (above) but the plant is an annual, smaller, not or little over 30 cm in height, and tends to sprawl due to its thin weak stems. Lvs are sparser, bluish-green, the segments linear, averagely finer. Fls in small umbels of fewer rays, white or pink; frts greyish-green to dark grey, larger (4–8 mm long) than Caraway, with pale ridges, strongly scented, less sweet and more pungent than Caraway.

Names: Fr.: Cumin; It.: Cumino; Sp.: Comino; Ger.: Kreutzkümmel; Dtch.:

Komijn; Dan.: Spidskommen; Gr.: Kyminon; Russ.: Kmin; Yug.: Kumina.

Uses: Although Cumin has been used as a Caraway substitute in Europe, for pickling, flavouring sauerkraut and such purposes, its stronger, sharper flavour makes it unsuitable for bakery or sweet dishes. Anyone familiar with Indian, Middle Eastern or Arab cooking will immediately recognise Cumin as one of the most pervasive aromas of those countries. It is used in a great variety of different dishes, either freshly ground, or the whole seeds roasted or fried, and is an essential ingredient of curry powders. In Europe its traditional uses are mostly confined to those areas which have been influenced by Turkish or Arab cooking.

Origin, distribution and cultivation: Cumin is a native of Turkestan. Its natural range either also extended to the eastern Mediterranean, or it was brought there at a very early date, for it was cultivated in Greece and the Levant in classical times. Its spread to North Africa, which with India is one of the areas of major production, was probably due to the Arabs. In Europe, Malta, Sicily, Greece, Turkey and Cyprus are the main growers while wild plants in most of the Mediterranean attest to areas of former cultivation. It was also grown in the past in central Europe, where hot summers allowed. Today nearly all the seed of commerce is imported, mainly from India.

Similar plants: Caraway (above). The confusion between these two plants has entered many popular books in which Cumin is attributed with the uses and geographical distribution of Caraway.

'Black Cumin' is a term used to designate the darker-seeded varieties of Cumin, and also *Nigella* (p. 120), a plant belonging to the buttercup family.

Pimpinella anisum
ANISE
(p. 186)

Description: An annual with erect branching ribbed stems 60–70 cm in height, sometimes growing to 1 m or more. Lower lvs on long stalks, simple, broadly ovate or heart-shaped, coarsely toothed; upper lvs once pinnate, the narrow, often linear lobes more or less ternately or pinnately lobed. Umbels convex, with ca. 10 rays. Fls small, white. Frt globose to ovoid, brown with paler ribs.

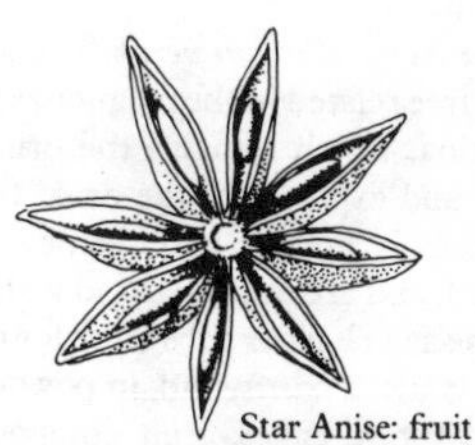
Star Anise: fruit

Names: The frt is commonly known as Aniseed.
Fr.: Anis; It.: Anice; Sp.: Anis, Matalahuva; Ger.: Anis; Dtch.: Anijs; Dan.: Anis; Gr.: Glikanison, Anithon; Russ.: Anis; Yug.: Anis.

Uses: Anis is cultivated for the frts which are rich in the essential oil anethol, which is found in lesser concentration in Sweet Fennel and some other plants. The frts are used in much Indian cooking, and are chewed, like Fennel seeds, after meals. In Europe they only have a limited culinary use, but the oil, obtained by maceration in alcohol or by steam distillation, is used in perfumery, for flavouring confectioneries, and above all as the basic flavour of those southern European drinks which turn cloudy with the addition of water: French *pastis* (*Pernod*, *Ricard*, *Berger*), Greek *ouzo*, Turkish and Levantine *raki* or *arrak*, etc., and the liqueurs called *anisette.* These drinks are in turn used as a flavouring in cooking, especially in France and in Spain.

Origin, distribution and cultivation: Anise is a native of the Near East and was used by the ancient Egyptians, Greeks and Romans. Cultivation spread in the Middle Ages to most of Europe, including Britain, where it is no longer grown because the plants will only fruit in exceptionally warm summers. Commercial production exists in all the Mediterranean countries, and in most of central Europe, from Belgium and France eastwards to the Soviet Union. Because it has little domestic use it is mostly grown on a field scale.

Similar plants: The simple basal lvs distinguish Anise from the other cultivated umbellifers.

Star Anise *Illicium verum* is a small evergreen tree related to the magnolias and native to China, which remains the principal producer and exporter of the dried frts. These, surprisingly, are rich in the same essential oil, anethol, and are imported and widely used in Europe as a cheaper substitute for true Anise, for flavouring *pastis*, and, in powder form, in sweet dishes, cakes, fruit compotes, etc. It is an important article in Chinese cooking in which it is used mainly in pork and duck recipes, and often enters the composition of soy sauces.

The frt is unmistakeable: a star-shaped woody structure about 3 cm across with 7 to 9 radiating beak-shaped carpels gaping on the upper side; each contains a shiny brown ovate flattened seed.

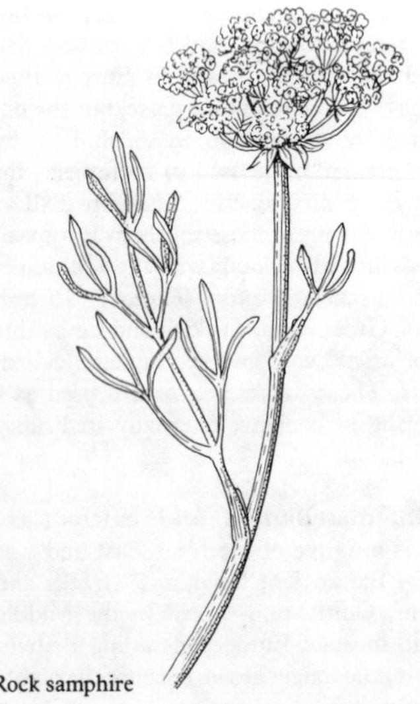

Rock samphire

Crithmum maritimum

SAMPHIRE

Description: A fleshy spreading perennial standing up to 30 cm, with solid ridged stems. Lvs 2- to 3-pinnate, with rounded fleshy segments similar in appearance to the stems. Umbels 3–6 cm across, many rayed, with many narrow bracts and bracteoles. Fls 2 mm across, greenish-yellow. Frt 6 mm long, ovate, purplish, with thick ridges.

Names: Often called Rock Samphire, referring to its habitat, in order to distinguish it from Marsh Samphire (*Salicornia* spp.). Fr.: Fenouil de mer; It.: Finocchio marino; Sp.: Hinojo marino; Ger.: Meerfenchel; Dtch.: Zeevenkel; Dan.: Stranddild.

Uses: Samphire is strongly aromatic and salty; it is usually pickled for use as a savoury, and sometimes eaten cooked in butter as a vegetable.

Origin, distribution and cultivation: Samphire occurs on sea cliffs, rocks and shingle on the Channel, Atlantic and Mediterranean coasts. It has never been cultivated except by a few amateur enthusiasts, and has scarcely any commercial value, but it is still sometimes gathered in England, and can be found, either fresh or pickled, on southern European markets, especially in Spain.

Similar plants: See Marsh Samphire (p. 245).

VALERIANACEAE

Valerian Family

A small family of herbs with opposite lvs, without stipules, and small fls in heads or umbel-like cymes. It takes its name from Valerian *Valeriana officinalis*, a tall (up to 130 cm) perennial with pinnate lvs up to 20 cm long and terminal umbel-like heads of small pinkish-white fls which recall the previous family, the Umbellifers. Valerian is cultivated to a small extent in the Netherlands, Belgium, Germany and eastern Europe purely as a medicinal plant; the parts gathered are the roots and rhizomes which contain an essential oil with mildly sedative properties.

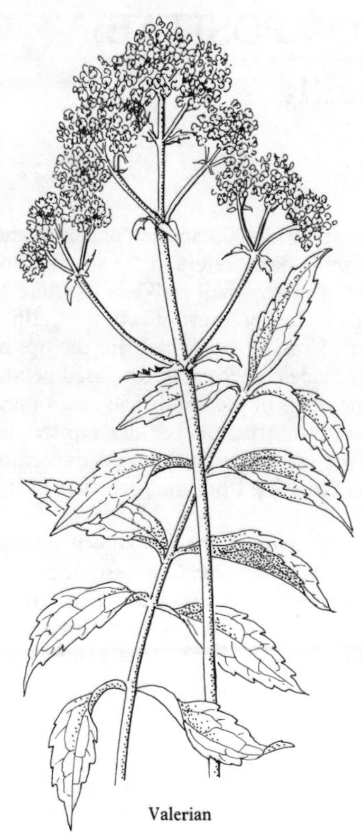

Valerian

Valerianella locusta agg.
CORNSALAD

(p. 188)

Description: The mature plant with flowering stems is a slender annual, not or slightly hairy, growing up to 30 cm in height, with branching stems (habit depends on soil fertility, water, and density of planting). Lvs blunt, more or less broadly obovate or spoon-shaped, the basal lvs untoothed, those on upper parts of stems narrow, with a few irregular teeth. Fls in terminal heads 1–2 cm across, blue or pale mauve, with 5 lobes and 3 stamens; frt a small (1–2.5 mm long) nutlet.

The wild spp. which comprise this aggregate (*V. locusta*, *V. eriocarpa* (Italian Cornsalad), *V. dentata*, *V. carinata*, *V. rimosa* and perhaps others) are identifiable by the structure of the frts. *V. locusta* has the largest frt, 2.5 x 2 mm, moderately flattened and distinguished from all but *V. carinata* by the minute, scarcely visible persistent calyx (conspicuous in other spp.). *V. eriocarpa* has small (1.2 x 0.8) hairy frts with long (1 mm) calyx teeth.

The cultivated varieties are roughly divided between large 'seeded' forms (cf. *V. locusta*) and small-seeded ones which may be Italian Cornsalad or hybrids involving these two and other spp.

The plant is usually seen as a rosette of basal lvs, for it is pulled before the flowering stems develop.

Names: Syn.: *V. olitoria.* Also known in English as Lamb's Lettuce.
Fr.: Mâche; It.: Erba riccia; Sp.: Lechuga de campo; Ger.: Feldsalat; Dtch.: Veldsla; Dan.: Vårsalat; Gr.: Nardidion; Russ.: Valeriana kolosovia; Yug.: Motovilec.

Uses: A fine-flavoured salad plant. It is little-known in Britain, but is one of the most prized and expensive winter salads on the continent, particularly in France, the Low Countries, and Italy, where it is widely available from grocers.

Origin, distribution and cultivation: *V. locusta* is recorded in the wild from the whole of Europe up to 60° N. *V. eriocarpa* is a more southern species which has become naturalised further north, including Britain. Cornsalads have been gathered in the wild at least since Roman times; the cultivated forms evolved from kitchen-garden plants and were developed mainly in the 19th century. Today they are widely grown on the continent.

Similar plants: Young plants resemble Lettuce seedlings.

ASTERACEAE (COMPOSITAE)

Daisy Family

The largest family of flowering plants with about 20,000 species of herbs and (especially in the tropics) shrubs. The older family name refers to the structure of the inflorescences which are heads composed of many small stalkless fls (florets) attached to a flat or rounded disc (the receptacle). The florets are of two types, either tubular, more or less symmetrical, tipped with 5 small teeth which are the tips of fused petals, or strap-shaped, with a long flat blade composed of the fused petals, extending out to one side of the floret. The members of the family can be grouped according to whether all the florets are tubular (as in Artichoke) or all strap-shaped (Dandelion, Lettuce), or composed of both types, with tubular florets in the centre of the head and the strap-shaped (ray) florets radiating from the perimeter of the head (Chrysanthemum).

Naturally, many composites are cultivated for ornament, the best known of these belonging to the genera *Dahlia*, *Zinnia*, *Aster*, *Chrysanthemum*, *Cosmos* and *Senecio*, but relatively very few are economic. More surprisingly, in view of the vast distribution and number of species in the world, nearly all the useful species are from temperate Eurasia, the only exclusively tropical crop of any importance being Niger *Guizotia abyssinica* grown in Ethiopia and India as an oil seed plant.

Artemisia dracunculus
TARRAGON

(p. 192)

Description: A perennial herb with a rhizome and erect leafy stems ca. 60 cm in height, or taller if allowed to grow naturally. Lvs alternate, willow-like, linear-lanceolate, light green, 2–4 cm long. Fl-heads small, yellow, globose, without ray florets, numerous in loose terminal panicles. Frt a cylindrical achene without a ring of hairs or scales around the tip. Scent characteristic, unlike any other herb.

Names: *A. dracunculus* is often called French or German Tarragon in order to distinguish it from Russian Tarragon (*A. dracunculoides*).
Fr.: Estragon; It.: Dragoncello; Sp.: Estragon; Ger.: Estragon; Dtch.: Dragon; Dan.: Esdragon; Gr.: Trakhoúri; Russ.: Estragon.

Uses: A valuable and highly individual culinary herb. Tarragon vinegar, made by macerating fresh lvs in white wine vinegar, is widely used for salads, and is an ingredient of the Bordeaux types of mustard and of *sauce tartare.* The French have made the greatest use of this herb in such inventions as *sauce bearnaise*, chicken *à l'estragon*, etc. and by introducing it to many sauces (*verte, ravigote*), *fines herbes* mixtures for omelette, and butter and cream dishes. Because the supply is irregular (only occasional in Britain) much of the commercial crop is dried.

Origin, distribution and cultivation: The natural distribution of Tarragon extends from south-east Europe across north-central Asia to North America. It was used by the ancient Greeks, and spread westwards through Italy at an undetermined period. Today it is cultivated mainly in western Europe, especially in the Netherlands, France, Germany and Italy, and to a smaller extent in Britain and C. Europe. Since plants rarely set seed in cultivation, propagation is by cuttings or division of rootstock, so it is not a field crop, but grown for home use and in market-garden strips. The leafy stems are picked before the fls develop.

Similar plants: Russian Tarragon *A. dracunculoides* is an inferior substitute for Tarragon native to west and central Asia. It has paler, less smooth lvs and a more pungent but less sweetly aromatic taste. As it readily sets seed it is easier to cultivate, and is often sold under the guise of Tarragon on continental markets.

The simple lvs distinguish these two from other *Artemisia* spp.

Artemisia absinthium
WORMWOOD

(p. 192)

Description: An erect very aromatic perennial herb 30–100 cm tall with furrowed angled stems. Lvs alternate, finely divided into narrow, flat linear-lanceolate blunt segments which are silky-hairy above and below, therefore uniformly silvery-green. Fl heads cup-shaped, 3–4 mm across, pendulous, with blunt silky-hairy bracts and yellow fls without ray florets. Frt an achene similar to that of Tarragon.

Names: Fr.: Absinthe; It.: Assenzio; Sp.: Ajenjo; Ger.: Wermut; Dtch.: Alsem; Dan.: Havemalurt; Gr.: Agriapsidiá; Russ.: Poli gorkaya; Yug.: Pelin, Gorčina.

Uses: Wormwood was traditionally used all over Europe as a vermifuge (hence the name) and to cure various gastric disorders, and the essential oil, obtained by steam distillation, is still used in various pharmaceutical products. The medicinal uses are the origin of its introduction to alcoholic drinks, either as a flavouring, by steeping a sprig in a bottle of spirits, or in much greater concentration by using the essential oil. Vermouth, which takes its name from Wormwood via the German Wermut, was flavoured with this plant until its use was made illegal. While lvs used as a flavouring are harmless, in concentrated form Wormwood is a powerful addictive poison producing stimulant and euphoric effects independent of those of the alcohol, and resulting ultimately in severe brain damage. The adverse effects went unnoticed until the end of the 19th century when a particularly strong liqueur, called simply *absinthe*, became fashionable in France. The consequences of abuse led in 1915 to its being banned by law in France, incidentally diverting attention from the effects of ordinary alcoholism and thus sparing the French wine and spirits industry at a time when movements to ban or license alcohol were sweeping other European countries.

Illegally-made *absinthe* liqueurs are still to be had in parts of southern France, Spain and Italy, and milder forms are made in central Europe.

Origin, distribution and cultivation: Wormwood has a scattered distribution, growing on rocky hillsides, road verges and waste ground in the whole of Europe, including Britain, where it is uncommon. It was cultivated on a field scale in the south of France and northern Italy until the First World War for the vermouth and liqueur manufacturers, and on a smaller scale thereafter for the pharmaceutical industry, but wild plants have generally sufficed for the limited quantities needed for either purpose.

Similar plants: The very common wild Mugwort *A. vulgaris* differs from Wormwood in that the leaflets are more pointed, white-woolly below and hairless above. Hoary Mugwort *A. stellerana* has lf-lobes densely white-felted rather than silky-hairy. These and many other *Artemisia* spp. (especially numerous in southern Europe) are not strongly aromatic, or have distinctly unpleasant odours. See also Southernwood, below.

Mugwort and other *Artemisia* spp. were formerly used as culinary herbs, and are still found occasionally on small markets, especially in Spain.

Artemisia abrotanum
SOUTHERNWOOD

(p. 192)

Description: A perennial, more compact and woody than most *Artemisia* spp., with a bitter but not unpleasant lemony scent. Foliage dense, of finely divided grey-green segments. Fls small, in loose panicles, similar in structure to the preceding.

Names: Older common English names are Lad's Love and Old Man.
Fr.: Aurone, Armoise; It.: Abrotano; Sp.: Abrotano; Ger.: Eberries; Dtch.: Citroenkruid; Dan.: Ambra; Russ.: Kustarikovaya poli.

Uses: Formerly widely used for medicinal purposes. Plants are still cultivated for a limited production of herbal tea mixtures and as one of the substitutes for Wormwood in the manufacture of vermouths and liqueurs. The lvs may be used as a culinary herb.

Origin, distribution and cultivation: Southernwood is a native of western Asia which spread in cultivation to most of Europe during the Middle Ages. It is naturalised in Spain, Italy and other Mediterranean countries, but does not set seed, and rarely even flowers in Britain and the North, where it is only grown as a garden ornamental. It is still cultivated on a field scale in southern Europe for the production of leaves and essential oil.

Similar plants: The plant's woody, shrubby nature and characteristic scent distinguish it from other cultivated *Artemisia* spp.

Southernwood is also called *citronelle* in France, a name which causes confusion with other lemon-scented spp: true Citronella *Cymbopogon nardus* (a S.E. Asian grass used for flavouring food, and available dried from Chinese grocers in Europe), Verbena, Balm *Melissa officinalis* and others.

Chamaemelum nobile
CHAMOMILE

(p. 192)

Description: A creeping downy perennial herb with stems 10–30 cm long, strongly aromatic with a scent recalling apple. Lvs 1–5 cm long, 2- or 3-pinnate, the segments short, linear. Fl heads ca. 2 cm in diameter, solitary, on short erect stems; receptable conical, solid disc florets yellow, with oblong blunt scale at base of each; ray florets white, spreading.

Cultivated plants mostly belong to var. *ligulosa*, a very distinctive form in which all the florets are white and strap-shaped, like the double varieties of ornamental chrysanthemums. Intermediary forms are common, in which secondary rows of ray florets invade the disc florets.

Names: Also known as Roman or Sweet Chamomile. Syn.: *Anthemis nobilis*
Fr.: Camomille romaine; It.: Camomilla romana; Sp.: Manzanilla romana; Ger.: Römische Kamille; Dtch.: Roomse Kamille; Russ.: Pupavka blagorodnaya.

Uses: The flower heads are picked and dried to be used medicinally, usually in the form of infusions or chamomile tea. They have mild anti-inflammatory, antiseptic and stomachic properties useful in alleviating gastric disorders, menstrual pains and insomnia. The pleasant, refreshing taste of chamomile tea ensures a continuing demand that far exceeds specific medicinal use.

Origin, distribution and cultivation: *C. nobile* occurs naturally in western Europe, from Italy and Spain northward to Belgium and southern England where it is local, and, as in central Europe, most plants are escapes from cultivation. It is sometimes grown as a lawn plant, and on the Continent is cultivated as a field crop for the pharmaceutical industry.

Similar plants: German Chamomile (below).

Matricaria recutita
WILD or GERMAN CHAMOMILE

(p. 192)

Description: An annual, similar in appearance to Chamomile but often more erect, taller (up to 50 cm), usually with sparser foliage. The ray florets bend backwards, the tubular disc florets are simple, without scales, and the conical receptacle is hollow.

Names: Also known as Scented Mayweed. Syns.: *Chamomilla recutita*, *Matricaria chamomilla.*
Fr.: Camomille commune; It.: Camomilla comune; Sp.: Manzanilla común; Ger.: Kamille; Dtch.: Kamille; Dan.: Kamille; Russ.: Romashka sodáchia.

Uses: As Chamomile (above).

Origin, distribution and cultivation: This species has a far wider natural distribution than Chamomile, extending over the whole of temperate Europe but becoming rarer in the north (Scotland, Scandinavia) and ranging well into Asia. It is cultivated on the Continent as a field crop.

Similar plants: This sp. differs most markedly from Chamomile by the structure of the fl head: hollow receptacle and absence of bracts between disc florets. Pineappleweed (*M. matricarioides*) lacks ray florets and smells of Pineapple when crushed. Other related spp. have unpleasant scents, or are scentless.

Chrysanthemum cinerarifolium
PYRETHRUM

(p. 192)

Description: A perennial herb 30–65 cm tall. Stems and lvs bluish-green with short grey hairs. Lvs alternate, pinnate, with long stalks. Fl heads ca. 4 cm in diameter, disc florets yellow, tightly packed, ca. 5 mm long; ray florets white, 1.5 cm long, about 20 in number. Frt a pale brown 5-ribbed, 1-seeded achene.

Names: Pyrethrum properly applies to the complex of active substances, pyrethrin and cinerins, also found in other plants, and not to the species, but is the name always given to this crop.
Syn.: *Pyrethrum cinerarifolium.*
Fr.: Pyrèthre; It.: Piretro (di Dalmatia); Sp.: Piretro, Pelitre; Ger.: Dalmatische insectenblüte, Mutterkraut; Dtch.: Pyrethrum; Gr.: Pairithon; Russ.: Dalmatskaya romashka, Piretrum; Yug.: Pravi buhac.

Uses: Pyrethrum is the source of a highly effective insecticide which has many advantages over synthetic organo-phosphorus or chlorinated hydrocarbon poisons including its low toxicity to man and other vertebrates, making it particularly suitable for domestic use and the protection of foodstuffs. It is contained in the fl heads which must be ground to powder after rapid drying, but is more usually marketed as a concentrated liquid extract.

Origin, distribution and cultivation: *C. cinerarifolium* is a native of the Dalmatian coast of Yugoslavia, which was the principal producer until its cultivation was established in Japan and later in E. Africa. Kenya, where plants develop a higher percentage of the active substances, remains the principal producer, while the USA is the largest importer. The smaller-scale plantations in southern France, Switzerland and other parts of southern Europe are now largely obsolete, but the increasing demand for safe insecticides may well bring about an expansion of this crop in the future.

Similar plants: Inflorescences closely resemble those of the common Ox-eye Daisy *Leucanthemum vulgare* and several other wild European chrysanthemums, but the bluish-grey colour and the shape of the lvs are characteristic.

Pyrethrum is recognised as a genus by some botanists, and includes a number of ornamentals which should not be confused with *C. cinerarifolium.*

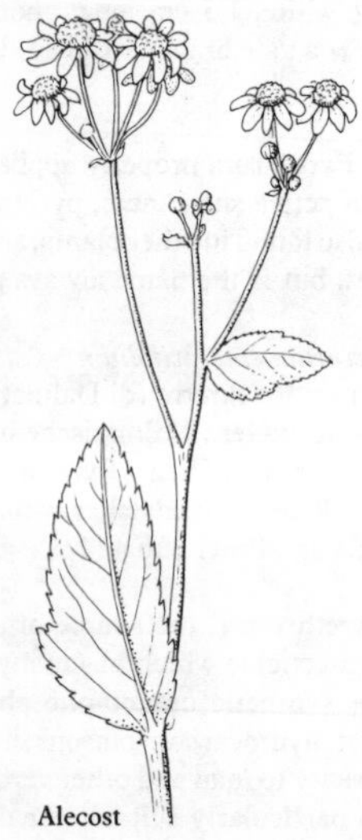

Alecost

Chrysanthemum balsamita ALECOST

Description: A perennial herb forming a clump of long-stalked ovate, simple lvs with slightly heart-shaped base and bluntly toothed margins, with blades 5–20 cm long. Flowering plants (rare in Britain and northern Europe) produce stems up to 1.2 m bearing loose clusters of fl heads 1–1.5 cm across with flat receptacle, yellow disc florets and white ray florets.

Names: Also known as Costmary, Balsam Herb, Mace, and Bibleleaf (USA).

Syn.: *Tanacetum balsamita.*
Fr.: Balsamite; Ger.: Marienblett; Dtch.: Vrouwenmunt; Dan.: Rejfan; Russ.: Pizhma.

Uses: The earliest use, and the commonest today, is as a culinary herb. The rather spicy lvs can be used as a pot-herb or fresh for flavouring salads and cooked dishes. On the continent they are used to flavour certain liqueurs. From the Middle Ages, until the now widespread use of Hops was adopted, Alecost was used for flavouring beer.

Origin, distribution and cultivation: Alecost is a native of western Asia. It was cultivated by the Egyptians, Greeks and Romans, and spread in the Middle Ages to central and western Europe where it remained a common garden crop until the 18th century. Today it is only grown in home-gardens, and does not enter commerce. As seed is not set in north-west Europe, it is propagated by division of rootstock.

Similar plants: The clumping growth habit and large simple lvs are quite different from the other economic *Chrysanthemum* spp. The plants resemble Sorrels more closely than they do any other grown as an agricultural or garden crop, but can be distinguished by the bluntly toothed, not entire lvs which taste mildly spicy but not sour.

Garland Chrysanthemum *C. coronarium* is very extensively grown as a leaf vegetable in China and Japan. It has been tried in Europe and could become a commercial crop in the future. This sp. forms clumps of deeply lobed lvs up to 20 cm long on short (1 cm) stalks which are more likely to be mistaken for a Crucifer such as Rocket or Land Cress than for other composites, but the lvs are rougher in texture, and plants allowed to flower have typical chrysanthemum fl heads.

Inula helenium ELECAMPANE

Description: A perennial herb covered in soft grey hairs with a tuberous rootstock. Stems erect, thick, 40–150 cm tall, furrowed. Lvs simple, elliptical, spirally arranged, the basal ones very large, up to 40 cm long, the upper ones clasping stem; all lvs very thickly hairy on undersides, greyish. Fl heads 6–8 cm in diameter, daisy-like, with all florets yellow, the ray florets narrow; involucre large, with many rows of bracts, the outer ones lf-like.

Names: Fr.: Aunée officinale; It.: Inula, Elenio; Sp.: Enula campana; Ger.: Helenakraut, Alant; Dtch.: Alant; Dan.: Alant; Russ.: Devyasil vsoki.

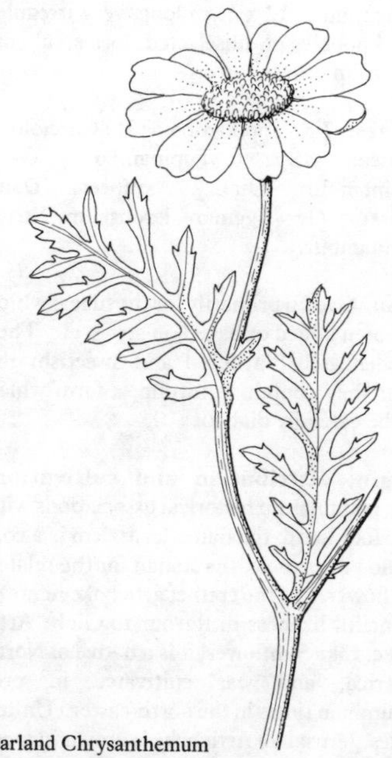

Garland Chrysanthemum

Uses: The rootstock yields an essential oil used in perfumery and medicinally, usually in the form of infusions or in herbal tea mixtures for the treatment of bronchitis and disorders of the stomach or gall bladder.

Origin, distribution and cultivation: This species is native to the Apennines and the Balkans but it does occur throughout the whole of Europe, including Britain. It is cultivated to a small extent in the Netherlands, Belgium, France, Germany and in central and eastern Europe as a field crop. The roots of second-year plants are lifted in the autumn.

Elecampane

Similar plants: Other (wild) composites with yellow fls. The deep receptacle with large lf-like bracts, and thickly hairy, grey-green foliage are characteristic features.

Helianthus annuus
SUNFLOWER

(p. 190)

Description: A familiar tall (0.8–3.5 m) annual herb with a tap-root that may descend to 3 m and a usually unbranched stem, round at first, becoming thick, angular and slightly woody. Lower lvs opposite, heart-shaped, 30–10 x 20–5 cm, on long stalks; upper lvs alternate, smaller, ovate. Fl heads terminal, 10–40 cm across; disc florets numerous, brown; ray florets ca. 6 x 2 cm, with 2 nerves, yellow. Frts ('seeds') variable, at least 1 cm long, flattened, slightly 4-angled, narrowed to base, whitish, brown, black, or white or grey with black stripes.

Ornamental varieties exist with red or red-striped ray florets, as well as double forms.

Names: Fr.: Tournesol; It.: Girasole; Sp.: Tornasol; Ger.: Sonnenblume; Dtch.: Zonnenbloem; Dan.: Solsikke; Gr.: Helianthos; Russ.: Podsolnechnik; Yug.: Sončnice.

The generic name and all the vernacular

names given above, meaning 'sun flower', 'sun seeker' or 'turn (to) sun', refer to the flower's phototropism so nicely described by Thomas Moore: 'As the sun flower turns on her god, when he sets/The same look which she turn'd, when he rose.'

Uses: Sunflower was originally cultivated as a food plant, and many crops in southern Europe are still grown exclusively for the seeds which are roasted in their husks and eaten as a snack. The principal ecoomic use of sunflower is as an oil seed crop. The oil, expressed from seeds, is a high-quality cooking and salad oil which is in increasing demand because it is 'polyunsaturated', a type thought not to build up cholesterol in arteries. The oil is also used in the manufacture of margarine and compound cooking fats, and in industry.

The residual cake of pressing is a high-protein food for livestock, and the whole plants, including threshed fl-heads can be fed to cattle. Some crops may be grown only for this purpose, or as a green manure.

Origin, distribution and cultivation: Cultivated or 'large-seeded' Sunflower (var. *macrocarpus*) evolved under cultivation by Indians from the wild *H. annuus*, which occurs in western North America from southern Canada to northern Mexico. Seeds were brought to Spain in 1510, and thereafter the plant spread, as an ornamental rather than a crop plant, to the whole of Europe. Cultivation of Sunflower as an oil seed crop began in Germany or in Russia in the 18th century. The Soviet Union is now the world's largest producer, and with the exception of North America and Argentina, the remaining bulk of world production comes from European countries, chiefly Rumania, Bulgaria, Hungary, Yugoslavia and Turkey. Substantial crops are also grown in other central European countries and throughout the Mediterranean.

Similar plants: Jerusalem Artichoke.

Helianthus tuberosus
JERUSALEM ARTICHOKE

(p. 190)

Description: A herb with stems 1–3 m tall, similar to Sunflower but perennating by stem tubers. The stems are more branched, slenderer. Lvs mainly opposite, ovate, often coarsely toothed, with broad-winged stalks. Fl heads much smaller, 4–8 cm in diameter, with yellow disc and ray florets; tubers numerous, whitish or yellowish, crisp-fleshed, up to 12 x 6 cm long, very irregular and knobbly in unselected forms, almost smooth in others.

Names: Fr.: Topinambour; It.: Carciofo di Giudea; Sp.: Tupinambo; Ger.: Topinambur; Dtch.: Aardpeer; Dan.: Jordskok; Gr.: Agginara ierousalim; Russ.: Topinambur.

Uses: Grown primarily for the tubers which are eaten boiled or baked, in stews, etc. They are delicately flavoured and sweetish; the sugar they contain is insulin, a form which can be eaten by diabetics.

Origin, distribution and cultivation: This plant has no historical associations with the Holy Land: the name Jerusalem is a corruption of *girasole*, the Italian for the related Sunflower, and the epithet artichoke refers to a fanciful likeness in flavour to Globe Artichoke. Like Sunflower, it is a native of North America, and was cultivated in pre-Columbian times in the north-eastern United States. Jerusalem Artichoke is grown in most European countries in home- and market-gardens, rarely as a field crop. Plants only flower in Britain and northern Europe after an exceptionally long warm summer. Propagation is by replanting tubers.

Similar plants: *H. tuberosus* is unlikely to be confused with Sunflower, but closely resembles related spp. such as *H. rigidus* which are grown for ornament. The latter has larger (6–10 cm) fls, and untoothed lvs on very short stalks.

Cynara scolymus
GLOBE ARTICHOKE
(p. 190)

Description: A herbaceous perennial thistle-like plant usually grown as a triennial, with stout erect stems branching towards apex, 80–180 cm tall. Lvs up to 75 cm long, greyish-green, pinnately lobed. Fl heads globose, dull grey-green flushed with purple in some varieties, variable in size, ca. 5–10 cm across, with numerous rows of overlapping tough fleshy bracts surrounding a central cluster of violet-blue tubular disc florets. The bracts are usually blunt or notched at apex, but end in a sharp spine in a few Mediterranean varieties, which are smaller, less succulent, and thought to be closer to the original wild form.

Many cvs exist, differing in fl head size, colour and quality, the latter being also affected by soil and climate. Varieties with smaller, less fleshy heads which are sometimes superior in flavour tend to come from the hotter, drier Mediterranean climate. The largest and most succulent are those which were developed in the mild moist climate of Brittany.

Names: Fr.: Artichaut; It.: Carciofo; Sp.: Alcarchofa; Ger.: Artischoke; Dtch.: Artisjok; Dan.: Artiskok; Gr.: Agginára ydrogeios; Russ.: Artishok; Yug.: Articoka.

Most of these names are corruptions of the Arabic *al-kharsuf*.

Uses: Artichokes are cultivated for the fl heads, cut when they are immature, long before the bracts open to expose the developing florets. The whole heads are usually boiled, the parts eaten being the tender fleshy bases of bracts, and, after removing the fibrous mass of developing florets, the fleshy receptacle or 'heart'. These are best eaten hot with *sauce hollandaise* or melted butter, or cold with vinaigrette, but the hearts may be baked, fried, used in delicate stews and in many other ways. Small, very immature entire heads are cooked, preserved in oil and eaten whole, especially in Italy.

Origin, distribution and cultivation: Globe Artichoke originated in the Mediterranean; it is not known as a wild plant, and some botanists believe it to be derived from *C. cardunculus*, wild Cardoon, at a very early date, for it was certainly known as a food plant to the Greeks and Romans. The large succulent forms cultivated today were probably only developed during the Renaissance.

The plant does not necessarily require very warm summers, but it is intolerant of frost; this largely determines its present distribution in Europe, which ranges throughout the Mediterranean, but with more intensive cultivation in the western countries, Italy, France and Iberia, and northwards through the whole of France to the Netherlands and southern England. The mild, almost frost-free climate of Brittany has made that one of the prime producing areas, but further north the plants may need protection in winter. For this reason it is little-grown in the harsher continental climate of central Europe. The species is unstable, and seedlings are unpredictably variable. It is therefore usually propagated by offshoots from the better plants.

Similar plants: Cardoon, below.

Cynara cardunculus
CARDOON
(p. 190)

Description: A perennial plant cultivated as an annual. Cardoon is closely related to the Globe Artichoke, and similar in structure, but the cultivated form is usually a taller plant, up to 2.5 m, with longer (ca. 1 m) lvs of a paler grey-green, this difference being accentuated by blanching (see below). Fl heads are smaller, less fleshy, with spiny bracts.

Cultivated varieties are sometimes classed as a distinct form, var. *altilis.* The wild form grows to about 1 m, is very spiny, with much smaller fl heads.

Names: Fr.: Cardon, Carde; It.: Cardone; Sp.: Cardo; Ger.: Kardone, Kardonen-artischoke; Dtch.: Kardoen; Dan.: Kardon; Gr.: Agriagginára; Russ.: Artishok ispanski.

Uses: Cardoon is cultivated for the blanched lf-stalks and midribs, eaten as a boiled vegetable, usually with white or cheese sauces such as *béchamel*, or with butter, garlic and anchovy sauces like the Italian *bagna cauda.*

Origin, distribution and cultivation: Cardoon evolved by selective cultivation of the wild form beginning in classical times in the Mediterranean. Although it is a labour-intensive and a rather unproductive crop, it is widely grown in Spain, in France as far north as Paris, and in Italy, and to a lesser extent in other Mediterranean countries. Cardoons were formerly grown by a few market-gardeners in England, but the plant is now virtually unknown there except as an ornamental.

Plants are sown from seed and harvested in the same year. Blanching of the lvs was formerly achieved by earthing up, but is now usually done by tying the lvs together in bundles and surrounding them with a packing of cardboard, canvas, or opaque plastic sheeting.

Similar plants: Artichoke (above). The method of husbandry (blanching by packing materials for Cardoon, free growth in rows on large surfaces in the case of Artichoke) makes the two spp. unmistakeable in the field.

Cnicus benedictus
BLESSED THISTLE

Description: A thistle-like plant 10–65 cm tall with branching reddish stems covered in gossamer-like hairs. Lvs pinnately lobed or toothed, spiny, with prominent white veins below, the lower ones 10–30 cm long. Fl heads solitary, 2–3 cm across, enveloped by upper lvs which hide all but the tips of yellow florets and bracts, the latter ending in long branching brown bristles.

Names: Fr.: Chardon béni; It.: Cardo santo; Sp.: Cardo santo; Ger.: Benediktenkarde; Dtch.: Gezegende distel; Dan.: Benedictenertidsel; Russ.: Benedikt aptechi.

Uses: The fls are gathered as the source of a drug used in the treatment of gastric and digestive disorders.

Origin, distribution and cultivation: A native of the Mediterranean region which is widely naturalised in most of Europe as a result of past cultivation. As its specific name suggests, the plant was probably originally cultivated in monastery herb gardens in the Middle Ages. It is cultivated as a field crop in many central European countries, but in Britain exists only as a casual wild species.

Similar plants: Many spp. of thistle, but these have purple fls.; *Carthamus* spp. and *Scolymus* spp. (only in the Mediterranean) do not have red stems, and fl heads are freer, not enveloped by upper lvs.

Carthamus tinctorius
SAFFLOWER

(p. 192)

Description: A herbaceous annual up to 1.3 m, branched, more or less spiny; branches rigid, cylindrical, pale grey-green. Lvs dark green, shiny, oblong to lanceolate with spines on margins and at tip, ca. 12 x 3 cm. Fl heads at ends of branches, ca. 3 cm in diameter, with spreading spiny bracts and onion-shaped involucre with a narrow opening through which the dense mass of orange tubular florets protrude, rather like an orange thistle head. Frt a pale grey quadrangular achene, ca. 8 mm long.

Names: Fr.: Carthame; It.: Cartamo, Falso zafferano; Sp.: Cártamo; Ger.: Saflor, Färberdistel; Dtch.: Saffloer; Dan.: Saflor; Russ.: Saflor; Yug.: Barvilni žafran.

Uses: Safflower is grown mainly as an oil seed crop, the oil being used locally (India, Egypt) for cooking and lighting purposes, elsewhere mostly in the manufacture of paints, varnishes, soap, etc. The decorticated seed pulp may be used as stock feed. The dried florets contain the yellow, rather fugitive dye carthamin (safflower carmine) used to colour cloth (in India), cosmetics (mixed with French chalk it makes *rouge*), or food: rice, stews, etc. In Poland, the florets are used locally in bread and cakes. In Egypt market vendors label large basketfuls of florets 'Saffron' in the hope of tempting uninformed tourists.

Origin, distribution and cultivation: Safflower is only known in cultivation, with primary centres of distribution in Afghanistan, Egypt, and Ethiopia. Today it is mainly grown in these and in other semi-tropical countries including the USA, India and the Middle East, but crops are also planted in south-east and eastern Europe, and in the Soviet Union. In the South of France and other parts of south-west Europe the plant is naturalised as the result of obsolete cultivation.

Similar plants: See Blessed Thistle (above).

Taraxacum officinale agg.
DANDELION
(p. 188)

Description: This aggregate comprises hundreds of spp. only separable by a specialised botanist. Dandelions are variable perennial herbs with a tap-root and a basal rosette of lanceolate to obovate, more or less deeply lobed or toothed lvs. Fl heads 2–6 cm across, solitary, borne on shallow unbranched stems which release abundant milky latex when broken; florets yellow, all strap-shaped. Fruiting head familiar, the long branching pappus of each seed forming a whitish feathery globe.

Names: Fr.: Pissentlit; It.: Dente de leone; Sp.: Diente de león; Ger.: Löwenzahn; Dtch.: Molsla; Dan.: Løventandsalat; Gr.: Agriorádiko; Russ.: Oduvanchik; Yug.: Maslačak.

Uses: In Britain Dandelion is sometimes used for making dandelion 'wine', but otherwise is thought of as an obsolete edible plant; on the Continent, particularly in France and Italy, it is recognised as a fine salad plant, particularly when combined with bacon. The bitterness of some lvs can be attenuated by soaking them for a couple of hours before use, or by blanching for a few seconds.

People seen gathering whole sackfuls of the plants on the Continent are almost certainly feeding domestic rabbits.

Origin, distribution and cultivation: This familiar weed is so common all over Europe that it is not cultivated, except in home-gardens in France, where improved forms (giant, curled, thick-leaved) were developed in the 19th century.

Similar plants: The combination of characters is sufficient to distinguish Dandelion from many similar wild yellow-flowered composites.

In the Soviet Union a related sp., *T. kok-saghyz* has been used as a source of rubber, obtained from the latex in the roots.

Lactuca sativa
LETTUCE
(p. 188)

Description: An annual hairless herb forming a dense basal rosette of thin-bladed large lvs and later, tall, branched, leafy flowering stems 30–100 cm in height. Fl heads numerous in a dense panicle with small arrow-shaped bracts; florets few, all strap-shaped, pale yellow, protruding from an involucre 10–15 mm long of blunt lanceolate bracts. Frt an achene 3–4 mm long, narrowly obovate, flattened, with 5–7 ribs on each side, white, greyish or brown.

The very numerous cvs of this species fall into 4 main varieties:

var. *capitata*, **Cabbage Lettuces**. These are the most widely grown. Lvs are broad, forming a compact, cabbage-like head with a firm crisp heart. Most forms have rather limp, usually better-flavoured lvs, but some, such as 'Webb' and 'Iceberg' have thicker, very crisp lvs. Others, like the 'Batavias' (not to be confused with 'Batavia' Chicory, p. 274) have very crinkled lvs.

var. *crispa*, **Leaf Lettuce**. These kinds form a very loose head of deeply lobed or curled lvs which can be picked individually from the growing plant.

var. *romana* (syn.: var. *longifolia*), **Cos Lettuce**, has crisp elongate lvs forming narrow upright heads.

var. *angustana* (syn.: var. *asparagina*), **Celtuce**, also known as Asparagus or Stem Lettuce, is a Chinese variety which bolts rapidly, forming a stout succulent edible green stem conspicuously marked with horizontal lf-scars. The basal lvs are narrow, lanceolate, alternate, unpalatable, and not forming a head.

Names: (Cabbage Lettuce): Fr.: Laitue pommée; It.: Lattuga a cappucio; Sp.: Lechuga arrepollada; Ger.: Kopfsalat; Dtch.: Kropsla; Dan.: Hovedsalat; Gr.: Marouli; Russ.: Salat; Yug.: Salata.
(Cos Lettuce): Fr.: Laitue romaine; It.: Lattuga romana; Sp.: Lechuga romana; Ger.: Bindesalat; Dtch.: Bindsla; Dan.: Bindsalat; Gr.: Marouli; Russ.: Zipivi letni.

Uses: Lettuce is the world's most widely cultivated salad crop. The lvs are eaten dressed, on their own or as the basis for many mixed salads. They may also be used cooked like spinach or in soups. The young stems of Celtuce are eaten as a cooked vegetable.

Origin, distribution and cultivation: Lettuce is not known in the wild, but is closely related to Prickly Lettuce *L. serriola* and Least Lettuce *L. saligna* and probably arose as a hybrid of these and of other spp. in the East Mediterranean. Lettuce was cultivated by the ancient Egyptians, Greeks and Romans, and improved and widely spread by the Arabs. Since the era of European colonisation it has been introduced to every continent and is grown everywhere except in the hottest tropical lowlands.

Cabbage and Cos Lettuces are primarily a market-garden crop, but are often grown on a field scale, and are present in every kitchen garden in Europe. Leaf Lettuces belonging to var. *crispa* are grown for home use and are rarely found in commerce. Celtuce is widely cultivated in China and Japan, but in Europe is an infrequent crop, mainly confined to private gardens.

Similar plants: Cos Lettuce might be confused with some of the Chinese *Brassica* leaf vegetables, p. 225. See also the forms of *Cichorium*, below, which are always fleshier, with a characteristic, rather bitter flavour.

Cichorium intybus
CHICORY
(p. 188)

Description: The wild plant is a perennial with a stout tap-root giving rise to elongate lvs sparsely covered in short erect hairs, with pointed, shallow to pinnate lobes, and erect annual stems up to 1.5 m which bear small undivided lvs. Fl heads clear blue, 2.5–4 cm across, in leafy spikes; achenes pale brown, angular, narrowed to base, with a terminal ring of short finely divided scales.

The numerous cultivated forms of this species can be grouped into the following categories:

'Wild' Chicory: grown as a grassland herb in ley mixtures.

Varieties grown for their roots: These include Wild Chicory, whose roots are gathered to feed rabbits, and very large-rooted forms such as 'Magdeburg', 'Soncino' and 'Chiavari'. The roots are similar in appearance to cylindrical white carrots, but usually more irregular.

Varieties close to the wild form modified by blanching in the dark for use as a vegetable; these take two distinct forms:

'Witloof', also known as 'Belgian' or 'Brussels Chicory' has broad lvs with white midribs forming a compact elongate bud-shaped head called a *chicon*.

'Barbe de Capucin' forms long etiolated stalks and midribs with lf-blades reduced almost to 'wings' towards apex.

A form similar to this, but not or only partly blanched, with long stalks and midribs but with more lf-blade in the form of ragged lobes (similar to deeply-lobed Dandelion lvs) is 'Catalonia Chicory'. Both these forms are sometimes called 'Asparagus Chicory'.

Broad-leaved forms forming lettuce-like heads: 'Red Treviso' has elongate, dark wine-red lvs with thick midribs forming a loose head more or less intermediate in shape between a *chicon* and a Cos Lettuce. 'Sugar Loaf' is similar in shape, with pale green lvs. 'Grumolo' has broad dark green lvs in a loose rose-like head. 'Radicchio' includes a number of cvs which form lettuce- or cabbage-like heads of variegated red and green or completely red lvs with white midribs. The best known are 'Red Verona', with a loose head, and 'Castelfranco' with a tight head of crisped lvs somewhat like a Webb lettuce.

Names: Fr.: Chicorée; It.: Cicoria; Sp.: Achicoria; Ger.: Zichoriensalat; Dtch.: Chichorei; Dan.: Jules salat, Cikorie; Gr.: Radiki; Russ.: Chikori salatni; Yug.: Radič, Čikorija.

Note: There is much confusion between the names Chicory and Endive, the latter properly meaning forms of the following sp., *C. endivia*, particularly in France where in popular usage Witloof is called *endive* and Scaroles and curly Endives are known as *chicorée.*

Uses: 'Wild' Chicory is sown as a forage plant in mixed leys, and the roots are often used to feed rabbits.

'Root' Chicories may also be used for fodder, but most crops are either grown as a root vegetable, or for use as a coffee substitute, either mixed with coffee, or used on its own. Originally a cheap *ersatz*, Chicory has become appreciated in its own right, especially as a breakfast beverage in France, where advertisers stress its healthier properties.

The bitter Chicories such as 'Catalónia' (the commonest winter green vegetable in southern Italy), or 'Barbe de Capucin', which although highly esteemed has become commercially obsolete, are always cooked, usually boiled to remove the bitterness, and served with white or cheese sauces, or sautéed with various seasonings. 'Witloof' *chicons* are eaten raw, shredded, as a salad, or whole and cooked. The classic recipe in its homeland of Belgium, Holland and northern France is to wrap each boiled *chicon* in a slice of ham and bake them in *sauce béchamel* topped with a grating of fresh cheese.

Broad-leaved Chicories such as 'Radicchio', mainly of Italian origin, can likewise be dressed as salads, or cooked; in Italy they are usually seasoned with oil and lemon juice, or sautéed with garlic and spices. The roots of all the cooking varieties (except 'Witloof') are cooked together with the lvs if not too old and stringy.

Origin, distribution and cultivation: Wild Chicory occurs throughout Europe except the far North. Botanists disagree on whether records by Pliny and other classical writers refer to this sp. or to Endive. If, as seems probable, the latter is correct, the first records of Chicory in cultivation date from the 16th century. In any case the various cvs are of relatively recent origin. 'Radicchio' was developed and is still mainly produced in Italy, and is exported to northern Europe as a winter vegetable. 'Witloof' is a winter vegetable of Belgian invention, and is mainly associated with that country and with neighbouring Holland and northern France. It is now the most widely available Chicory in north and western Europe, and is also grown in Britain, Germany and other countries.

To obtain *chicons*, the large first-year roots of selected varieties are used. The tips of the roots, and all but the basal 3 cm of foliage are cut off, and the roots replanted indoors in the dark, the tops either covered in light soil, or left uncovered but packed closely together, and forced at a constant temperature of ca. 18° C. Root crops for coffee-substitute are mainly grown in France, the principal consumer, always as a field crop. The same varieties grown as a vegetable are cultivated, more widely, on a smaller scale.

Similar plants: This species is very close to Endive (below), with which it is often confused (see names, above). The lvs of *C. intybus* are minutely prickly-hairy, at least in parts, whereas they are quite hairless in *C. endivia.*

Wild plants or forms with deeply lobed lvs such as 'Catalonia' might be mistaken for Dandelion (for which see p. 273).

Cichorium endivia
ENDIVE

Description: The standard or wild plant is very similar to Chicory, but lvs are quite hairless and typically less deeply lobed. Stems are shorter, and the achenes are larger, with a ring of larger scales at apex.

The cultivated forms are fewer than those of Chicory, and generally form larger heads. The two main types are Escarole or Scarole, sometimes classed as var. *latifolia*, with heads of rather twisted and convoluted lvs with margins only finely and slightly toothed; Batavian Endive is the best known of this type. The other type, referred to var. *crispa*, has equally large heads of narrow, deeply toothed curly lvs. In commerce the term 'endive' is sometimes restricted to these forms, of which some of the best known cvs are Ruffec, Green-curled, Pancaliere, and Pavia.

Names: Fr.: Endive (see above, under names of *C. intybus*, for the popular misuse of terms); It.: Indivia; Sp.: Escarola; Ger.: Endivie; Dtch.: Andivij; Dan.: Endivie; Gr.: Antidi; Russ.: Endivi; Yug.: Endivija.

Uses: The rather bitter lvs may be used, raw or blanched in boiling water, in salads, or they may be cooked in the same way as Chicory.

Origin, distribution and cultivation: The natural distribution of Endive extends from the Himalaya, where it may have originated, to the Mediterranean. The confusion between this sp. and Chicory extends to records from classical times. If those refer to the former and not, as many botanists believe, to Endive, then its origin in cultivation is unknown. Today it is grown in most of Europe as well as in Asia as an annual to be harvested in winter. It is mostly planted in market-garden strips.

Similar plants: Chicory (see above). Scaroles resemble some forms of lettuce, but the lvs have sharply toothed margins, and the bitter taste is characteristic.

Tragopogon porrifolius
SALSIFY
(p. 188)

Description: A hairless biennial with a simple or little-branched stem 50–100 cm tall. Lvs very long, narrow, almost parallel-sided to narrowly lanceolate, with parallel veins, resembling those of garlic, etc., their bases broadened and half encircling the stem. Fls dark pink to dark red or purple, with narrow involucral bracts 3–5 cm long, as long as or longer than ray florets, the latter only spreading open for a few hours a day. Frt bearing a large parachute-like pappus, like Dandelion. Tap-root cylindrical, white-skinned.

Names: Sometimes called Oyster Plant. Fr.: Salsifi; It.: Barba di Becco; Sp.: Salsifi blanco; Ger.: Haferwurz; Dtch.: Haverswortel; Dan.: Havrerod; Gr.: Lagolachano; Russ.: Kosloborodnik poreclistnyi; Yug.: Vrtna kozja brada.

Uses: Cultivated for the root which is a luxury vegetable. The delicate, rather nutty flavour (the likeness to oysters is wildly fanciful) is best appreciated by eating the boiled roots on their own with melted butter, but many fine cream and cheese recipes exist. Part of the commercial crop is canned.

Origin, distribution and cultivation: A native of the Mediterranean region and naturalised over parts of central and northern Europe, including Britain. Superior forms of Salsify were originally developed in Italy, probably during the Renaissance, and came to Britain via France in about 1700. The plant is cultivated as an annual for harvesting in late autumn. Though almost unknown in Britain except to a few gardeners, it is a popular vegetable in France and other parts of western Europe, and widely cultivated in home- and market-gardens.

Similar plants: Scorzonera (see below). The white root, seen without lvs, is similar in appearance – but not in scent – to Chicory, Celeriac, etc. (see pp. 274 and 254).

Scorzonera hispanica
SCORZONERA
(p. 188)

Description: Similar in structure to Salsify (above), but a usually shorter plant, ca. 50 cm in height, with a white-fleshed tap-root with brown to blackish skin. Lvs are less linear, distinctly long-lanceolate, more narrowed to base, not clasping stem. Stems are more branching, with smaller, scale-like lvs towards apex, bearing solitary yellow dandelion-like fls with ray florets much longer than sepal-like bracts.

Names: Also called Black Salsify.
Fr.: Scorzonère; It.: Scorzonera; Sp.: Salsifi negro; Ger.: Schwartzwurz; Dtch.: Schorsoneer; Dan.: Skorsonerrod; Gr.: Maúro lagókhorto; Russ.: Skortsoner; Yug.: Črni koren.

Uses: As Salsify. Scorzonera is even more prized, and usually more expensive than Salsify. Like the latter and Jerusalem Artichoke, the roots contain insulin, a form of sugar that can be eaten by diabetics.

Origin, distribution and cultivation: Scorzonera, a native of the Mediterranean and western Asia, was first developed as a cultivated vegetable in Italy. The Latin specific epithet was given because it was introduced to France and northern Europe from Spain, where it had achieved early popularity. It is grown by home- and market-gardeners, mainly in western Europe, especially Spain, France and Italy, but remains little-known and unavailable from greengrocers in Britain.

Similar plants: Salsify. The blackish roots distinguish it from all other European root crops.

SOLANACEAE

Nightshade Family

A medium-sized family of some 2000 species of herbs, shrubs and small trees widely distributed around the world, but especially numerous in the tropics. The plants are sometimes spiny, and have simple or variously dissected lvs without stipules. The fls are radially symmetrical with parts usually in fives, the corolla variable, fused into a tube but mostly with widely spreading lobes. The frts are berries of a characteristic structure (cf. Tomato) or a dry capsule.

The family includes a number of poisonous plants which are used medicinally, such as Deadly Nightshade, Thorn Apple *Datura stramontium* and Mandrake *Mandragora officinalis*; also the drug Tobacco, as well as a number of food plants, some of which are of outstanding economic importance, such as the Potato, Sweet Peppers, the Tomato and the Aubergine. It is remarkable that the world owes all but one (Aubergine) of the food crops of this family to the pre-Columbian civilisations of South America.

Atropa bella-donna
DEADLY NIGHTSHADE

(p. 194)

Description: A tall perennial with stout stems, rather bushy in habit, standing up to 1.5 m in height. Lvs ovate, narrowed to stalks, alternate, the basal ones large, up to 20 cm or more in length, the upper small. Fls solitary or in pairs in lf axils or in forks of branches; corollas bell-shaped, slightly asymmetrical, stalked, 2.5–3 cm long, lurid violet-brown or violet-green. Frt a glossy black berry 1.5–2 cm across with persistent 5-lobed calyx. All parts of the plant are very poisonous, the cherry-like berries a dangerous lure to small children.

Names: Fr.: Belladone; It.: Belladonna; Sp.: Hieba mora; Ger.: Nachtschatten; Dtch.: Wolfskers; Dan.: Galnebaer; Gr.: Mpellantónna; Russ.: Krasavka.

Uses: Cultivated for the lvs which yield a number of drugs (atropine, hyoscyamine, scopolamine, etc.) components of many proprietary medicines used in the treatment of

KEY TO SWEET PEPPERS and CHILLIES

1	Plants annual; lvs large or small; fls and frts solitary; frts pendulous = *C. annuum*	(2)
2	Plants perennial; lvs small; fls and frts in clusters of 2 or more; frts erect = *C. frutescens*	(1)

heart disease, Parkinson's disease, etc. Atropine also dilates the pupils of the eyes, and is therefore a help in ophthalmic diagnosis and surgery. The specific name *bella donna* is owed to this property, for Italian and Spanish ladies of the late Renaissance used it as a cosmetic, artificially inducing a symptom which is normally one of emotional excitement.

Origin, distribution and cultivation: Deadly Nighshade is an uncommon wild plant of most of Europe, including England. It is cultivated as a field crop for the pharmaceutical industry mostly in eastern Europe, but also in Germany, France, the Netherlands and England.

Similar plants: See *Solanum intrusum*, (p. 278). Black Nightshade *S. nigrum* has fls with spreading white petals and fls and frt in clusters.

The name Deadly Nightshade is often given, erroneously, to another, though less poisonous sp., Bittersweet *S. dulcamara*, which has bright purple fls and ovoid frts green ripening to red.

Capsicum spp.
SWEET PEPPERS and CHILLIES

Sweet Peppers, Paprika and most Chilli Peppers belong to *Capsicum annuum*; some Chillies, including the smallest and most pungent varieties, belong to *C. frutescens*. The two spp. may be distinguished as shown in the key on this page.

Capsicum annuum
PEPPERS, CHILLIES
(pp. 194, 220)

Description: A variable shrub-like herb sometimes woody at base, erect and much branched, to 1.5 m in height. Lvs variable in size, simple, lanceolate to ovate with pointed tip, stalked, the blade thin, 1.5–12 cm long. Fls solitary, the corolla white or greenish deeply divided into 5 or 6 lobes, 10–15 mm across, with 5–6 stamens and bluish anthers. Frt a hollow, many-seeded berry very variable in size, shape and pungency according to cvs, yellow, red or brownish purple, often picked when still green.

Hundreds of varieties of this species are cultivated in the tropics, some of which are imported to Europe. The main forms grown locally are:

Sweet Peppers Very large (5–25 cm long) forms with a basal depression, more or less irregular in shape, slightly angled and not or rarely pointed at tip, with thick, mild flesh.

Paprikas Varieties with thinner flesh (therefore easier to dry). Hungarian varieties are long and pointed, Spanish ones are long top-shaped or round, not or only slightly pungent.

Chillies The name is applied to usually highly pungent forms of this species. Narrow conical in shape, variable in length from 3–1[illegible] cm or more, picked either green, or when ripe red or sometimes yellow.

Wrinkled Peppers are ovate, 3–6 cm long wrinkled, usually picked when still pale green, slightly pungent. Another similar form, imported to Europe from the West Indies, is extremely pungent.

Names: (Chillies): Fr.: Piment; It.: Peperoncino; Sp.: Pimiento, Guindilla; Ger.: Rote

Pfeffer; Dtch.: Spaansche Peper; Dan.: Spank peber; Gr.: Piperia; Russ.: Pepets kayenskaya; Yug.: Paprika.
(Sweet Pepper): Fr.: Poivron; It.: Peperone; Sp.: Pimiento dulce; Ger.: Paprika.

Uses:
Sweet Peppers are used as a vegetable, either raw, in salads, or cooked, grilled or stuffed; they form the basis of many southern European vegetable stews such as *ratatouille*, Italian *peperonata*, Basque *pipérade*, etc.
Paprika (Hungarian pepper, Spanish pepper) is a bright red powder made from thin-fleshed mild or slightly pungent varieties. It is used very liberally, as the basic flavouring of *goulash* and many other Hungarian dishes. An almost identical preparation, called *pimenton*, is made and widely used in Spain in such specialities as *romesco* sauce.
Chillies are the most important economic form of this species on a worldwide basis, but are little-used in European cooking except in some pungent Spanish dishes and in sauces such as the *rouille* of Provence. The frts may be used fresh, or dried and ground. Cayenne Pepper, mostly imported, is a similar product, but ground to powder rather than coarsely, and usually mixed with a little flour, salt, and other ingredients. Frts are often pickled in brine and eaten as a relish with Italian antipasti, Greek mezze, etc.
Wrinkled peppers are also used mainly in this way.

Origin, distribution and cultivation: *C. annuum* and other capsicums were widely cultivated in central and South America in pre-Columbian times. Seeds of *C. annuum* were brought to Spain by Columbus on his first voyage, and the Spanish and Portuguese disseminated varieties of this sp. and of *C. frutescens* in Africa and Asia in the following decades. Before the introduction of these plants the most pungent spice known in the Old World had been Black Pepper. The cooking of many African countries and of most of India, Ceylon and S.E. Asia, where hot chilli is ubiquitous, testifies to the fact that no other flavouring has so profoundly revolutionised traditional cooking on so large a scale.

Being an annual, this sp. can be grown in any temperate country with sufficiently warm summers. Sweet Peppers are grown as an outdoor crop throughout the Mediterranean, and in France eastwards through central Europe to Russia and beyond; in cooler climates (such as the Netherlands), they are grown under glass. Paprika varieties are extensively grown as a field crop in Hungary and neighbouring countries, and in Spain. The limited demand in Europe for pungent varieties largely restricts economic cultivation to the Mediterranean countries, especially Greece, Turkey and Spain.

Similar plants: *C. frutescens*, below.
The name pepper should not cause confusion with true Pepper, the frt of *Piper nigrum* and other related vines, belonging to a different family, which is only cultivated in the humid tropics.

Capsicum frutescens
BIRD CHILLIES
(p. 194)

Description: Similar to *C. annuum*, above. Plants are usually shrubby, rarely over 1 m in height, with generally smaller lvs. The fls and frts are in clusters of 2–5, the latter erect, usually red when ripe, 2–3 cm long, elongate or conical, extremely pungent. One variety, grown mainly for ornament, has spherical frts.

Names: Fr.: Piment enragé; It.: Peperoncino, Diavoletto; Sp.: Chile, Guindilla; Ger.: Roter Pfeffer; Gr.: Pipériés; Russ.: Pepets kayenskaya.

Uses: This is the sp. used in the hottest exotic dishes, and forms the basis for fiery chilli sauces or extracts such as *Tabasco.* It has little use in European cooking, except in a few southern Spanish dishes and in pickling mixtures, but may be used instead of pungent frts of *C. annuum* in *rouille*, etc. (see above).

Origin, distribution and cultivation: As *C. annuum.* This sp. is very widely grown and used in the tropics, but is rarely seen as a commercial crop in Europe, except in southern Spain and to a small extent in Greece, Cyprus and Turkey.

Similar plants: *C. annuum*, above. The frts are similar to the long conical frts of *C. annuum*, but smaller.

Nicotiana tabacum
TOBACCO

(p. 196)

Description: A perennial herb grown as an annual; reaches, if allowed to, 2 m in height with a thick, erect, unbranched stem. In plants cultivated for the lvs; the budding terminal inflorescence is removed, causing axillary buds to produce branches which are also removed. Lvs spirally arranged, stalkless or with winged stalks adnate to stem, the blade variable in size, ca. 50 cm long, ovate-lanceolate or elliptic, entire. Fls numerous on short stalks in racemes; calyx cylindrical, 1–2 cm long with 5 teeth; corolla funnel-shaped, 3–5 cm long, about 1 cm in diameter at apex where it is divided into 5 pointed lobes, pink (rarely white or red). Frt a 2-valved ovoid capsule containing several thousand minute seeds.

Many cvs exist; in Europe the only form which is notably different in structure is Turkish Tobacco, with very small lvs 7–15 cm long.

Names: Fr.: Tabac; It.: Tabacco; Sp.: Tabaco; Ger.: Tabak; Dtch.: Tabak; Dan.: Tobak; Gr.: Kapnos; Russ.: Tabak; Yug.: Tobak.

Uses: The addictive drug nicotine is consumed for pleasure in various forms: as snuff, chewing tobacco (both obsolescent in Europe) or by smoking the cured and fermented lvs in pipes, cigars or cigarettes. The overwhelming bulk of the European crop is grown for the manufacture of cigarettes. The distinctive flavours of the main types of tobacco produced in Europe, yellowish 'Virginia', French 'Caporal', cigar tobacco and Turkish tobacco depends less on the cvs used than on the method of curing (controlled drying) of the lvs: flue curing for 'Virginia', air curing for cigar and 'Caporal' types, or sun curing for Turkish tobacco; the degree of subsequent fermentation of the lvs also accounts for the differences in flavours, the darker tobaccos being more heavily fermented.

Origin, distribution and cultivation: Like all other members of the genus, Tobacco is a native of South America, where it was cultivated and smoked long before the Spanish conquest. It was first introduced to Europe in the 16th century and is now grown almost all over the world.

In Europe it is cultivated as an economic field crop in all countries except those where summers are too cool to produce crops of acceptable quality, such as Britain and Scandinavia, but the main bulk of lvs used by European manufacturers is imported. Dark 'Caporal' types are produced in France and to a lesser extent in Spain. Turkish tobacco, formerly among the most expensive in Europe, is now waning in popularity in favour of Virginia types, but the sight of lvs laid out on racks for sun curing is still fairly common in Greece, Bulgaria and Turkey in late summer and early autumn.

Similar plants: *N. rustica*, see below. The white-flowered garden ornamentals belong to other species of *Nicotiana*.

Nicotiana rustica
NICOTINE TOBACCO

Description: Similar to *N. tabacum*, but the lvs are borne on short stalks which are not winged, and the fls are greenish-yellow.

Uses: This sp. has a higher nicotine content than *N. tabacum*, but the flavour is rank. It is smoked to a certain extent in the Soviet Union, but is cultivated primarily as a source of nicotine and citric acids for industry, and as a source of nicotine for insecticides.

Origin, distribution and cultivation: This species reached Europe from South America before *N. tabacum*, but has now been entirely replaced as a source of tobacco by the latter. It is still grown as a field crop in the Soviet Union.

Similar plants: *N. tabacum*, see above.

Solanum tuberosum
POTATO
(p. 196)

Description: A perennial herb with rather weak trailing or more or less erect branching stems 0.3–1 m high. Lvs pinnate with smaller leaflets between the 3–4 pairs of main lobes. Fls white, red or purple, ca. 2.5 cm across, with yellow anthers joined into a cone-like structure. Frt a small inedible green or yellowish tomato-like berry 1.5–2 cm across; the tubers are very variable in size, shape and skin colour according to cv, numerous on each plant, borne at the tips of thin rhizomes radiating from the fibrous roots.

Several hundred cvs exist, differing in the quality of tubers, suitability to different soils and climates, and rate of growth. According to the times at which they mature, cvs are classed as first earlies (early summer), second earlies (late summer) and main or late crop (autumn or winter). New Potatoes are the product of early maturing crops.

Names: Fr.: Pomme de terre; It.: Patata; Sp.: Patata, Papa; Ger.: Kartoffel; Dtch.: Aardappel; Dan.: Kartoffel; Ger.: Patáta; Russ.: Kartofel; Yug.: Krumpir.

The English, Italian and Spanish names were transferred from the Sweet Potato (p. 286), an unrelated plant which reached Europe fifty years before the Potato.

Uses: The Potato is the most important vegetable in the world today, the tubers providing the main source of carbohydrates, after cereals, in European diets. Their greatest value lies in that a crop of potatoes yields nearly twice as much nutritional value per acre as the cereals. However, they are less concentrated as a food source than cereals because of their high water content, their storage life is shorter, and the cost of transport much greater. The tubers are cooked in a variety of ways too numerous and familiar to need mention. Secondary uses include the production of starch and dextrose, and of alcohol by fermentation, used industrially and as the basis of *schnapps*, *vodka* and other spirits.

Origin, distribution and cultivation: The Potato came from the Andes at altitudes over 2000 m, where together with several other native tuberous plants it was cultivated in pre-Columbian times. Having evolved in the cool damp conditions of that region, the Potato was particularly well-suited to the similar European climate. Potatoes were first brought to Spain about 1570, but more than two centuries were to elapse before they were appreciated as a food plant, except in Ireland (whose particularly wet climate is ill-suited to cereals), where they became a staple food crop in the 17th century. Such was Irish economic dependence on the Potato a century later that, when the crops failed in 1845–7 due to 'potato blight', over a million people died of starvation and there began a large-scale emigration that lasted several generations. Elsewhere in Europe Potatoes only became widely established after the beginning of the 19th century, largely due to the efforts at the end of the previous century of the French agronomist Parmentier.

Today, Potatoes are cultivated all over the world except in the lowland tropics. Europe, including the Soviet Union, which is the largest producer, accounts for 90% of the world's crop, which in terms of volume and value exceeds all other crops, including wheat. Potatoes are grown both as a field- and market-garden crop, usually on parallel earthed-up ridges.

Similar plants: See Potato-leaved Tomato, (p. 283).

Solanum melongena
AUBERGINE or **EGGPLANT**
(p. 196)

Description: A perennial erect branching herb 0.5–1.5 m high grown as an annual. All parts woolly, greyish, sometimes spiny. Lvs large, alternate, simple, ovate with shallowly lobed margins, 7–15 cm long, on 2–10 cm stalks. Fls solitary or in cymes of 2–5 opposite lvs, 3–5 cm across, the corolla violet with 5–6 lobes and 5–6 large free yellow anthers. Frts very variable, from the size of a hen's egg to 20 cm long, globose, ovoid, oblong, sometimes curved, with smooth shiny skin usually dark purple, sometimes creamy white, more rarely greenish or yellow.

The name Eggplant was first given to

varieties, rarely seen in Europe but common in Asia, with small white perfectly ovoid frts.

Names: Also sometimes known in Britain by its Indian name, Brinjal.
Fr.: Aubergine; It.: Melanzane; Sp.: Berengena; Ger.: Eierfrucht; Dtch.: Eierplant, Aubergine; Dan.: Aegplante; Gr.: Melitzana; Russ.: Baklazhani; Yug.: Jajčevec.

Uses: The cooked frts are used as a vegetable, boiled, fried, or stuffed, or sliced for such dishes as *moussaka* or in vegetable stews like *ratatouille* and *caponata*.

Origin, distribution and cultivation: Aubergine is a native of tropical Asia, from western India to S.E. Asia, where primitive, small-fruited forms are used alongside the large improved varieties. It was first cultivated in India at an early date but does not appear to have reached Europe until its introduction to Spain by the Arabs in the 8th century. Aubergines are cultivated out-of-doors, as a small field crop and in market- and home-gardens throughout the Mediterranean and central Europe. In Britain, the Netherlands and other cool countries it is grown to a small extent under glass.

Similar plants: See other spp. of *Solanum*, see below. The large lvs and very large frts make it unmistakeable.

Solanum intrusum
GARDEN HUCKLEBERRY

(p. 194)

Description: An annual herb growing to 1 m in height, similar in structure to Aubergine but not covered in a grey tomentum, and with much smaller lvs which are ovate and entire. Fls white, 7–10 mm across, the corolla with 5–7 long pointed lobes, and brownish-yellow anthers, borne in loose cymes of 5–20 or more. Frts globose or slightly flattened, purple-black, ca. 2 cm across.

Names: Syn.: *S. nigrum guineense.*

Uses: Suitable for cooking with sugar to make pie fillings, jellies and jams.

Origin, distribution and cultivation: The origin of this species, considered by some botanists to be an African subspecies of the cosmopolitan *S. nigrum* (see below), is uncertain; it is possible that it arose as a hybrid in cultivation in America, where it is more often grown than in Europe. Here it is little known to any but a few amateur gardeners, and is only rarely found in commerce.

Similar plants: *S. nigrum*, Black Nightshade, a weed which occurs all over the world including Europe, is a smaller plant (under 60 cm) with lobed lvs and smaller (6–8 mm) frts. The frts are mildly poisonous, but the lvs are gathered and eaten as a spinach in Greece, the Middle East and in Asia.

The lvs and small bitter frts of other wild *Solanum* spp. are likewise used as pot-herbs and stew ingredients in the tropics.

Lycopersicon esculentum
TOMATO

(pp. 194, 218)

Description: A variable annual herb, 0.5–2 m in height, either erect or spreading and sprawling, coarsely hairy, with characteristic odour. Lvs spirally arranged, pinnate or bipinnate with segments variously lobed or toothed, usually very narrow (entire in Potato-leaved Tomato). Fls borne in racemes of 4–12, drooping, ca. 2 cm across, with parts in fives or more often in sixes, the petals narrow, pointed, star-like, yellow, the yellow anthers forming a cone enclosing the style. Frt a yellow or red berry 2–15 cm across, globose or elongate sometimes irregular or with longitudinal furrows, or pear-shaped; most varieties have fruits with 2 cells containing many seeds, but some are multicellular, with fewer seeds.

The many cvs fall into one of three main varieties:

var. *cerasiforme*, **Cherry Tomato**, has fls with parts in fives, and very small (ca. 2 cm across), more numerous frts.

var. *pyriforme*, **Pear Tomato**, also has fls with parts in fives, and pear-shaped frts.

var. *commune*, including all other commercial varieties, has fls usually with parts in sixes, and small to very large globose, irregular or plum-shaped frts. var. *grandifolium*,

Potato-leaved Tomato, and var. *validum*, **Upright Tomato**, are included in this group by most botanical authors. The former is recognisable by its entire lvs; the latter is a stout, erect, very bushy plant.

Names: Syn.: *Solanum lycopersicon.* Fr.: Tomate; It.: Pomodoro; Sp.: Tomate; Ger.: Tomate; Dtch.: Tomaat; Dan.: Tomat; Gr.: Tomata; Russ.: Pomidor; Yug.: Paradiznik, Rajcica.

Uses: The Tomato is one of the world's most important vegetable, and a major culinary flavouring. As a vegetable it is eaten raw or cooked in a great variety of ways. For flavouring, whole peeled fresh or canned frts may be used in, stews, etc. Commercially-produced powders, concentrated purées or pastes, ketchups – and in the Mediterranean, sun-dried frts preserved in oil – all of these with a distinctive flavour suited to different dishes are widely used, and are essential to much Mediterranean, especially Italian, cooking.

Cvs vary greatly in flavour as well as in shape, water content and storage quality. The best-flavoured varieties, such as the French *Marmande*, are increasingly rarely available in northern Europe, where consumers have allowed producers and supermarkets, whose only concern is with yield, appearance and storage quality, to flood the market with insipid, gas-ripened frts of cvs such as '*Moneymaker*'.

Large quantities of tomatoes are also used to produce juice, soups and various commercial sauces.

Origin, distribution and cultivation: Cultivated tomatoes are thought to have been derived from the Cherry-Tomato (var. *cerasiforme*) which occurs in the wild in Peru and Equador, and was cultivated in Mexico in pre-Columbian times. Seeds were brought to Spain soon after the conquest of Mexico in 1523, and the plant spread to most of Europe within the same century. Tomatoes seem to have been used at the time in Spain, and in Italy, where improved cvs were developed which were to have a profound effect on Italian cooking; but in the rest of Europe they were regarded as little more than a curiosity until the end of the 19th century.

Today, Tomatoes are grown all over the world. In Britain and northern Europe crops are grown under glass; in central and southern Europe many fresh frt cvs are also grown under glass, while others are cultivated in the open in home- and market-gardens. Plum Tomatoes, originally developed in Britain, are grown as a sprawling field crop for the canning industry, mainly in Italy, southern France and Spain. Other varieties may be sprawling, erect and needing no support, or trained on strings and wires.

Similar plants: The entire lvs of Potato-leaved Tomato resemble those of the Potato plant, but the yellow fls and characteristic scent of lvs are typical of Tomatoes. See also the Tree Tomato, below, which has smaller, thick-fleshed, distinctly more pointed frts than the Plum Tomatoes.

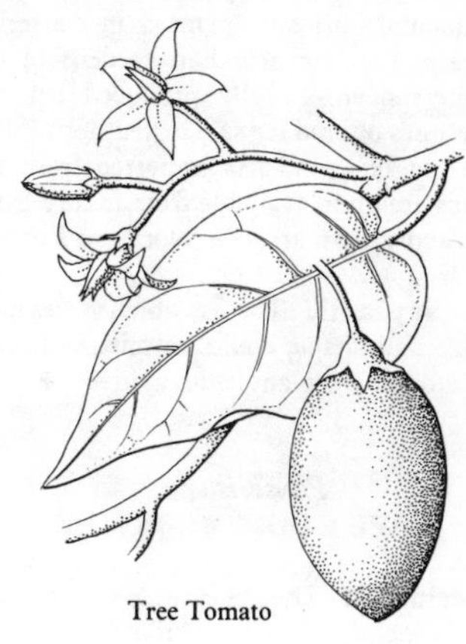

Tree Tomato

Cyphomandra betacea
TREE TOMATO

Description: A small (up to 6 m) short-lived tree with slender trunk and branches which starts bearing fruit in its second year. Lvs large, simple, entire, the blades ca. 15 cm long, heart-shaped with pointed tips, on 3–8 cm stalks. Fls white, the corolla deeply divided into 5 pointed lobes, and yellow anthers loosely joined in a cone. Frts about the size of a hen's egg, usually distinctly pointed at tip, yellow, orange or purple, internally like a Tomato.

Names: The frts are sometimes marketed in Britain under the Spanish name Tomatillo. Fr.: Tomate arborescente; It.: Pomodoro arboreo; Sp.: Tomate arból; Ger.: Baumtomate; Dtch.: Tomatzieboom; Gr.: Tomatiá; Russ.: Tomatnoye derevo.

Uses: The frts, which have a strong sweet flavour distinct from Tomato, are sometimes eaten raw, as a fruit, with the addition of sugar, rather than as a salad vegetable, but they are more often stewed.

Origin, distribution and cultivation: The Tree Tomato is a native of Peru. It has been taken to many tropical countries where it is cultivated commercially at medium and high altitudes. In Europe it is principally an ornamental curiosity, planted in conservatories in the North and in gardens in the Mediterranean. Locally produced frts are sometimes offered for sale in southern European markets, and frts imported from the tropics are often available from luxury fruiterers and supermarkets in Northern Europe.

Similar plants: The frt, which varies little in size and shape, could be mistaken for a Tomato but the plant is distinctive.

Physalis spp.
CAPE GOOSEBERRY, etc.

Description: The frts of these spp., globose berries enclosed in a loose inflated calyx (the 'bladder' or 'lantern') are very distinctive, but there is much confusion in nurseries, seed catalogues and popular literature between the few spp. cultivated in Europe, and the vernacular names are frequently transposed or used for more than one sp. For this reason, and to avoid further confusion, the vernacular names in other European languages are only given for the best-known sp., *P. alkekengi*. The key overleaf may help to identify the spp. grown in Europe, but new hybrids may not fit into the scheme.

Physalis pruinosa
GROUND CHERRY

Description: An annual with spreading branches, to 1 m in height or sometimes more, bushy, about as broad as tall. Lvs heart-shaped, shallowly toothed, greyish-green when young, softly hairy, with one basal lobe larger than the other, similar to Begonias. Fls yellow, ca. 1 cm across, the corolla shallowly divided into 5 lobes, each with a brownish blotch at base. Frt a globose berry ca. 2 cm across, yellow, entirely enclosed in the loosely fitting pale brown husk formed by the calyx.

Names: Also known as Strawberry- or Husk-Tomato, Dwarf Cape Gooseberry, etc. Syn.: *P. edulis*.

Uses: The sweet slightly acid frts are suitable for making jams, jellies, purées for tarts, etc.

Origin, distribution and cultivation: This sp. is a native of eastern and central North America. It is commonly gathered in the wild and cultivated there, but in Europe is less often planted than the following three spp. It is of no commercial importance and is only grown by amateur gardeners.

Similar plants: See key, above, and other *Physalis* spp., below.

Physalis peruviana
CAPE GOOSEBERRY

Description: A perennial usually grown as a half-hardy annual, similar in structure to the preceding. Lvs hairy but with bases equal, with slightly wavy or toothed margins. Fls small, white or yellow, the corolla slightly spotted with brown at base. Frts similar to *P. pruinosa*, somewhat larger, with a thicker, larger calyx.

Names: Syns.: *P. edulis*, *P. peruviana edulis*.

Uses: The fruits are somewhat less sweet than those of *P. pruinosa*; they are used in the same way.

Origin, distribution and cultivation: *P. peruviana* is a native of South America, probably, as its name suggests, of Peru. It was probably introduced to Spain at an early date, but only became known in Britain in the 19th century, from plants brought from the Cape of Good Hope; the Dutch had been cultivating it there since the 17th century. Although more often planted in Europe than *P. pruinosa*, it is scarcely more important economically, and only rarely found in commerce.

Similar plants: Other *Physalis* spp. (above and below).

Physalis ixocarpa
TOMATILLO

(p. 196)

Description: A perennial, usually grown as an annual, similar to the two preceding spp. but hairless. The fls are yellow with 5 purple-brown blotches, ca. 2 cm in diameter. Frts are either yellow or purplish and the husks sometimes veined with purple; when ripe the frt almost or entirely fills the husk, which tends to adhere to it and often has to be soaked off in water.

Many forms, some of them hybrids, are attributed to this sp. 'Sugar Giant' is the most distinctive of these, with much larger yellow frts incompletely covered by the husks. Jamberry, Golden Berry and Sugar Berry are names given to other cvs.

Uses: As the preceding spp.

Origin, distribution and cultivation: This sp. originated in Mexico, where, with other *Physalis* spp., it was cultivated before the Tomato, and which remains the main centre of production. Various improved forms, including hybrids, have recently been offered in European seed catalogues; these larger frts are likely to supersede the preceding spp. in popularity. The frts are sometimes offered for sale in southern European markets, but are as yet little-grown commercially in Europe.

Similar plants: Other *Physalis* spp.

Physalis alkekengi
WINTER CHERRY

(p. 196)

Description: Similar to the three preced-

KEY TO PHYSALIS sspp.

1	Calyx husks red; frt bright orange=*P. alkekengi*	**(2)**
2	Calyx husks greyish-brown; frts yellow or purplish=**3**	**(1)**
3	Lvs mostly unequal at base, with one lobe larger than the other; young lvs grey-green, slightly hairy; fls yellow with brown blotches at bases of corolla lobes; frt ca. 2 cm across, calyx husk loose=*P. pruinosa*	**(4)**
4	Lvs equal at base=**5**	**(3)**
5	Frts yellow, entirely enclosed by large loose husk, like spp. above; lvs hairy=*P. peruviana*	**(6)**
6	Frts yellow or purplish, almost or completely filling husk, the latter adherent; lvs hairless=*P. ixocarpa*	**(5)**

ing spp., but with bright orange frts loosely enveloped in a calyx husk which is red, or flushed with orange to red, later drying to pale brown.

Names: Also known as Bladder Cherry, or Chinese Lantern Plant. The following names are given often indiscriminately to this and the other *Physalis* spp. mentioned above:
Fr.: Coqueret, Amour en cage, Tomate-fraise; It.: Alchechengio, Pomodoro-fragola, Mirabello di Corsica; Sp.: Alquequenje, Capuli; Ger.: Kapstachelbeere, Ananaskirche, Erdkirche, Erdtomate; Dtch.: Lampionplant; Dan.: Jødekirsebaer; Gr.: Fysallída; Russ.: Meksikanski tomat, Bishiya peruanskaya.

Uses: Although the fruit is edible and can be used like those of other *Physalis* spp. it is grown principally as a winter ornamental, and is listed as such in seed catalogues.

Origin, distribution and cultivation: This is the only cultivated member of the genus which did not originate in America. Its natural range extends from the Caucasus through central Asia to China, and plants occur as an introduced sp. on calcareous soils in parts of southern Europe, including France. It is the most widely and commonly cultivated sp. in Europe, but is of no economic importance.

Similar plants: Other *Physalis* spp.

CONVOLVULACEAE

Bindweed Family

A family of about 1000 spp. of mostly annual and perennial herbs, many twining or creeping, but also some erect forms and even shrubs. Lvs are alternate, without stipules, usually simple. Fls with funnel-shaped corollas and 5 stamens. Frts usually a capsule.

The members are widely distributed around the world, including Europe, where Bindweed and Convolvulus are familiar either as ornamentals or as tenacious garden weeds. With the exception of Sweet Potato, which is of outstanding economic importance in the tropics, the family yields no useful products except a few potherbs.

Ipomeoa batatas
SWEET POTATO
(pp. 196, 214)

Description: A perennial herb grown as an annual. In cultivation it is seen as a tangle of thin (3–8 mm in diameter) green or purplish vine-like trailing stems 1–5 m long, bearing many spirally arranged lvs on mostly erect stalks. Lvs very variable in shape and size, entire, heart-shaped or more or less deeply lobed to deeply palmate, green, often flushed with purple. Fls like those of bindweed, 2.5–5 cm long, with funnel-shaped corolla purple in throat, paler, to lavender at margin. Frt a 4-seeded capsule 5–8 mm across. The underground tubers are very variable, with whitish, yellow, pinkish-brown to purple skins, more or less irregular, sometimes globose, usually pointed at one or both ends.

Names: Fr.: Patate (douce); It.: Patata dolce; Sp.: Batata; Ger.: Batate; Dtch.: Bataat; Dan.: Batat; Gr.: Glykopatáta; Russ.: Batata; Yug.: Batata.
These names all derive from the Carib Indian name *Batata.*

Uses: As Potato, but the slightly sweet flavour is inappropriate in many European dishes. The greater dry-matter content makes them particularly suitable for mashing.

Origin, distribution and cultivation: The disjunct distribution of Sweet Potato, which was cultivated in both South America and some of the Pacific Islands, as far west as New Zealand before the arrival of Europeans, has fuelled diverse theories about ancient human migrations across the Pacific. It is now generally accepted that the plant travelled westward from South America, whether carried by man or flotsam, and that Polynesians dispersed it in the Pacific. The spread of the Sweet Potato to the Indonesian and Philippine archipelagos and to mainland Asia did not follow from this initial westward movement; Columbus brought plants back on his first voyage in 1492, and the Spaniards and Portuguese exported them to their colonies once they were established in Europe.

Sweet Potato is now a very important crop in many tropical countries. Being more productive and easier to cultivate it has replaced traditional root crops such as Yams in many areas. In Europe it is only of minor importance. Spain is the main producer, and exports part of the crop to northern Europe. Small quantities are also grown in Italy and Greece. In the tropics, plants are easily propagated by stem cuttings, but where winters are too cold for the plants to survive tubers must be forced in spring to produce shoots that can be planted out.

Similar plants: Tubers which are not characteristically pointed resemble Potatoes, but plants are unmistakeable.

In southern Asia, a closely related sp., *I. aquatica*, is widely cultivated for the lvs, used as spinach. This plant usually grows in water, but some crops are planted on dry land, where they might be mistaken for Sweet Potato. Although, like Sweet Potato, the lvs are variable, they are typically much narrower, or with narrower lobes.

HYDROPHYLLACEAE

Phacelia Family

A small family similar in appearance and in the structure of inflorescences to the Boraginaceae, whose members are distributed in all the major regions of the world except Europe. A few spp. of Phacelia are grown for ornament, and one is sown as a field crop.

Phacelia tanacetifolia
PHACELIA
(p. 198)

Description: An erect annual herb with little-branching stems up to 120 cm in height. Lvs sparce, oblong-ovate, up to 25 cm long, fern-like, pinnately divided into delicate lobes. Fls many, blue or lavender, with very long protruding stamens, borne in dense, curling, branched cymes.

Names: Fr.: Phacelie; It.: Phacelia; Sp.: Phacelia; Ger.: Bienenbrot, Phazelie; Dan.: Honningurt; Russ.: Fatselia.

Uses: Phacelia, which is sometimes grown as an ornamental, is sown on farms as a green manure and break crop. It is particularly suited to estates with an apicultural interest, for the fls are good nectar producers.

Origin, distribution and cultivation: Phacelia is a native of western North America, from central California south to Arizona and New Mexico. It is a recent introduction to European agriculture and as yet is only grown in western Europe, particularly in Germany, the Low Countries, France and Britain. Because soil tends to compact under the plants, it is often sown in a mixture with clover.

Similar plants: None. The inflorescences are similar to those of the Boraginaceae, but the long stamens and finely divided lvs are unmistakeable.

BORAGINACEAE

Borage Family

A widespread family of herbs, usually roughly hairy. Lvs alternate, entire, without stipules. Fls borne on paired outwardly coiling branches with fls opening progressively from the base of fork, their parts in fives. Frt usually a 4 one-seeded nutlet.

The family, which contains only one economic crop species, takes its name from Borage *Borago officinalis*, an old-fashioned medicinal and culinary herb. This is now only grown in a few private gardens, mainly in France, where the fls may be lightly fried as a garnish for cooked dishes, and the young lvs, which taste faintly of cucumber, are sometimes added to salads. The plant, which is a native of the Mediterranean but widely naturalised further north including Britain, stands up to 60 cm, is bristly-hairy, with large ovate stalked lower lvs and narrower, wavy-edged stalkless upper lvs; the 20–25 mm wide bright blue fls are borne in loose, branched inflorescences.

Symphytum x *uplandicum*
RUSSIAN COMFREY

(p. 198)

Description: A variable perennial herb with branching stems up to 1.5 m in height. Basal lvs broadly lanceolate, bristly-hairy, on stalks; upper lvs smaller, unstalked. Fls drooping in cymes at tops of stems, the corolla broadly tubular, dull pinkish-purple, the calyx with pointed teeth. Frts rarely produced in crops, 4–5 mm across, rough, black.

Names: Fr.: Consoude; It.: Sinfito, Consolida; Sp.: Sinfito, Consueldo; Ger. Beinwell, Wallwurz; Dtch.: Smeerwortel Dan.: Kulsukker; Gr.: Stekoúli; Russ. Okopnik.

Uses: Russian Comfrey is grown as a fodder crop for cattle. The plants are usually wilted before feeding, or used for silage.

Origin, distribution and cultivation: Russian Comfrey is a hybrid of Common Comfrey *S. officinale* and Prickly Comfrey *S. asperum*. It was first introduced to Western Europe from Russia in about 1870, but the present range of forms probably arose from further back-crosses with the parent spp. It is now little grown as a field crop, mainly because it must be propagated vegetatively by root cuttings or crown division. It may be more often seen on mixed farms in central and eastern Europe than in Britain.

Similar plants: Of the two original parent spp., Common Comfrey (once widely cultivated as a medicinal plant and still used as an ingredient of many brands of proprietary medicines for its healing properties and in compresses and liniments) is closest in appearance to Russian Comfrey, differing typically by its lvs being adnate to the stem and in the white or purple fls. Prickly Comfrey has smaller lvs which are not adnate to the stem, and bright blue fls with blunt calyx teeth. This sp. was formerly cultivated as an agricultural crop, and like the other two is now widely naturalised in Britain and the rest of Europe.

LAMIACEAE (LABIATAE)

Mint Family

A distinctive family of herbs and shrubs with 4-angled stems and simple lvs in opposite pairs, without stipules. Fls arranged in whorls in axils of often lf-like bracts, the whorls either separate or grouped to form a long terminal spike. Fls with 5-toothed calyx, often 2-lipped; corolla tubular, often 2-lipped, the lower lip often divided into 3 lobes; stamens 2 (rarely), or 4. Frt composed of 4 nutlets.

The family is widely distributed, with the greatest concentration of spp. in the Mediterranean region. Although few spp. are grown as agricultural crops the family is of considerable economic importance; many species are glandular and highly aromatic, with a great range of distinctive scents even within single genera. It includes all the most important European culinary herbs, and a few others used in perfumery; others are grown as ornamentals. Many of these herbs are now grown on other continents, which have contributed few useful products of their own. These include Patchouli *Pogostemon cablin*, a small shrub native to the Philippines, grown in Indonesia, Brazil, etc. for the perfume industry, and three spp. cultivated for their edible tubers: Chinese Artichoke (p. 299), Hausa Potato *Plectanthrus esculentus*, grown in Africa, and *Coleus parviflorus* in S.E. Asia.

Bergamots (*Monarda* spp.) are North American aromatic plants of this family used in perfumery and for flavouring iced drinks, etc. They should not be confused with the Bergamot Orange (p. 107).

Oregano

Origanum vulgare
WILD MARJORAM or **OREGANO**

Description: A perennial erect, often bushy, slightly downy herb 30-60 cm in height. Lvs 1–4.5 cm long, ovate, stalked, usually untoothed, with more or less strong characteristic sweet scent. Fls in dense rounded terminal panicles. Lower bracts lf-like, upper bracts mauve; calyx with 5 short equal teeth, the tube hairy inside; corolla 2-lipped, longer than calyx, purplish.

Names: Syn.: *Marjorana vulgare.*
Fr.: Origan; It.: Origano; Sp.: Oregano; Ger.: Oregano; Dtch.: Origan; Dan.: Merian; Gr.: Rigani; Russ.: Dushitsa obiknovennaya.

Uses: The wild plants of Britain, northern Europe and even of the moister regions of the North Mediterranean are of little value as a culinary herb, and are only used occasionally as a hardy substitute for Sweet Marjoram (below), but those of the hot dry areas of southern Italy, Greece, etc. have a distinctive pungent peppery flavour. It is the classic herb flavouring of Neapolitan pizza and many grilled meat dishes in southern Italy and Greece (see also similar plants, below). In S. European markets it is usually sold fresh or dry in bundles; for commercial export only the dried lvs are retained.

Origin, distribution and cultivation: *O. vulgare* occurs in the wild in most of Europe including Britain where it is the only native marjoram. In N. Europe it is largely confined to dry, calcareous soils. It is cultivated to a certain extent, but much of the commercial crop is still gathered in the wild, often from jealously guarded localities. Italy is the greatest producer and consumer.

Similar plants: See other marjorams, below. In Greece at least ten different varieties and species of marjoram, including *Marjorana onites* (p. 291), *M. heracleotum*, *M. paniflorum* and *M. smyrnaicum*, all called *rigani* are gathered in the wild and used in the same way, especially with grilled meat.

Marjorana hortensis
SWEET or **KNOTTED MARJORAM**
(p. 202)

Description: An annual, sometimes biennial herb or sub-shrub with an erect branched stem 30–60 cm tall. The greyish lvs are opposite, ovate, short-stalked. Fls small, white or purplish, arranged in very small dense round clusters or 'knots' in lf axils.

Names: Syn.: *Origanum marjorana.*
Fr.: Marjolaine; It.: Maggiorana; Sp.: Mejorana; Ger.: Majoran; Dtch.: Majoraan; Dan.: Merian; Gr.: Mantsourana; Russ.: Mayoran tsapovi.

Uses: Sweet Marjoram is a more delicately flavoured herb than Oregano, with a scent related to, though sweeter than, thyme. It is one of the most important kitchen herbs, with a wide variety of uses, either on its own or in herb mixtures. Like many other spices and herbs the essential oils are lost in prolonged cooking, therefore the fresh or dried lvs are best added late in the process.

Origin, distribution and cultivation: Sweet Marjoram is a native of the Mediterranean, and has been cultivated in much of Europe since ancient times. It is essentially a European herb, little-used in the East or elsewhere. The dried lvs of commerce are mostly cultivated, but some are gathered in the wild in southern Europe.

Similar plants: Other marjorams. The 'knots' of fls of *M. hortensis* are characteristic.

Marjorana onites
POT MARJORAM
(p. 202)

Description: A perennial plant smaller than the two preceding spp., 20–35 cm tall, forming dense sprawling clumps of reddish stems and smaller lvs. Fls mauve to white, ca. 8 mm long, in whorls on long stems.

Uses: This herb is hardier than Sweet Marjoram, and often grown for this reason, although it is less fragrant and often rather bitter. It is used in the same way, as a culinary herb with meat dishes, in strongly flavoured sauces, etc.

Origin, distribution and cultivation: *M. onites* has a wide distribution in the Mediterranean, and is often cultivated in kitchen gardens further north, including Britain, as a source of fresh lvs. The lvs of commerce are both wild and cultivated.

Similar plants: Other marjoram spp.

Melissa officinalis
BALM

Description: A vigorous erect hairy, little branched perennial herb 30–60 cm tall, lemon-scented when crushed. Lvs ovate, pointed, the lowest heart-shaped, deeply toothed and with strongly impressed veins, on short stalks. Fls with 2-lipped, bell-shaped calyx, the upper lip very hairy, flat, with 3 very short triangular bristle-pointed teeth; corolla ca. 12 mm long, 2-lipped, upward curving, white.

Names: Fr.: Mélisse citronelle; It.: Melissa; Sp.: Citronmeliss; Ger.: Zitronenmelisse; Dtch.: Citroenkruid; Dan.: Citronmelisse; Gr.: Valsamódentro; Russ.: Limonnaya myata aptechnaya.

Uses: Formerly widely grown for its mild medicinal properties, Balm is now a little-used kitchen herb. The pleasantly lemon-scented lvs are used fresh (preferably) or dried, in omelettes, in home-made wine cups or iced drinks, and in several commercial liqueurs such as *Bénédictine* and *Eau de Mélisse des Carmes.* It is more widely used as a general culinary herb in Spain, and also for flavouring milk.

Origin, distribution and cultivation: Balm is a native of the eastern Mediterranean, but was introduced to all but the most northerly parts of Europe in ancient times; it was first brought to Britain by the Romans. Balm is rarely available from greengrocers, but fresh plants grown by smallholders may be had on country markets in France, Spain, etc.

Similar plants: Balm resembles calamints (*Calamintha* spp.), but the deeply-toothed lemon-scented lvs are distinctive.

Lavandula officinalis
TRUE LAVENDER
(p. 200)

Description: An evergreen sub-shrub with much-branched woody stems forming a dense hemispherical clump. All parts of the plant with characteristic scent. Woody stems long (20–30 cm), densely covered in opposite, small, green, entire, linear lvs. Flowering stems leafless, unbranched, rising well above the leafy stems to 60 cm in height. Fls small, bluish, 2-lipped, easily separated from the spike-like terminal panicles.

Names: Syn.: *L. angustifolia.* Also known as Garden Lavender.
Fr.: Lavande vraie, – femelle; It.: Lavanda vera; Sp.: Lavanda real; Ger.: Echte Lavendel; Dtch.: Lavandel; Dan.: Lavandel; Gr.: Levanta; Russ.: Lavanda; Yug.: Lavenda.

Uses: The essential oil, obtained by steam distillation from the flowering shoots and lvs, is of a higher quality than that yielded by the other two cultivated forms (below). This more expensive 'alpine' or 'French' lavender essence is used principally in perfumes, colognes and toilet articles and to a lesser extent in the pharmaceutical industry. The dried fls are used as natural 'air fresheners', to repel moths in linen cupboards, etc.

Origin, distribution and cultivation: True Lavender occurs as a smaller, more sparsely branched wild plant in the north Mediterranean, from Spain to Greece. It is cultivated as a garden ornamental in much of Europe, including Britain, but sufficient concentration of essential oil is only produced in suitably hot dry climates, and commercial cultivation, which only began at the beginning of this century, is confined to south-east France, where it is grown on a field scale, usually at 700–1200 m altitude. The parallel rows of clumps make lavender fields readily recognisable even before the plants flower in June.

Similar plants: See Broad-leaved Lavender and the hybrid *L. intermedia* (*Lavandin*) below. Other wild lavenders occur in Europe. The fls of French Lavender *L. stoechas* are often gathered and dried in southern France to perfume linen. This sp. and *L. dentata* are easily distinguished from the cultivated forms by the flowering stems which are leafy to apex, and their panicles of fewer fls crowned by large purple petal-like bracts.

Lavandula latifolia
BROAD-LEAVED LAVENDER
(pp. 200, 217)

Description: Differs from True Lavender in that the woody stems are much shorter, the flowering stems are longer, branching, making the overall size of the clump larger, from 30–80 cm in height. Young lvs opposite, woolly-whitish, narrowly spoon-shaped, not linear. Fls purple, not easily detached from panicles; all parts of the plant have a more camphor-like scent.

A hybrid of this sp. and of True Lavender, sometimes treated as a distinct sp., *L. intermedia*, and called *Lavandin* in France, has characters intermediate between the two.

Names: Syn.: *L. spica.*
Fr.: Aspic, Lavande à larges feuilles, – mâle; It.: Spigo; Sp.: Espliego; Ger.: Breitblättriger Lavendel; Gr.: Platyfilli levanta; Russ.: Lavanda shirokolostnaya; Yug.: Despic.

Uses: Pure *L. latifolia* produces *essence de spic* or *huile d'aspic*, now almost entirely replaced by the essential oil of the much cultivated hybrid, *Lavandin.* This plant yields four times more oil per volume of plants than True Lavender, but it is of inferior quality, with a distinct camphor scent, and therefore not used in fine perfumery but to scent some soaps, 'air fresheners', furniture polish and similar products. 'English' or 'Mitcham' lavender comes from this plant. The dried fls are used in the same way as those of other lavenders.

Origin, distribution and cultivation: Broad-leaved Lavender is a native of the Mediterranean and is grown to a small extent as a field crop in south-east France. The hybrid, *Lavandin*, is by far the most widely grown of the three commercial forms, especially in the south of France where it is cultivated at lower (400–700 m) altitudes than True Lavender. It is also the source of commercial English lavender.

Similar plants: Other lavenders, see above.

Rosmarinus officinalis
ROSEMARY
(p. 200)

Description: A densely branched bushy evergreen shrub with characteristic aromatic scent, up to 2 m in height. Lvs lavender-like, 2–3.5 cm long, linear, 1–3 mm broad, leathery, folded inwards along margin, dark green above, hairy-white below. Fls in small clusters on upper branches; calyx 2-lipped, the upper broadly ovate, the lower with 2 triangular lobes; corolla 2-lipped, the lower lip ovate, the upper divided into 3 narrow lobes, lilac with 2 violet stamens and curved style projecting.

Names: Fr.: Romarin; It.: Rosmarino, Ramerino; Sp.: Romero; Ger.: Rosmari; Dtch.: Rozemarijn; Dan.: Rosmarin; Gr.: Dentrolívano; Russ.: Rosmarin; Yug.: Ružmarin.

Uses: Rosemary is used fresh or dried as a culinary herb throughout the Mediterranean and to a lesser extent in central and northern Europe. It is usually included in herb mixtures, in small quantities, because the strongly resinous, slightly camphory scent can be overpowering. This quality makes it particularly useful, on its own, to counteract the fattiness of lamb and other grilled meat, for which purpose it is very widely used in Italy. Distilled Rosemary oil is used extensively in perfumery, toilet articles, disinfectants, etc.

Origin, distribution and cultivation: Rosemary is a native of the Mediterranean, where it is especially common in the western half, on dry limestone hills near the sea. It has been used as a culinary and medicinal herb since classical times, and was introduced at an early date to other parts of Europe where winters are not too severe, notably western France northward to England. The plant is so common in the Mediterranean that little commercial cultivation is necessary; the best herbs are picked in the wild in hot arid situations. Plants grown in England and northwest France have comparatively little savour.

Similar plants: The dense bushy habit and leathery linear lvs are reminiscent of Lavender, but the scent and fl arrangement are quite different.

Hyssopus officinalis
HYSSOP

Description: A variable herb, the different forms of which are sometimes divided into sspp or varieties. It is a perennial with stems slightly woody at base, 20–65 cm high, green, almost hairless. Lvs opposite, widely spaced, 1.5–3 cm long, narrowly oblong-lanceolate, without stalks. Fls arranged in long dense terminal spike-like inflorescences, with bracts as long as fls; calyx 4–5 mm long, tubular, 15-nerved, with 5 subequal teeth; corolla 2-lipped, 1–1.3 cm long, normally violet-blue, but sometimes white or pink.

Names: Fr.: Hysope; It.: Issopo; Sp.: Hisopo; Ger.: Ysop; Dtch.: Hysop; Dan.: Isop; Gr.: Ýssopos; Russ.: Issop.

Uses: Hyssop was formerly widely grown as a medicinal plant. It is now an unimportant herb with a bitter, slightly minty flavour. It is used in many liqueurs, and less frequently as an additive to soups, stews, or salads.

Origin, distribution and cultivation: Hyssop occurs naturally in all of southern Europe except western and central Spain; in central Europe northwards to the North Sea, it is found sporadically as an escape from cultivation. It has been grown in herb gardens since classical times, but is now rarely seen except as an ornamental, and is not available in commerce.

Similar plants: Summer and Winter Savory (below). The deeper blue fls of this sp. are arranged in larger, denser, more distinctly terminal inflorescences.

Satureja montana
WINTER SAVORY

(p. 200)

Description: A perennial aromatic subshrub with erect or trailing branching stems 10–45 cm tall. Lvs opposite, fairly widely spaced on stems which bear a distinct ridge between each pair of lvs, linear to narrow-lanceolate, 0.8–2.2 cm long, leathery, stalkless or almost so. Fls arranged in small clusters in upper lf axils; calyx 10-nerved, with 5 subequal teeth; corolla with a bell-shaped tube 6–7 mm long, white, pink, or pale violet, 2-lipped, the upper lip flattened, the lower 3-lobed.

Names: Fr.: Sariette vivace; It.: Savore, Santoreggia selvatica; Sp.: Sabroso; Ger.: Winter Bergminze; Dtch.: Winterbonenkruid; Dan.: Vintersår; Gr.: Lákhano tou milánou; Russ.: Chabor.

Uses: The lvs of this sp. are used in the same way as those of Summer Savory (below) but are generally considered inferior.

Origin, distribution and cultivation: Winter Savory is a native of the Mediterranean. It is less often cultivated than Summer Savory, although it has the advantage of being somewhat hardier and of providing lvs over a longer period. Savorys are principally a kitchen garden crop, and not normally available commercially except as an ingredient of dried herb mixtures.

Similar plants: Summer Savory, below, is an annual, less bushy plant with smaller fls, and the stems lack the ridge between each pair of lvs. Other wild spp. of *Satureja* may be used locally in southern Europe. See also Thymes (pp. 296–297).

Satureja hortensis
SUMMER SAVORY
(p. 200)

Description: An aromatic branching, erect or straggling annual herb or sub-shrub 10–45 cm tall, similar to *S. montana*, but stems are without a ridge between pairs of lvs, and the fls are larger, white, pale lilac, or purplish.

Names: Fr.: Sariette annuelle; It.: Santoreggia; Sp.: Ajedrea de jardín; Ger.: Bohnenkraut, Kölle; Dtch.: Bonenkruid; Dan.: Sår; Gr.: Ferinó lákhano tou Milánou; Russ.: Chaber sadovi.

Uses: Savory has a biting, thyme-like but more bitter flavour. It is most commonly used dried in herb mixtures, in sausages, meat dishes, stuffings, etc. Its most valuable and traditional use, especially in France and in central Europe, is in bean and pea dishes. Essential oil, obtained by distillation, is produced for flavouring processed foods.

Origin, distribution and cultivation: Summer Savory is a native of the Mediterranean, and was cultivated by the Romans, who probably first introduced it to northern France and Britain. It is now mainly a kitchen garden crop, but is also grown commercially, especially in western Europe and the Mediterranean.

Similar plants: Winter Savory (above); Thymes (pp. 296–297).

Ocimum basilicum
BASIL
(p. 200)

Description: A delicate erect annual growing to ca. 35 cm, little-branched, the stems with opposite pairs of broadly ovate, entire or slightly toothed long-stalked lvs. Lvs wrinkled between veins, but smooth, pale green, somewhat resembling beech lvs. Fls 1–1.5 cm long, white often tinged with pink or purple, with broad, slightly lobed upper lip and very long lower lip, arranged in whorls in upper lf axils. All parts of plant with characteristic aroma. Some varieties have lvs flushed with red, or entirely purple.

Names: Syn.: *O. americanum.*
Fr.: Basilic; It.: Basilico; Sp.: Albahaca; Ger.: Basilienkraut; Dtch.: Basilicum; Dan.: Basilikum; Gr.: Vassilikos; Russ.: Bazilik; Yug.: Bražiljka, Basilika.

Uses: Basil is one of the finest of all culinary herbs, with a distinctive, rich yet delicate flavour which has a particular affinity with tomato. It may be used fresh on a tomato salad, on grilled tomatoes *'provençal'*, tomato sauces, juice, etc. Basil has many other culinary uses, particularly with fish, poultry, and dishes cooked in wine and garlic. It is the essential ingredient of Provençal *pistou* soup, and of Genoese *pesto*, a paste made of basil, garlic, cheese, pine nuts, etc. The lvs should be used fresh, as the flavour of dried lvs is quite different, and inferior. The only satisfactory way of preserving basil is in olive oil with a little salt.

Origin, distribution and cultivation: *O. basilicum* is probably a native of India, where other *Ocimum* spp. occur. It has been cultivated in the Middle East since ancient times, and remains an important herb in Turkish and Arab cooking. It was grown and used by the Greeks and Romans, but its spread to central and northern Europe was restricted by climate: Basil is a semi-tropical plant with no resistance to frost. Italy, in particular Liguria, is probably the major commercial producer in Europe. The herb has been little-used or known in Britain and northern Europe, but in recent years young potted plants which can be kept in the kitchen as a source of fresh lvs have become available from many greengrocers.

Similar plants: See Bush Basil, below. In tropical Asia other spp. such as Hoary Basil *O. canum* and Holy Basil *O. sanctum* are used. *O. basilicum* is often known as Sweet Basil in order to distinguish it from these and from 'Wild Basil', a name sometimes given to Calamints, and 'Basil Thyme' *Acinos arvensis*.

Ocimum minimum
BUSH BASIL

(p. 200)

Description: Bush or Dwarf Basil is similar in structure to Sweet Basil, but is a smaller, more compact plant 10–25 cm high, with smaller lvs. Some ornamental varieties have variegated or differently coloured lvs.

Uses: This sp. is mainly grown as an ornamental, for the flavour is inferior to that of Sweet Basil.

Origin, distribution and cultivation: Bush Basil is a hardier plant than *O. basilicum*; its origin is uncertain but it has been known in the Mediterranean since classical times. It is more commonly grown than Basil in England, but it is of no commercial importance.

Similar plants: Basil (above).

Salvia officinalis
SAGE

(p. 200)

Description: A variable sp. with a large number of varieties. Sage is a perennial subshrub with more or less trailing or erect stems up to 45 cm long. Lvs opposite, stalked, oblong-ovate to lanceolate, with bluntly toothed margins, wrinkled above, felted-hairy, and persistent. Fls in whorls in terminal spikes, 2-lipped, white or more or less bluish or reddish violet.

Some of the varieties are distinctively coloured, with lvs golden green, or with stems and lvs shot with crimson or purple. The flavour varies greatly according to varieties and provenance. Most forms are more appropriate for ornament than as a herb; the best culinary varieties are the blue-flowered Narrow-leaved Sage and the broad-leaved variety, which is often non-flowering.

Names: Fr.: Sauge; It.: Salvia; Sp.: Salvia; Ger.: Salbei; Dtch.: Salie; Dan.: Salvie; Gr.: Faskomiliá; Russ.: Shalfei; Yug.: Žalfija.

Uses: Sage is a powerful and highly individual herb; its use should accordingly be restricted to certain dishes, and it is not suitable for all herb mixtures. Good use has been made of this herb in Britain in such traditional recipes as sage and onion stuffing for goose, in cheeses, and to add flavour to the sometimes bland ways in which pork is cooked here. In Germany and the Netherlands it is associated with eels. The Italians use it most ubiquitously, particularly with veal and liver, in sausages, and with roasted small birds.

Much of the commercial crop is grown for essential oil obtained by steam distillation and used in the liqueur, food, perfume and pharmaceutical industries.

Origin, distribution and cultivation: Sage is a native of the north Mediterranean coast and is widely naturalised in southern Europe. It was used by the Romans, and was grown in most herb gardens but its use appears to have been purely medicinal until a later date. The most aromatic plants are gathered in the wild, especially in Dalmatia, which also exports sage honey, but it is grown commercially in many countries including England, both as a culinary herb and for the production of essential oil.

Similar plants: Many other spp. of *Salvia* occur in the wild in Europe. Some of them are used locally as cooking herbs, or for herbal teas or medicines. The best-known of these is perhaps Three-lobed Sage *S. triloba*, a larger plant, up to 1.5 m in height; its best distinguishing character is that many (but not all) the upper lvs have 2 small lobes at the base, thus forming a 3-lobed lf. This is the basis of an infusion sold in cafés in the eastern Mediterranean, called *faskomelo* in Greek.

Salvia sclarea
CLARY

(p. 200)

Description: A biennial plant usually grown as an annual, with an erect, little-branched stem and lvs concentrated towards base, partly forming a rosette. Lvs large, opposite, almost stalkless, broadly ovate, irregularly shallowly lobed or toothed, with a wrinkled surface like Sage. Fls white, violet, or pink, with 2 lips, the upper lip narrow, strongly arched, with protruding style, the lower convoluted in 2 lobes, subtended by a very large, concolorous, sharply pointed bract.

Names: Fr.: Orvale, Sauge sclarée; It.: Erba moscatella, Selarea; Sp.: Salvia silvestre; Ger.: Muskatellersalbei; Dtch.: Scharlei; Gr.: Gorgógianni; Russ.: Shalfei muskati.

Uses: The large highly aromatic lvs were used in the past, especially in Germany, for flavouring wine in imitation of muscatel. Today the plant is grown almost exclusively for the production of an essential oil, called muscatel oil or sage clary, used to flavour vermouths and liqueurs, and in perfumery, soaps, etc.

Origin, distribution and cultivation: Clary is a native of the Mediterranean which has long been grown in other parts of Europe as an ornamental, as a medicinal plant, and because – like other sages – it is attractive to bees. It is now cultivated on a very small scale as a field crop in parts of central and southern Europe.

Similar plants: Other non-cultivated spp. such as Wild Clary *S. verbanacea.*

Thymus vulgaris
GARDEN THYME

(p. 202)

Description: A small perennial sub-shrub, in northern Europe often cultivated as an annual, with much branched square ascending stems, woody at base. Lvs evergreen, opposite, very small, 4–8 mm long, linear to elliptic, almost stalkless, with margins curved inwards, white-felted below, with a strong scent of thyme. Fls white, pink or violet, 2-lipped, the lower lip divided into 3 lobes.

There are many varieties of this sp. differing in flavour, lf shape and habit. 'English' thyme is a broad-leaved var.; that known as 'French' thyme has much narrower lvs.

Names: Also known as Common or French Thyme.
Fr.: Thym; It.: Timo; Sp.: Tomillo; Ger.: Thymian; Dtch.: Tijm; Dan.: Timian; Gr.: Thimari; Russ.: Timyan; Yug.: Timijan.

Uses: Thyme is one of the most important European culinary herbs, with uses too numerous to mention. Because the lvs are leathery and contain little water in the living plant, they dry without excessive loss of flavour, and are most often used in this form in northern Europe. Sprigs of Garden Thyme are, with Parsley and Bay, one of the essential parts of *bouquet garni*, and the lvs enter the majority of dried herb mixtures. Garden Thyme adds a deep aromatic quality to many dishes, especially in combination with onions, garlic and wine. The essential oil, thymol, has a wide range of uses in the manufacture of liqueurs, perfumes, pharmaceutical products and toilet articles.

Origin, distribution and cultivation: *T. vulgaris* is a very common plant of southern Europe, with a natural range extending beyond the strict limits of the Mediterranean. This and other thymes have been used as a culinary herb at least since classical times. In southern Europe, which produces the most aromatic plants, they are usually picked in the wild, but elsewhere Garden Thyme is cultivated both as a commercial crop and for home use.

Similar plants: See *T. serpyllum*, below. Many other spp. of thyme are native to Europe, some of which are cultivated on a small scale. Some spp. are most easily identified by their individual scents: Lemon Thyme *T. citriodorus*, a plant with a more creeping habit than Garden Thyme, has distinct lemony undertones. It is often cultivated by home-gardeners, and sometimes on a commercial scale, for it is particularly useful with dishes of rich fatty meats such as duck or lamb. Caraway Thyme *T. herba-barona* is likewise recognisable by its distinct caraway scent. This sp. is a native of Corsica and Sardinia, and is occasionally grown elsewhere.

The common Wild Thyme *T. drucei* of Britain and the coastal areas of western France is of no value as a herb, for it is very faintly scented. It can be recognised by the flat lvs and square stems which are densely hairy on 2 opposite faces only. Large Thyme *T. pulegioides*, is fairly strongly scented, and often used. This sp. stands up to 25 cm in height, has square stems hairy at angles, and broad (up to 6 mm) lvs with slightly upwardly curled margins. 'Spanish Thyme' (p. 119) belongs to a different genus.

Thymus serpyllum
BRECKLAND THYME

Description: Similar to *T. vulgaris*, above, but distinguished by the stems which are almost round in section. The roots and lower stems tend to be more mat-forming, and the pink or violet fls are arranged in larger, denser, more rounded terminal heads.

A number of ornamental varieties exist, mostly differing in fl colour (pink, white or red) and mostly with larger fl heads; var. *lanuginosa* has entirely woolly-white lvs.

Names: Also known as Continental Wild Thyme, sometimes as Mountain Thyme. Fr.: Serpolet; It.: Serpillo; Sp.: Serpoleto; Ger.: Feldthymian; Dtch.: Gewone tijm; Dan.: Smalbladet timian; Gr.: Agriothimaro; Russ.: Chabrets.

Uses: As Garden Thyme, above.

Origin, distribution and cultivation: *T. serpyllum* is a common native of southern and central Europe on sandy heaths and grasslands, but in Britain occurs naturally only in the Breckland. It is the second most widely cultivated thyme and its commercial use is either as fresh bunches on continental markets, or in dried herb mixtures.

Similar plants: Other thymes, above.

Mentha spp.
MINTS

Mints are often difficult to name, not only because of the large number of wild ones and the variability of cultivated spp., but because many of them hybridise freely. The key overleaf will help to determine the main economic spp. provided the plants are in flower. (Economic spp. in bold).

Mentha spicata
SPEARMINT

(p. 202)

Description: An erect perennial herb 30–90 cm tall, more or less hairless. Lvs lanceolate, pointed, finely toothed. Fls mauve, in terminal spikes 3–10 cm long; bracts very narrow, longer than fls; calyx and fl-stalks usually hairless, the corolla hairless, with stamens protruding.

Names: Fr.: Baume verte, Menthe verte; It.: Mentastro verde; Sp.: Menta verde, Hieba buena, Punitaguda; Ger.: Grüne Minze; Dtch.: Kruizemunt; Dan.: Krusemynte; Gr.: Dyósmos; Russ.: Myata koposovaya.

Uses: This is one of the commonest garden and commercial mints, especially in Britain. It is the species used in British mint sauce for lamb, etc., and is otherwise used for the same culinary purposes as other mints. The essential oil is used to flavour toothpaste, chewing gum and confectioneries, and many pharmaceutical products.

Origin, distribution and cultivation: Spearmint is a native of central and southern Europe. It was introduced to Britain by the Romans, and now occurs there as in most of Europe as an escape in ditches, damp wasteland, etc. It is grown on a commercial scale and in kitchen gardens, more extensively in Britain than on the Continent, where for culinary purposes *M. rotundifolia* is preferred.

Similar plants: Other mints: 'See key, above. The unstalked lanceolate lvs of Horse Mint *M. longifolia* give it a resemblance to Spearmint but they are hairy above, and woolly-grey beneath. This is a common sp.

throughout Eurpe, not used in the west, but cultivated in the Middle East and perhaps also in south-east Europe.

Mentha x *piperata*
PEPPERMINT

(p. 202)

Description: This is a fairly variable hybrid of Water Mint *M. aquatica* and *M. spicata*, with consequent intermediate characters. The lvs are borne on short stalks, usually ovate or lanceolate, finely toothed, somewhat wrinkled and hairy. Fls are borne in short terminal spikes which are sometimes so short as to resemble the globose heads of *M. aquatica*; scent characteristic, relatively pungent.

'White' Mint, with green stems, and 'Black' Mint, with dark, purplish stems, are two of the cultivated forms of this sp. The former is said to be of better quality but, as with most labiates, this depends largely on climate and other local factors.

Names: Fr.: Menthe anglaise, – poivrée; It.: Menta pepe, – piperita; Sp.: Hierbabuena, Menta piperita; Ger.: Edelminze, Hausminze; Dtch.: Peppermunt; Dan.: Pebermynte; Gr.: Mínthi i piperódis; Russ.: Myata perechnaya; Yug.: Ljuta metvica.

Uses: This mint is rarely used as a culinary herb, for the essential oil it contains includes menthol which has an anaesthetic action which would deaden the flavours of cooked foods. Oil of Peppermint, obtained by distillation, has a very wide range of uses in flavouring sweets, chewing gum, cordials and liqueurs, of which *crème de menthe* is the most obvious example and pharmaceutical and related products such as toothpastes.

Origin, distribution and cultivation: This hybrid was mainly developed and exploited in Britain, but the many industrial uses of the essential oil which ensued soon led to commercial cultivation on the Continent, where it is more common as a wild escape than in Britain. It is not a kitchen- or market-garden plant, but is grown in large plots for industry in England, the Netherlands, Germany and other countries.

Similar plants: See key, (p. 299).

Mentha rotundifolia
ROUND-LEAVED MINT

Description: An erect perennial herb up to 80 cm in height. Lvs unstalked or almost so, broadly ovate or round, 2–5 cm long, bluntly toothed, wrinkled, more or less hairy but not felted below. Fls in long terminal spikes, white, pinkish or mauve.

Names: Syn.: *M. suaveolens.*
Fr.: Menthe à feuilles rondes; It.: Menta selvatica; Sp.: Matapulgas; Ger.: Rundblättrige Minze; Gr.: Platyfilli minthi.

Uses: Round-leaved Mint, with its subtle undertone of apple or pineapple, is one of the finest culinary spp., suitable for any dish for which mint is appropriate.

Origin, distribution and cultivation: *M. rotundifolia* is a native of the western half of Europe and of North Africa; in the East it is confined to the Balkans. It is widely cultivated in kitchen- and market-gardens on the continent and in Britain.

Similar plants: *M. citrata*, Eau de Cologne Mint, also known as Lavender, Orange or Bergamot Mint, is a similar round-leaved southern European sp. which is often grown in gardens, to be used fresh in drinks, and is cultivated on a small scale for the essential oil. It is most easily recognised by the characteristic scent, reminiscent of orange blossom. *M.* x *niliaca*, a common wild sp. is very similar to Round-leaved Mint, but lvs are sharply toothed, usually more distinctly pointed, and lack the apple scent. It is of no culinary value.

Mentha pulegium
PENNYROYAL

Description: A prostrate creeping perennial herb up to 30 cm long. Lvs very small, 10–20 mm x 5–10 mm, ovate, bluntly toothed. Fls in widely separated whorls in lf axils, mauve, with calyx and outside of corolla downy.

KEY TO MINTS		
1	Fl whorls in dense terminal leafless heads or spikes=**2**	(10)
2	Fls in spikes=**3**	(9)
3	Lvs stalked, lanceolate; scent characteristic, of peppermint=**Peppermint**	(4)
4	Lvs more or less unstalked=**5**	(3)
5	Fl-stalks and calyx tubes hairless; lvs almost hairless, lanceolate; scent of British mint sauce=**Spearmint**	(6)
6	Fl-stalks and calyx hairy; lvs hairy=**7**	(5)
7	Lvs lanceolate or narrowly oblong, more or less hairy above, densely hairy beneath=**Horse Mint**	(8)
8	Lvs round or ovate, 2–5 cm long, bluntly toothed, often apple- or pineapple-scented=**Round-leaved Mint**	(7)
9	Fls in rounded heads, often with extra whorls beneath=**Water Mint**	(2)
10	Fls in whorls in lf axils widely spaced on stem, not forming heads or spikes; stem tips leafy=**11**	(1)
11	Larger, usually erect plants, comparable to those above; lvs at least 1.5 cm broad; calyx teeth equal=**Corn Mint and others**	(12)
12	Small creeping plant with ascending stems; lvs ovate, 0.5–1.5 cm long, less than 1 cm wide=**Pennyroyal**	(11)

Names: Fr.: Pouliot; It.: Puleggio; Sp.: Poleo; Ger.: Flohkraut; Dtch.: Polei; Russ.: Myeta bopotnaya.

Uses: This sp. scarcely merits inclusion as a crop plant. It was used by the Romans as a flea repellent. The bitter minty taste of the lvs is inappropriate for culinary purposes, although it is used successfully in English North Country black puddings and in some Spanish sausages.

Origin, distribution and cultivation: Pennyroyal is widely distributed in Europe, including Britain, partly as a result of ancient introduction from southern Europe. It is commonly grown in gardens, between flagstones, etc., but has no economic use.

Similar plants: Among cultivated spp.: none.

Stachys affinis
CHINESE ARTICHOKE
(p. 202)

Description: An erect herb growing to 45 cm in height related to and closely resembling Woundwort. Lvs rough, in opposite pairs on square stem. Fls white to red in a loose terminal spike, but rarely produced in cultivated plants. The roots produce numerous trailing stems which either turn up to form new plants or bear at their tips the distinctive tubers 2–7 cm long, elongate, conical or tapering at each end, knotty because ringed with sharp constrictions.

Names: Syn.: *S. sieboldii.*
Fr.: Crosne; It.: Tuberina; Ger.: Japanknollen.

Uses: The small tubers are one of the finest and most delicate of all 'root' vegetables. They may be eaten hot or cold after blanching in water or stock.

Origin, distribution and cultivation: This vegetable is a native of China. The first viable tubers to reach Europe were sent from Peking to Paris in 1882, and planted at Crosne. They have been grown ever since in France, where tubers are available from seed merchants, and as a vegetable, from greengrocers, but they remain practically unknown in the rest of Europe.

Similar plants: The plant is similar to many ornamental or wild European labiates such as other *Stachys* spp. and also bear a resemblance to nettles *Urtica*, but cannot be confused with any of the other crop plants. The tubers are unmistakeable.

MUSACEAE

Banana Family

A family of giant herbs, originally from S.E. Asia, having only two genera, *Ensete* and *Musa*. The many varieties of Banana, or plantain, are sterile hybrids which consequently do not bear specific scientific names, but are known by commercial cv. names. Only one of these, the hardiest, is cultivated in our region.

Musa cv. Dwarf Cavendish
CANARY BANANA

(p. 218)

Description: A tree-like perennial herb ca. 2 m high arising from a corm; the 'trunk' is a pseudostem composed of the overlapping thickened bases of lvs. These are large and handsome, the lamina becoming torn and tattered, thus reducing resistance to wind. The flowering stem is pushed up through the centre of the pseudostem and emerges at the apex, gradually bending over to hang downwards. Male fls are sheathed in conspicuous large red bracts borne at the apex of the stem; the sterile female fls from which the seedless frt develop without fertilisation are borne further up. The whole bunch of some 100–

Canary Island Banana

180 frts is attached in semi-circular groups of ca. 10 frts, called hands. Frts green, ripening to pale yellow, short, with blunt tips.

Names: Fr.: Banane; It.: Banana; Sp.: Plátano, Banana; Ger.: Banane; Dtch.: Banaan; Dan.: Banan; Gr.: Banana; Russ.: Banan; Yug.: Banana.

Uses: Eaten raw as a fresh fruit; occasionally cooked.

Origin, distribution and cultivation: Dwarf Cavendish Banana originated in S. China; it was brought, via Mauritius, to England, where it was described by Paxton after flowering in the greenhouses at Chatsworth, the Cavendish family house. It was taken from here for commercial cultivation to the Pacific, and reached Spain and the Canary Islands early in the last century. In Europe it is cultivated mainly in the Canary Islands, but also on a smaller scale in southern Spain, and in Cyprus.

Like other Banana cvs, propagation is done by planting suckers arising from the corm. Frts are produced and harvested about eleven months after planting, after which the 'trees' are cut down and new suckers planted.

This variety, distinguished from the imported tropical cvs which make up the overwhelming bulk of fruits consumed in Europe, by their smaller size, with blunt tips and thinner skin, does not travel well and so is mostly grown for the home markets of the producing countries.

ARACEAE

Arum Family

This family of some 1500 species is distributed around the world, but species are most numerous in the humid tropics. Perhaps the most familiar members to most Europeans are the Arum lilies (Lords-and-ladies, Cuckoo Pint), and *Monstera* and *Philodendron*, grown as ornamental house plants. Sweet Flag *Acorus calamus* is another member of the family which was formerly cultivated in Europe for its aromatic rhizome which could be candied or used in perfumery.

The family is best characterised by the type of inflorescence, with small flowers tightly packed on a large tubular spadix enclosed by a spathe.

Colocasia esculenta TARO

Description: A large herb, up to 2 m tall, with an underground corm giving rise to a whorl of large (20–60 cm) peltate lvs with pointed apex and rounded basal lobes. Inflorescence (not produced in many cvs) enclosed in a spathe ca. 20 cm long.

C. esculenta has two recognised varieties, the nominate form and var. *antiquorum* which differs in the structure of the inflorescence and because the corm is smaller and normally produces many, much larger, side tubers (only a few small tubers produced in var. *esculenta*). Both forms have many cvs differing in the colour of lvs and petioles, which may be spotted or streaked with purple, and in the colour (white, yellow or greyish pink) of the tuber flesh.

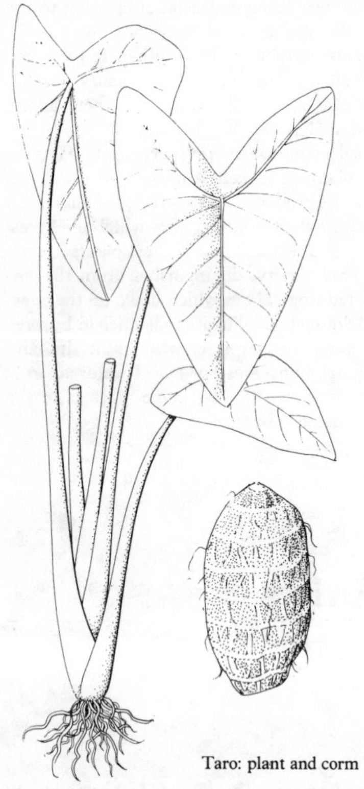

Taro: plant and corm

Names: Fr.: Colocase; It.: Colocasia; Sp.: Malanga; Ger.: Kalo, Karibisher Kohl; Gr.: Kologasi; Russ.: Kolokaziya.
Taro is the Polynesian name; *Dasheen* and *Cocoyam* are its names in the W. Indies and West Africa respectively.

Uses: Taro is cultivated for the starchy corms which are treated in the same way as potatoes: boiled, baked, or sliced and fried.

Origin, distribution and cultivation: *C. esculenta* probably originated in S.E. Asia. It reached China in ancient times, and the Polynesian peoples took it with them on their eastward migrations across the Pacific, where it remains one of the most important staple food crops. It is widely cultivated elsewhere in the humid tropics, particularly in S.E. Asia, West Africa and the West Indies, as a crop of secondary importance. It reached the Mediterranean in classical times, and is cultivated now on a commercial scale in Cyprus.

Taro requires very damp, even marshy soil. It is propagated by planting the cut tops of corms, or the entire side tubers.

Similar plants: In Europe: none. In the tropics several species belonging to other genera (*Xanthosoma, Alocasia*) of the Arum family are cultivated for the same purpose.

IRIDACEAE

Iris Family

A family best known for its many ornamental species – Gladiolus, Iris, etc. They are all herbaceous, with rhizomes, bulbs or corms, and narrow upright lvs often sheathing the stem. Fls relatively large, with parts in threes.

Apart from the Saffron Crocus described below, one other member of the family merits mention in the context of this book: *Iris florentina*, a typical Iris with large white fls often flushed with pale blue which occurs wild throughout the Mediterranean. It is cultivated on a small scale among vines or in dry sunny clearings in the hills of Tuscany for the powdered rhizome, called Orris Root, used in perfumery, particularly in combination with violet, the scent of which it resembles. It is also used as a flavouring for certain liqueurs.

Crocus sativus
SAFFRON
(p. 198)

Description: Fls lilac-purple, darker at base, the red stigmas protruding, often drooping sideways between petals. Lvs narrow, not striped with white, appearing at the same time as fls in autumn.

Names: Fr.: Saffran; It.: Zafferano; Sp.: Azafran; Ger.: Safran; Dtch.: Saffraan; Dan.: Safran; Gr.: Safróni; Russ.: Shafran; Yug.: Safran.

All these names derive from the Arabic *asafar* meaning yellow.

Uses: As a colouring and flavouring agent for food. Saffron was very widely used in medieval and renaissance cooking. It contains a high proportion of a very concentrated yellow dye, but because it is water-soluble, is not suitable for fabrics (the 'saffron' robes of buddhist monks are dyed with turmeric or safflower – see below), but is ideal for cooking. It also contains essential oils with a characteristic flavour which combine particularly well with seafoods and garlic. For this reason it has been retained, indeed is essential, in a few European dishes: *bouillabaisse* and its accompanying *rouille*, *paella valenciana*, *zarzuela*, and *risotto milanese.* Saffron cakes, or buns, remain an old tradition in Cornwall.

Origin, distribution and cultivation: Saffron Crocus is assumed to be a native of the Near East, perhaps derived from the wild *C. pallasi*, but has been in cultivation in the Mediterranean since ancient times. The Phoenicians are credited with introducing it to their colonies at Marseille and North Africa; in the 9th century the Arabs brought it to Spain, which remains one of the major producing countries.

Saffron was formerly cultivated in most of Europe (it was introduced to England in the reign of Edward III, when Saffron Walden in Essex became a centre of cultivation until the beginning of this century), but today it is only grown commercially in the poorer parts of Mediterranean countries. The decline of Saffron, and its very high price, are due to the intense labour required: it is variously estimated that between 75,000 and 400,000 stigmas are necessary to produce 1 lb of Saffron, and these must be individually hand-picked as soon as the flowers open during the two-week flowering period in autumn, and rapidly dried for storage.

The crocus is propagated by planting secondary corms about 12 cms apart; they are allowed to flower and are harvested for four seasons, after which they become susceptible to disease, and so are dug up and new corms planted.

Similar plants: The Saffron Crocus is not unlike the poisonous Meadow Saffron *Colchicum autumnale*, but the latter has 6, not 3 stigmas; the common Autumn Crocus *C. nudiflorus* is also similar, but its lvs die before the flower appears in autumn. *C. pallasi* which grows wild in Greece and Crete is even closer, but may be distinguished by the paler, orange, stigmas which do not project beyond the petals. The corms of *C. cancellatus*, another species confined to the Near East, from Greece to Jordan, are commonly sold for food on Levantine markets. The corms are distinguished by the particularly coarse network of fibrous scales which cover them.

Because it is so expensive, Saffron is often adulterated; for this reason it is best to avoid the powdered form and buy the dried stigmas instead. These should be red, with a strong scent and a pungent bitter-sweet taste, and should swell rapidly when dropped in water, releasing a stream of red dye which dilutes to yellow.

The name 'saffron' is sometimes applied to two other plants which have nothing in common with *C. sativus* except that they produce a similar yellow dye:

Turmeric the powdered rhizome of *Curcuma longa*, a plant belonging to the ginger family, is the usual yellow ingredient of curry powders. It is grown and used in S. India, Ceylon and S.E. Asia, where Saffron is absent, and is imported to Arabia and the Near East where it is used as a cheap substitute for Saffron. It is a useful spice, and invaluable for those dishes (in Europe, mainly Indian) which require it, but is disastrous when used instead of Saffron in the European seafood dishes mentioned above, for the flavour is quite different. In England it is used, among other things, in piccalilli.

Safflower (see p. 272). The dried florets are sold as a dye in Egypt, and to tourists under the guise of Saffron.

LILIACEAE

Lily Family

This widespread family includes some trees, shrubs and climbers, but most are herbs with rhizomes, corms or bulbs, often with basal lvs. Fls often showy, in few- or many-flowered heads, with parts in threes, with 6 perianth segments and 6 stamens. Frt a berry or capsule. The family is often divided, with justification, into several distinct families, with the Alliums removed to a family Amarillidaceae or Alliaceae. Taken in its broad sense, the Liliaceae includes a number of ornamental plants belonging to exotic genera such as *Agapanthus.* Most of the food plants of this family belong to the native European and North Asian genus *Allium*, which in addition to the cultivated forms described below includes such familiar wild species as Ramsons.

Alliums are bulbous unbranched perennials with a characteristic strong smell. Fls are small, often bell-shaped, borne in round heads or umbels.

KEY TO ALLIUM spp.		
1	Lvs flat or V-shaped in section, not hollow; flowering stem (scape) solid=**2**	**(10)**
2	Large rhizome present; bulb scarcely developed=**Chinese Chives**	**(3)**
3	No rhizome present=**4**	**(2)**
4	Bulb consisting of a number of segments (cloves) enclosed in a whitish papery membrane; inflorescence small, usually bearing aerial bulbs=**Garlic**	**(5)**
5	Bulb often obsolete, otherwise consisting of two thickened bladeless leaf bases, with several axillary bulbels=**6**	**(4)**
6	Bulb and axillary bulbels well developed; plant resembles a robust Garlic, but fls borne in a large umbel, as in Leek (see also Kurrat, below)=**Great-headed Garlic**	**(7)**
7	Bulb not (Leek), or poorly developed, without axillary bulbels=**8**	**(6)**
8	Larger plant, 40–100 cms tall; lvs broader, 1.2–4 cms wide. Very widely cultivated in N. and western Europe=**Leek**	**(9)**
9	Smaller, under 40 cms tall; lvs not more than 1.6 cms broad, similar to Chinese Chives. Near East, Greece etc.=**Kurrat**	**(8)**
10	Lvs cylindrical and hollow; scape hollow (except Rakkyo)=**11**	**(1)**
11	Lvs slender, less than 5 mm broad; scape rarely more than 5 mm in diameter; plants form clumps=**12**	**(14)**
12	Bulb well developed; scape solid=**Rakkyo**	**(13)**
13	Bulb scarcely developed; scape hollow=**Chives**	**(12)**
14	Lvs stouter; scape at least 6 mm, up to 2.5 cms in diameter=**15**	**(11)**
15	Lvs distinctly flattened on upper surface; perianth segments ('petals') white, pink or purple, and shorter, 3–6 mm long; bulb very large in proportion to stem (*Allium Cepa*)=**16**	**(20)**
16	Bulb large, usually single and circular in cross section; inflorescence normally without aerial bulbs=**Onion**	**(17)**
17	Bulb smaller, either single and poorly developed, or producing many slightly asymmetrical lateral bulbels and shoots=**18**	**(16)**

KEY TO ALLIUM spp.

18	Ground bulb poorly developed; inflorescence with many bulbs which often produce leaves and lateral bulbels while still on the plant=**Tree Onion**	**(19)**
19	Ground bulbs always well developed, producing lateral bulbs; infloresence normally without aerial bulbs=**Shallots, Ever-ready Onion,** and **Potato-** or **Multiplier Onion**	**(18)**
20	Lvs not flattened, round in cross-section; perianth segments yellowish, and longer, 6–8 mm; bulbs slender=**Welsh Onion**	**(15)**

Allium tuberosum
CHINESE CHIVES
(p. 204)

Description: A small Allium growing in dense clumps from a prominent rhizome; bulbs not or scarcely formed. Lvs flat, linear, grass-like, 15–25 x 0.3–0.7 cms; scape solid, slightly flattened, up to 45 cms long. Inflorescence a small rather loose umbel of white, widely spreading fls; perianth segments ca. 6 mm long with a green or reddish-brown stripe on the underside.

Names: Syn.: *Allium odorum.* Known to Chinese (Cantonese) grocers in Europe as *'Gau Tsoi'.*
Fr.: Ciboulette tubéreuse; It.: Cipollina tuberosa.

Uses: Grown for the leaves which are eaten blanched or green, and for the scapes with unopened inflorescences, which are used as a green vegetable. Both have a mild garlic-like or delicate onion flavour. In Chinese cooking the leaves are widely used finely chopped to flavour soups, noodle dishes and omelettes.

Origin, distribution and cultivation: As the English name suggests, this plant originated in China where it is of ancient cultivation, later spreading to Japan and the whole of the Far East. It is now commonly available from Chinese grocers in Western Europe, who import it direct from the Far East, but a few market-gardeners have begun commercial production in Europe. There is no reason why this excellent and easily cultivated species should not find more favour with gardeners and consumers in the future.

In Northern China and Japan Chinese Chives are grown from seeds, but as these are rarely set in hotter climates, it is propagated vegetatively, like most other *Allium* spp., in tropical countries.

Similar plants: The presence of a rhizome is the most singular characteristic of this species, but of course this cannot be seen in cut plants. The only other *Allium* with similar sized flat leaves is Kurrat (see p. 308), but the latter is restricted to Greece and the Near East. Chinese Chives is the only Allium cultivated for the unopened flower heads, so it is easily recognisable in this form.

Allium sativum
GARLIC
(p. 204)

Description: Mature plant 30–60 cms tall. Lvs linear, flat, 1–2.5 cms broad, slightly folded longitudinally, with a 'keel' on underside. Inflorescence not usually produced; when present the scape is round, coiled at first (remaining coiled in some varieties); spathe whitish, long and pointed; the umbel produces small aerial bulbs which displace the small whitish fls (these sometimes absent) with white or pinkish perianth segments (each ca. 3–4 mm long); anthers protruding.

Bulb composed of a number of 'cloves', roughly the shape of citrus fruit segments arranged around the stem, enclosed in the white, pinkish or sometimes even purple dry outer scales of the original parent bulb. Bulb grows entirely underground.

Names: Fr.: Ail; It.: Aglio; Sp.: Ajo; Ger.: Knoblauch; Dtch.: Knoflook; Dan.: Hvidlog; Ger.: Skordor; Russ.: Chesnok; Yug.: Češnjek.

Uses: Garlic is one of the world's most important flavouring agents, and is used extensively in almost all the countries in which it will grow. It is also invaluable in a general diet for health. Not only is it rich in vitamin C, but stimulates bile production and gland stimulation, reduces the build-up of cholesterol, is an antispasmodic, a vermifuge, and antibiotic, particularly effective in preventing bacterial infections. These properties have long been recognised empirically even among primitive peoples in many parts of the world who not only used it as a specific remedy, but magically, to ward off evil spirits, the vectors or agents of disease.

Prejudice against Garlic in Anglo-Saxon countries may be due in part to the climate of England: Garlic grown in cold or damp areas, like bulbs that have gone soft and discoloured from too lengthy storage, is sour and ill-flavoured. Aversion to Garlic probably derives as much from misuse: raw Garlic, used in such dishes as *aioli* in Provence or the *skordalia* of Greece is very pungent and leaves a fearful redolence on the breath. Raw Garlic is also somewhat indigestible, whereas cooked Garlic, is on the contrary, an aid to digestion. Provencal '40 clove chicken' and similar dishes demonstrate this admirably; the whole cloves are baked in fat for as long as it takes to cook the meat, until they acquire a creamy consistency with a mild nutty flavour; each diner may eat a dozen or more cloves with relish and impunity. Garlic then becomes a vegetable in its own right rather than just a flavouring agent.

A certain quantity of the commercial crops is dried and powdered for the same flavouring uses in the kitchen. These preparations are far less strong in flavour than the fresh article.

Origin, distribution and cultivation: Garlic is believed to have originated in central Asia, perhaps derived from the wild *A. longicuspis*. It was in cultivation in Egypt more than 5000 years ago, and has been used in Europe continuously since the classical era. It is the second most important economic *Allium* crop after onion, and is therefore widely cultivated on a field scale as well as in market- and home-gardens. It is propagated by planting single cloves, generally in spaces of about 15 x 30 cms.

Similar plants: Excluding the characteristic bulb, Garlic resembles Great-headed Garlic (see overleaf), and Rocambole (see below). Ramsons *A. ursinum* is a common wild European species which is occasionally cultivated by the home-gardener and used for flavouring. It may immediately be distinguished from Garlic by its broad elliptical lvs and white, star-like fls in a loose umbel.

Allium scorodoprasum
ROCAMBOLE, SAND LEEK

Description: Very like Garlic, but with sparser, stiff upright lvs with rough edges. Inflorescence a small compact umbel of aerial bulbs mixed with long-stalked fls from which the stamens do not protrude, both reddish-purple.

Names: From the Danish meaning 'rock onion'.
Fr.: Rocambole, Echalote d'Espagne; It.: Rocambola, Aglio romano, Aglio di Spagna; Sp.: Rocambole; Ger.: Rockenbolle, Schlangenknoblauch; Dtch.: Slangenlook; Dan.: Skov løg; Gr.: Praso annou; Russ.: Luk prirechni.

Uses: As Garlic, but its milder flavour makes it more suitable for certain dishes.

Origin, distribution and cultivation: Rocambole is a native of Europe, east to the Caucasus and Syria. In Northern Europe it grows in relatively dry rocky or sandy places (in Britain on the coasts of Scotland and northern England). It is now rarely cultivated, and only on a small scale for domestic consumption, having lost much favour since the last century, but is still gathered wild and offered for sale in some countries.

Similar plants: The purple-skinned varieties of Garlic, from which it can be distinguished by its purple flowers and bulbils (both whitish in garlic).

The name 'rocambole' is now most often applied to varieties of true Garlic *Allium sativum*, which have coiled scapes.

Allium ampeloprasum
LEEK, KURRAT
and **GREAT-HEADED GARLIC**
(p. 204)

Description: A variable species represented by 3 cultivated varieties which, among the other *Allium* spp. with plane, not hollow lvs, are distinguished by the large (5–10 cm) dense umbel in which the purple to pale pink fls are not displaced by bulbils, with a non-persistent papery bract, by the absence of a rhizome, and, when bulb is present (Great-headed Garlic) this consists of two swollen bladeless storage lvs surrounded by the bases of foliage lvs, with axillary bulbils.

Leek (var. *porrum*) is a large biennial, 40–100 cms tall, not or scarcely forming a bulb. Lvs V-shaped, keeled, with thin blades 1–2–4 cm broad; scape solid, pithy.

Kurrat (var. *kurrat*) is similar but smaller, with narrower lvs, and bulb sometimes more developed.

Great-headed Garlic (var. *ampeloprasum*), a perennial, resembles a very large Garlic plant (until it flowers); lvs 10–35 mm broad; bulb always well developed, 2-lobed, with axillary bulbils not enclosed together in a papery outer membrane.

Names: (Leek): Fr.: Poireau; It.: Porro; Sp.: Puerro; Ger.: Breitlauch; Dtch.: Prei; Dan.: Porre; Gr.: Prasson; Russ.: Luk porei; Yug.: Por.

Uses: Leek The edible part is the elongated blanched bases of foliage lvs which are always cooked, usually boiled and used in combination with other vegetables in soups, stews, etc. but also on their own ('Poor man's asparagus'). They combine particularly well with creamy sauces (such as *béchamel*) in pies or with bacon or ham.

Kurrat is grown for the green foliage lvs which are used raw, chopped in the same manner as Chives. **Great-headed Garlic** is cultivated for the bulb, which is intermediate in flavour between onion and garlic, but milder than either.

Origin, distribution and cultivation: Wild *A. ampeloprasum*, the ancestor of these three varieties and also known as Wild Leek or Great Round-headed Garlic, occurs in its natural state around the Mediterranean from the Atlantic Isles to the Middle East, and has spread to much of central and northern Europe, including the British Isles. Var. *porrum* was already in cultivation in the Middle Ages, and today is mainly a crop of N. Europe, with France as the major producer.

Leek has a greater resistance to cold than Onion; indeed flowering is induced by cold spells. Since bulbs are not produced, growth is continuous and the plants can be harvested over a long period. Leeks are grown from seed, either sown under glass in winter for transplanting in spring, or sown in the open in spring. They are planted in deep furrows, and the soil drawn up around the 'stalks' to exclude the light. Most crops are on large market-garden-plot scale, but Leeks are also grown extensively by the home-gardener.

Kurrat is mainly a produce of the Arab countries of the Near East, but it is cultivated to a small extent in the Balkans. It is also grown from seed and like Leeks has an extended harvesting period. Great-headed Garlic is presumably also of ancient cultivation in Europe, although it scarcely differs from its wild ancestor. It is cultivated only on a small scale as a home-garden crop.

Similar plants: Leek is unmistakeable due to its size. Kurrat may be confused with Chinese Chives (see p. 306). Great-headed Garlic might be confused with true Garlic; see key (p. 305), and description above.

'Pearl Onions', produced in central Europe and Italy and used almost exclusively for pickling, from a form of *A. ampeloprasum*, are small white bulbs consisting of a single storage leaf which multiply when the scape is removed.

Allium cepa
ONION, SHALLOT, etc.
(p. 204)

Description: A very variable species. The description applies principally to var. *cepa*; aberrations are described in the list of main varieties below.

A biennial herb usually grown as an annual, 30–100 cms tall. The lvs, which are produced in succession from the bulb, have cylindrical blades, at first solid then becoming hollow, glaucous, slightly to markedly flattened on upper surface, erect but not very stiff, often bending over when fibres are broken. Bulb variable according to cv, typically large and globose, oblate or ovoid, composed of concentric thickened white leaf bases; the outer thin papery layers may be silvery white, pale or dark brown, to reddish-purple; inflorescence is large, globose, composed of numerous, usually greenish-white fls with relatively short stamens and irregularly but widely opening perianths; bracts are 2–3, persistent; the scape is up to 100 cm long, at first solid, becoming hollow, and swollen below the middle.

Three main varieties, each divided into numerous cultivars, are recognised:

1. var. *cepa* **Common Onions** The great majority of commercial bulbing onions belong to this group. The many cvs vary not only in flavour, pungency, size and colour, but also in storage quality and in their suitability for different climates: bulbing is induced by photoperiod, and many successful northern European cvs dependent on 14–16 hours of daylight in summer will not develop in southern countries. The bulbs of this group are large and usually single. Spring Onions, such as cv 'White Lisbon' also belong to this group, but are harvested when immature. The inflorescence typically lacks bulbils.

2. var. *proliferum* **Tree Onion**, **Catawissa Onion**, etc. These forms often have poorly-developed bulbs, but the infloresence bears bulbs which can produce lvs and scapes bearing further bulbils, whilst still attached to the primary inflorescence. The exiguous bulbs and bulbils of these onions make them of little commercial value.

3. var. *aggregatum* This group is divided into three distinct forms:

Shallot often called var. *ascalonicum*, or even considered as a distinct species, *A. ascalonicum* is by far the most important form of *A. cepa* after the Common Onion. It is a smaller plant than most Common Onions, producing a cluster of slightly asymmetrical bulbs from a single planted bulb of the same size, the bulbs being separate, not enclosed in a common outer set of scales. Different cvs are recognisable by the colour of their skins – grey, pinkish, or golden-brown, which have subtly different flavours. Like Common Onions, the inflorescence does not normally produce bulbils.

Ever-ready Onion is a perennial with lvs and bulbs narrower than those of common onions. It produces several bulbs each year.

Potato, or **Multiplier Onion** produces quite large oblate bulbs together with many lateral bulbs enclosed in the same outer scales which produce their own bulbs and foliage if left for a second year. They do not normally flower, and propagate by bulb division.

Names: (Common Onion): Fr.: Oignon; It.: Cipolla; Sp.: Cebolla; Ger.: Zwiebel; Dtch.: Ui; Dan.: Løg; Gr.: Krommion, Kremmydi; Russ.: Luk repchati; Yug.: Navadna cebula. (Shallot): Fr.: Echalote; It.: Scalogno; Sp.: Chalote; Ger.: Schalotte; Dtch.: Sjalot; Dan.: Skalotteløg; Ger.: Sallóti; Russ.: Luk nemetski, Shalot.

The various names for shallot derive from the Palestinian city of Ascalon, but the attribution probably results from a Roman confusion with another, blue-flowered, wild Onion of the Near East. 'Scallion', variously used for shallot and for other long-necked bulbs, especially by North Americans, is also cognate with Ascalon, via the Old French *Eschalogne.*

Uses: Onion is the single most universally appreciated flavouring plant, a basic ingredient in the kitchens of all the civilised nations for as long as it has been in cultivation, and rapidly becoming indispensable wherever it is introduced. It can be eaten raw, as a garnish, or cooked as a vegetable in its own right, but its main use is as a flavouring agent. Onions have several distinct flavours, depending on how much, and at what heat they are cooked, and these various flavours are appropriate to different dishes. If a recipe calls for chopped onion to be gently sweated in butter and water, it should not be sizzled in hot fat, which produces a rank, somewhat acrid taste.

Shallots, used largely for pickling, are underestimated as a fresh flavouring by unsophisticated cooks, but are justly appreciated by the discerning, particularly in France. Their virtue lies in a stronger flavour than the milder (eg. Spanish) Onions, but without the strong pervasive smell of all Common Onions. Shallots should never be browned, as this makes them bitter. Reduced in wine or wine vinegar, they form the bases of sauces which are some of the glories of French provincial cooking.

Ever-ready and Multiplier Onion have the advantage for the home-gardener of providing a steady source of bulbs, in small quantity, over a long period. Tree Onion has very pungent bulbs, but is little used.

There is an increasing demand, mainly from food processing companies, for dried onion products, in rings, flakes or powder. These have the advantage of reducing transportation and storage costs and assuring a more uniform flavour, but for the home consumer offer only a negligible convenience to be weighed against the inevitable loss of quality.

Origin, distribution and cultivation: Onion is of such ancient cultivation in its native Turkistan that its wild ancestor, if still extant, has been lost sight of. It was a staple article of diet in Ancient Egypt (the Israelites, grumbling about conditions on their flight to Canaan ca. 1500 BC, harked back to the onions they used to eat there (Numbers XI, 5)). Egypt remains the world's principal exporter of Onions, the country's second most valuable export crop after cotton. Great Britain is the greatest importer, consuming more than a quarter of a million tons a year, of which she produces less than a fifth. All European countries produce Onions, but Spain, Italy and Turkey lead the export trade.

Common Onions are usually propagated by seed, but the home-gardener, and to a lesser extent market gardeners, also plant 'sets'. These are small bulbs produced under special conditions which are dependent on temperature and are planted in the next year to give an early crop of large bulbs. Another method of cultivation used by commercial growers is transplants: densely sown plants are pulled up after two and a half months, their foliage pruned, and replaced at wider intervals.

Similar plants: See key, p. 305. *A. cepa* can be distinguished from all other cultivated *Allium* spp. by cutting a section through a leaf: it is hollow, but not cylindrical, somewhat flattened, with a concave upper (or inner) face, and convex outer surface.

Allium schoenoprasum
CHIVES
(p. 204)

Description: A small, strongly tillering, tussocky herb, 15–40 cms tall. Bulbs are small, narrowly oblong, white, 1–3 cm long, 0.5–1.5 cm broad. Lvs narrow, 0.1–0.2 mm thick, hollow, tubular, 10–30 cm long, occasionally tinged with purple at base, but light green, only slightly glaucous; umbel is born on a slender hollow scape. Fls pinkish-mauve, opening first at top of umbel, then progressively towards base; spathe short, unbeaked, persistent.

Names: Fr.: Ciboulette; It.: Cipollina; Sp.: Ceboletta; Ger.: Schnittlauch; Dtch.: Bieslook; Dan.: Purløg; Gr.: Krómmio to skhoinópraso; Russ.: Luk scoroda; Yug.: Drobnak.

Uses: The leaves are the part used, raw and chopped, as a garnish or in soups, omelettes, salads, etc. They cannot be dried, but frozen chives are marketed in the USA.

Origin, distribution and cultivation: *A. schoenoprasum* occurs wild in most of the holarctic region (Europe, N. Asia, N. America). They appear to have been cultivated in Europe since the 16th century and today are widely grown, mainly in the home-garden where they provide a continuous source of leaves as well as being ornamental. The demand from caterers and grocers assures a limited production on market-garden scale. Propagation is by seeding or by division of a clump.

Similar plants: Spring Onion (see *A. cepa*) have much thicker lvs. Chinese Chives (p. 306) are quite different, having plane, not fistulose lvs. Rakkyo (see p. 311) is the most similar species.

Allium chinense
RAKKYO

Description: Similar to Chives (p. 310) in its bunching habit, size and very narrow hollow lvs, but these are 3- to 5-angled, not so stiffly erect, and of a brighter green, and bulbs are well developed, ovoid. Lvs usually 3 to a bulb, die down in early summer and new lvs from lateral bulbs grow with inflorescences in early autumn; scape solid, bearing a flattened umbel with 15–20 lavender fls on long pedicels.

Names: Rakkyo is the Japanese name for this *Allium.* It is known to Chinese (Cantonese) grocers in Europe as *Kiu Tsoi* or *Heung Kiu Tsoi.*
Fr.: Ciboulette de Chine; It.: Cipollina della China; Sp.: Ceboletta de China; Ger.: Chinesische Schnittlauch.

Uses: Rakkyo is used almost exclusively for pickles.

Origin, distribution and cultivation: *A. chinense* is a native of central and eastern China, which with Japan is still the main area of cultivation. It is scarcely cultivated in Europe except by a few home-gardeners, but may follow other Chinese vegetables which have been adopted by European market-gardeners in recent years. Pickled Rakkyo is exported both by Japan and the United States. It is propagated by transplanting small bulbs.

Similar plants: Chives (p. 310). The bulbs resemble those of young onions, but differ in that they do not contain bladeless scale lvs; all scales are the bases of foliage lvs.

This is one of the *Allium* spp., together with Shallots, etc. known in America as 'Scallions'.

Allium fistulosum
WELSH ONION
(p. 204)

Description: A variable, freely tillering *Allium* sp. 40–80 cm high, closely resembling *A. cepa*, but bulbs are small, narrowly oblong, slightly asymmetrical like Shallot, white or pink. Lvs hollow, very acute, not flattened dorsally near apices. Fls open first at summit of umbel, then progressively outward; no aerial bulbils are produced in the umbel.

Names: The English name probably derives from the German *welsche* (foreign), so called when the plant was first introduced to Germany from central Asia in the Middle Ages. It has no connection with Wales. *A. fistulosum* (fistulose: hollow, refers to the lvs) is also known in English as Japanese Bunching Onion.
Fr.: Ciboule; It.: Cipoletta; Sp.: Ceboletta; Ger.: Winterheckenzwiebel; Dtch.: Piplook, Indische prei; Dan.: Pibløg; Russ.: Luk dudchaty, - batun; Yug.: Čebula zimska.

Uses: Being milder than Onion or even than Shallot, Welsh Onion requires less cooking, and is often eaten raw, including the green parts, like spring onion. It is the proper *Allium* sp. to use in any Chinese recipe calling for Onion.

Origin, distribution and cultivation: *A. fistulosum* is not known in the wild state, but is closely related to *A. altaicum* from Mongolia. It has been in cultivation in China since prehistoric times, and is the main *Allium* sp. there, as in Japan and most of S.E. Asia. In Europe it is little known, only cultivated by home-gardeners, more frequently in France and Italy. It is propagated by seed.

Similar plants: The bulbs of Welsh Onion might easily be confused with those of Shallot, but tend to be less swollen, and with rougher outer scales. The plant resembles Shallot, particularly because of its bunching growth habit, and other forms of *A. cepa* except in that its lvs are round in cross-section, not flattened on upper surface.

The name 'Welsh Onion' is sometimes erroneously applied to Ever-ready Onion (see *A. cepa*, p. 309).

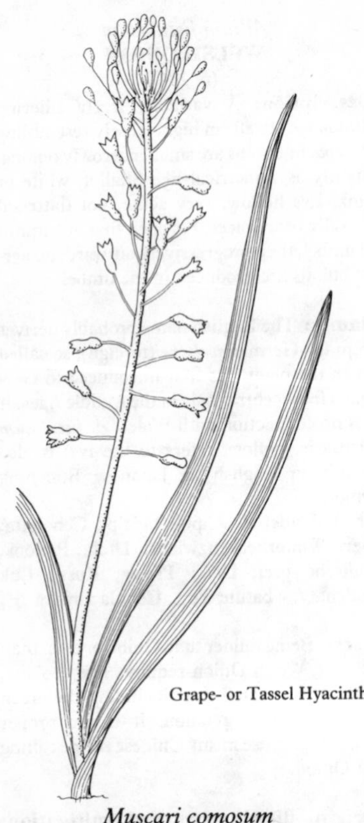

Grape- or Tassel Hyacinth

Muscari comosum
GRAPE HYACINTH

Description: This plant looks very much like one of the *Allium* spp., but the inflorescence is an elongate spike, not a bracted umbel. Lvs are linear, rather limp and tending to collapse, semi-cylindrical, 5–15 mm broad. The flowering spike, up to 60 cm in height, is surmounted by a somewhat flat-topped tassel of small, long-stalked sterile mauve fls; beneath, the larger fertile fls on stalks about as long as the corolla are erect, purple and tightly bunched near apex, greenish brown, laterally spreading and less dense on lower part. The bulbs resemble small brown-skinned onions, but lack the characteristic allium scent, and do not separate easily into lf base layers.

Names: This sp. is also known as Tassel Hyacinth, in order to distinguish it from other Grape Hyacinths.
Syn.: *Leopoldia comosa.*
Fr.: Muscari; It.: Giancinto; Sp.: Jacito de penacho; Ger.: Träubel; Dtch.: Pluim hyacint; Dan.: Dusk Hyacint; Gr.: Klimatódis yákinthos; Russ.: Gadyuchni luk.

Uses: The bulbs of this plant and of some other *Muscari* spp., especially *M. atlanticum*, which occurs in Britain, are eaten in many Mediterranean countries, but especially in Italy and in Greece. They are rather bitter, and must be boiled in a large volume of water with a little vinegar, after which they are preserved in oil, or served as antipasto, in salads, etc.

Origin, distribution and cultivation: *M. comosum* occurs throughout central and southern Europe. It is sometimes cultivated in gardens, but the wild plants, which are abundant on waste land, in orchards, fields, etc., provide most of the bulbs of commerce. These are sometimes available from Greek or Italian grocers in northern Europe, and are exported as far as North America.

Similar plants: *M. comosum* is distinguished from *M. atlanticum* and other Grape Hyacinths by the tassel of long-stalked sterile fls at the top of the flowering stem. The bulbs of *M. atlanticum* and of others may be used in the same way.

Asparagus officinalis
ASPARAGUS
(p. 198)

Description: Members of the genus *Asparagus* differ so strikingly in appearance from *Allium* spp. that their place in the same family is at first far from obvious. *A. officinalis* is a perennial rhizomatous plant with annual stems standing ca. 1.5 m in height. The lvs of the feathery, fully developed stems are scale-lvs, triangular and adpressed to the stem; their function is carried out by needle-like cladodes, which are modified stems borne in clusters in the axils of scale-lvs. Fls small, yellowish or green, borne singly or in twos or threes in the axils of branchlets; male and female fls usually on separate plants.

The parts eaten are the young shoots or 'spears' cut when they are 20–30 cm tall. Different cvs vary in thickness and in colour, from very fleshy and white with green tips to green, or green with purple tips and scale lvs. Wild and more 'primitive' forms are slender and more pigmented.

Names: Fr.: Asperge; It.: Asparagio; Sp.: Espárrago; Ger.: Spargel; Dtch.: Asperge; Dan.: Asparges; Gr.: Sparággia; Russ.: Sparzha; Yug.: Šparga.

Uses: Asparagus spears are a luxury vegetable, best eaten boiled or steamed with hollandaise sauce or with melted butter, with or without cheese, or cold with vinaigrette. They are also used for soup. Large quantities are canned, with inevitable loss of flavour.

Origin, distribution and cultivation: *A. officinalis* is one of several native European *Asparagus* spp. It occurs in sandy places, near river banks, etc., throughout central and southern Europe and in North Africa and western and central Asia. It was cultivated by the ancient Egyptians, Greeks and Romans, but appears to have been abandoned during the Middle Ages, except by the Arabs, until it became fashionable once more in 17th century France. Asparagus is now cultivated throughout Europe on light or sandy soils, by home- and market-gardeners, sometimes on a large field scale. Wild shoots are gathered all over southern Europe and are available in local markets from April to July.

Similar plants: 'Wild Asparagus' usually means the narrow green shoots of *A. officinalis* which are gathered in the wild, but those of other native European sp., especially *A. acutifolius* are also gathered and sometimes sold on markets under this name. The shoots of this sp. resemble very thin shoots of *A. officinalis*, but the scale lvs are narrower, thorn-shaped, the lower ones hard and spiny, and they are much stronger in flavour. The mature stems are quite different in appearance, somewhat resembling Juniper, for the cladodes are stout and spiny.

The shoots of another member of the Lily family, Butcher's Broom *Ruscus aculeatus* are also used as an Asparagus substitute in southern Europe, though they are somewhat bitter and require more cooking. The tips resemble an artists' paint brush, with a smooth stem bearing only a few long widely spaced scale-lvs.

The Asparagus 'leaves' used by florists are those of *A. plumosus*, a purely ornamental South African species.

POACEAE (GRAMINAE)

Grass Family

A very large homogenous family of about 10,000 spp. widely distributed throughout the world, its species often dominating the vegetation of large natural areas such as prairies, steppes, savannas, and the overwhelming surface of farmland, in the form of meadows, downs, leys and cornfields.

Grasses are not popularly thought of as flowering plants because their fls are very simple and inconspicuous. The family is similar to the sedges, below, but the stems are round with conspicuous nodes, the lvs are in 2 rows, and the structure of inflorescences is characteristic.

The inflorescence consists of spikelets arranged either in loose or dense panicles (eg. Millet), in spikes (Wheat) or in racemes. Each spikelet consists of a group of alternating bracts; the 2 lower, sterile, bracts are called glumes; above these are one or many pairs of scales, the outer one of each pair being the lemma which may or may not be awned. (In cultivated spp. in which both forms exist, the awned or 'bearded' form is the more primitive; thus Durum Wheat is closer to the wild ancestors of Wheat than is the beardless Bread Wheat.) The inner scale of each pair is the palea, enclosing the floret and later the 1-seeded frt or 'grain'. The structure of the lvs, and particularly of their bases at the junction with the stem provide characters which enable identification of grasses even at an early vegetative stage. The number of parallel veins and the direction, clockwise or anti-clockwise, in which the blade may be twisted vary between spp. The lf base, or sheath, may form a complete tube around the stem, or it may be split; in some spp. the split extends downwards almost or quite to base. At the top of the sheath, where the blade begins, there is usually a thin projecting rim, the ligule, which varies in different spp. (this character has not been used in the key given below), and the basal angles of the blade are often extended in a pair of claw-like lobes, the auricles, which also differ in shape according to spp.

The Graminae constitute the single most important economic plant family in the world. The grain crops described below provide the staple diet for most of the world's populations, and every year about one twentieth of the total land surface of the globe is occupied by them. Grain crops are the very material basis of human civilisations. The neolithic revolution in agriculture, which took place between the tenth and fifth centuries BC, occurred when these crops were taken into cultivation, enabling the land to support much larger sedentary populations, with many people living in towns. Until that time, almost the whole population was engaged in the finding or production of food. With the regular, annual supply of staple food guaranteed by grain crops, human occupations diversified, leaving food production to one section of society, the farmers, while others could devote their time to the trades, arts and sciences which are the basis of civilisation. This revolution occurred more or less concurrently in different parts of the world, with different species used in each major region: wheat in the Middle East, Europe and northern Asia (supplemented by Rye, Barley and Oats, especially in areas unsuited to Wheat cultivation), Rice in southern Asia, Maize in the New World, and, to a lesser extent, Sorghum and Millets in Africa.

The overwhelming importance of the Graminae in agriculture does not rest solely on the grain crops. Although forage grasses (not treated in this book) are not popularly thought of as crop plants, they are of outstanding economic importance. Grassland, whether natural or in sown leys, is one of the mixed farmer's greatest assets. The advantage of grasses over other forage crops, which die when their foliage is stripped, is that grasses thrive under grazing, repeatedly putting up new shoots and tillers, and thus maintaining a perennial source of forage or fodder. Grass for fodder may be cut and fed to cattle fresh or as silage, or dried as the sole or chief constituent of hay.

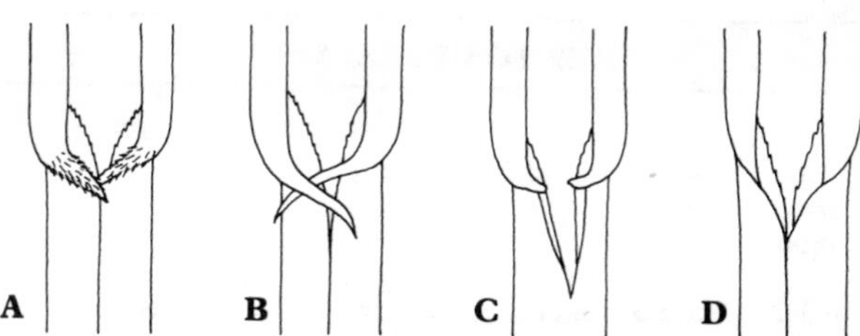

Leaf bases showing development of ligule and auricles in **A**: Wheat; **B**: Barley; **C**: Rye; **D**: Oats

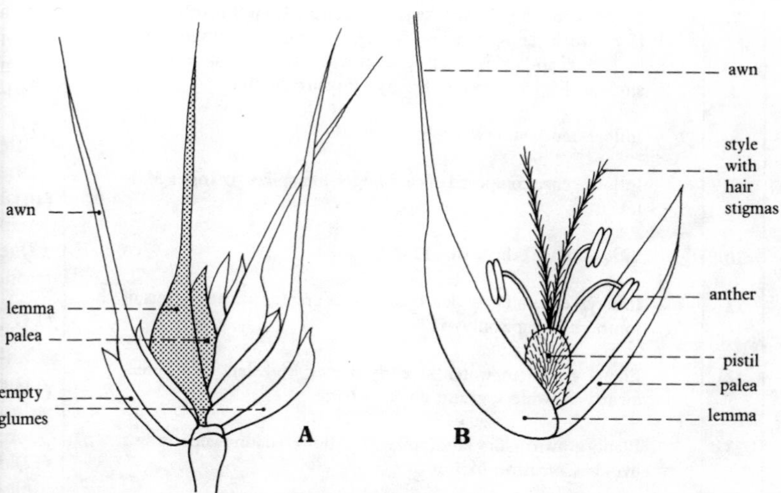

Schematic spikelets (**A**) and single flower (**B**) of awned wheat

KEY TO CEREALS

1	Usually larger plants, 1–4 m tall; lvs broad, mostly more than 2.5 cm wide, tending to spread and curve downwards = **2**	(6)
2	Large (1–4 m) plant with very broad (5–15 cm) lvs; male fls in terminal tassel, female fls and cobs in axils of middle lvs on stem = **Maize**	(3)
3	Medium or large plants; lvs 1–13 cm broad; fls and grains all in terminal bisexual inflorescence = **4**	(2)

KEY TO CEREALS

4	Inflorescence a large compact panicle; grains large (4–7 mm), globose, white or dark reddish-brown; spikelets/grains in pairs or in threes, with one stalkless, the others on short stalks=**Sorghum**	(5)
5	Inflorescence a bulrush-like spike, very dense, the grains free from lemma and palea at maturity, the surface of spike usually smooth=**Bulrush Millet**	(4)
6	Smaller plants, under 1.5 m; lvs narrow, less than 2.5 cm across, more erect and grass-like=**7**	(1)
7	Inflorescence a bulrush-like spike differing from Bulrush Millet (5, above) in being more lax, the mature grains partially enclosed by lemma and palea; each spikelet with 1–3 bristles, the whole surface of spike therefore bristly=**Foxtail Millet**	(8)
8	Inflorescence otherwise=**9**	(7)
9	Inflorescence composed of ca. 5 finger-like spikes=**Finger Millet**	(10)
10	Inflorescence otherwise=**11**	(9)
11	Inflorescence a fairly dense panicle of erect branches (crops of southern Europe only)=**12**	(14)
12	Plants grown in water in early stages; spikelets 1-flowered, awned or awnless; grains oblong=**Rice**	(13)
13	Plants grown on dry land; spikelets 2-flowered, unawned; grains ovoid=**Common Millet**	(12)
14	Inflorescence a lax panicle of spreading branches or with branches only on one side (Oats), or a spike=**15**	(11)
15	Lvs with ca. 12 veins, usually twisted anti-clockwise from base; auricles absent; inflorescence a panicle=**Oats**	(16)
16	Lvs twisted clockwise from base; inflorescence a spike=**17**	(15)
17	Lvs with ca. 20 veins; auricles long, slender, hairless; spikelets in clusters of 2–3 at each node, awned=**Barleys**	(18)
18	Lvs with ca. 12 veins; spikelets solitary at each node, awned or awnless=**19**	(17)

KEY TO CEREALS		
19	Auricles very short, hairy; glumes very narrow, 1-nerved=**Rye**	(20)
20	Auricles long, blunt, hairy; glumes broad, 3-nerved=**Wheats**	(19)

Young plants of the last four cereals can be identified by examining the lf-sheaths with a lens. These are hairless in Oats and Barley (Barley with large auricles, Oats without); in Wheat the lf-sheaths are densely covered with short hairs; those of Rye are similar but with conspicuous long hairs intermingled with the short ones.

Farmers and all those familiar with the limited number of varieties of these cereals grown locally in any one area do not depend on the characters used above to identify them. They can usually tell the crops apart at a glance, even from a great distance, by the colour. Looking across fields anywhere in Britain or north-west Europe in spring or early summer, before the plants turn straw-coloured, the bright pale green of Barley contrasts vividly with the darker, rather glaucous green of Bread Wheat and the grey-green of Rye. These distinctions have not been used in the key because they are only relative, and do not apply to the whole range of varieties within each species.

Zea mays
MAIZE

(p. 208)

Description: A large annual with a single stem usually 2–3 m high, but varying from 1–6 m, 2–4 cm in diameter, with ca. 14 nodes. Lvs alternate, spreading on either side of stem, 10–20 in number, with long-lanceolate blades 30–150 cm x 5–15 cm. Male inflorescence a 'tassle' up to 40 cm long at apex of stem; female inflorescence an ear or 'cob', born in axils of middle lvs about half way up stem, 1, 2 or 3 per plant, the cob and grains sheathed in ca. 10 overlapping modified lvs, called the 'husk'.

A great many cvs are recognised, which fall into one of 5 major groups according to the structure of the grain and their uses:

1. Flint Maize Grains very variable in colour, from white through yellow to red, purple or almost black, smaller than Dent Maize, with rounded ends, consisting mainly of hard endosperm with a little soft starch at centre.
2. Dent Maize Larger grains, also variable in colour but usually yellow or white, containing a greater proportion of soft starch extending to the apex and which shrinks on drying, producing a characteristic dent.
3. Popcorn A more primitive form with small grains and an even higher proportion of hard endosperm than Flint Maize. On heating, the steam produced inside the grain causes it to explode, the small quantity of endosperm expanding to form a fluffy mass around the everted hull.
4. Sweet corn Grains are shiny and translucent when immature, becoming wrinkled when dry but remaining broader than Flint Corn. The endosperm has a relatively high sugar content because less of it is converted to starch during growth.
5. Waxy Maize So called because the starch consists entirely of amylopectin, which has a waxy appearance.

Names: Fr.: Maïs; It.: Granturco, Mais; Sp.: Maíz; Ger.: Mais; Dtch.: Mais; Dan.: Majs; Gr.: Aravositos; Russ.: Kukuruza, Mais.

Uses: Although the nutritional value of Maize is lower than that of most other cereals it is the most important cereal in the world after Wheat and Rice. Dent and Flint Maizes are grown as a human food, as fodder for livestock, as an oil-seed crop and as the source of other substances used in industry. They are staple foods in many tropical countries but this use is confined in Europe to Italy and the South-Eastern countries, where it is of secondary importance. In Italy *polenta*, the medium-ground flour, is used in a variety of ways. N. America produces grits (coarsely ground flour), cornflakes and other breakfast cereals, corn-flour (very finely ground), and other commercial food products. The bulk of the European crop is used as fodder, the smaller grains of Flint Maizes being preferred for poultry, the larger and starchier Dent varieties for meal in cattle and pig fodders. Oil seed crops are mostly grown in America.

Sweet Corn is grown on a small scale as a vegetable. Popcorn and Waxy Maize are not European crops; the former is grown almost exclusively in America, while Waxy Maize is used in the Far East to produce a tapioca-like starch.

Origin, distribution and cultivation: Maize is the native grain crop of the New World where it has been cultivated in a wide range of environmental conditions, from sea-level to over 3000 m, from Chile to southern Canada, for more than 5000 years. The species, which arose entirely in cultivation, is structurally very different from its wild ancestors, plants with tiny cobs 2–3 cm long not sheathed in modified lvs. Indeed Maize cannot reproduce without human agency, as the peculiar structure of the ear prevents it from shedding its seed.

Maize has many advantages over other cereals, including a wide tolerance of different climates, the highest yield of grain per man-hours of labour, resistance to depredation by birds, etc., and for these reasons it was spread throughout the world soon after the Spanish conquest. It remains the most important of all crops in the United States, and has supplanted, or is in the process of doing so, native grain crops in many tropical countries, such as Millets in parts of Africa and Hill Rice in S.E. Asia, and is widely grown as a secondary crop almost everywhere else. Southern England, the Netherlands and North Germany form the northern boundaries of cultivation in Europe, where it is grown on a very large scale, with the Soviet Union, Rumania and Yugoslavia leading production. France also exports Maize, but the other West European countries together form the world's largest importer.

Similar plants: In the earlier vegetative stages Maize resembles Sorghum, below.

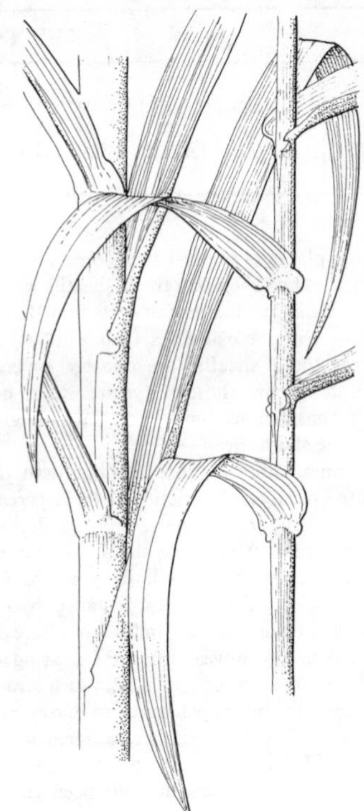

Sugar Cane (A) and European Cane (B)

Saccharum officinarum
SUGAR CANE

Description: A very tall grass, 2.5–6 m in height. The culm or cane is composed of joints 5–25 cm long, 1.5–6 cm in diameter, the internodes cylindrical or sometimes swollen in the middle, barrel-shaped, and variable in colour, usually green, often flushed with red or purple, the surface somewhat waxy. Lvs alternate in 2 rows on either side of stem, about 10 in number when in full growth, the lower half or more of stem usually bare as older lvs die and drop off; lf-blades ca. 1 m long, 2–10 cm broad, with sharp cutting, often toothed margins. Canes are cut before inflorescence; this is a tassle, a loose feathery-silky terminal panicle 25–50 cm long.

Names: Fr.: Canne à sucre; It.: Canna de zucchero; Sp.: Caña de azucar; Ger.: Zuckerrohr; Dtch.: Suikerriet; Dan.: Sukkerrør; Gr.: Zakharokálamo; Russ.: Sakhari trotnik.

Uses: Originally a food crop, used for chewing or as a source of the very sweet juice extracted by crushing the canes. Sugar Cane is the earliest and still the most important source of commercial sugar (see origins of Sugar Beet, p. 243), obtained by reduction of the sap. The refined sugar is indistinguishable from that of Sugar Beet. Other commercial products are molasses, refined syrup and rhum. Industrial methyl alcohol, acetone, butane and food yeasts including baker's and brewer's yeasts are manufactured from molasses.

Origin, distribution and cultivation: *S. officinarum* is one of 6 spp. of *Saccharum*, all from the Old World tropics. This sp., which originated in New Guinea and neighbouring islands, was taken to most of the inhabited islands of the Pacific and westward to Malaysia by early Polynesians. It is now grown principally for sugar and the various industrial derivatives. Sugar Cane was introduced to parts of Europe - Cyprus, Crete, Spain - in the 8th century by the Arabs. Their Sugar Cane industry thrived, particularly in Spain, until Columbus took canes to the West Indies on his second voyage in 1493. Thereafter those islands became the chief producers and the centre of the industry which depended on and fuelled the West African slave trade. Sugar Cane is now grown on a vast scale in most tropical countries. A little is still grown in S.E. Europe and in Spain, but no longer for the international sugar trade.

Similar plants: European Cane or Giant Reed *Arundo donax* is the only European grass large enough to be mistaken for Sugar Cane. It is much commoner than Sugar Cane in the Mediterranean where it occurs wild in marshy areas or by rivers, and is often planted as windbreaks at the edges of cultivated fields, on the banks of dykes, etc. This plant has thinner stems with lvs persistent right to base.

Sorghum bicolor agg.
SORGHUM
(p. 208)

Description: A usually annual grass with a single stem 0.5–3 cm in diameter, 1–6 m in height, but some modern cvs, including ones grown in Europe may stand only 50–100 cm tall. Lvs 7–24 according to cv, alternately spreading and curving downwards, the sheaths long, overlapping, encircling stem, with short white hairs at base; auricles triangular or lanceolate; blade long-lanceolate, 30–130 x 1.5–13 cm. Inflorescence a dense panicle, almost globose to oblong, erect, or in some cvs with stem recurved to almost 180 degrees, so head is pendent; spikelets in pairs, one stalked and sterile, the other stalkless, 1–10 mm long. Grains globose to ovoid, 4–8 mm long, variable in colour according to cv: white, yellow, reddish to purple-brown.

The taxonomy of the cultivated *Sorghum* spp. is complicated. Several hundred forms exist which are considered by some botanists to belong to about 30 distinct species and by others to subspecies or varieties of a single species, *S. bicolor*. Most forms grown in Europe belong to *S. bicolor sensu strictu*: **Grain** or **Sugar Sorghums**, with a high sugar content in the stems, and elongate, compact heads, or to *S. dochna*, Broom Sorghum, in which the inflorescences have long lateral branches. Among the better known exotic forms are **Gaoliang** *S. nervosum*, an important crop in China, with much laxer heads, **Durra** *S. durra* and **White Durra** *S. cernuum*, with pearly white grains, both grown in the Middle East, from Sudan to India, **Guinea Corn** *S. guineense*, and **Milo** *S. subglabrescens*.

Names: Syns. (of *S. bicolor sensu lato*): *S. vulgare*, *Andropogon sorghum*. Other common names include Great Millet and Sorgo. Fr.: Sorgho; It.: Sorgo; Sp.: Zahina, Sorgo; Ger.: Mohrenhirse, Durra; Dtch.: Sorghum; Gr.: Sorgo; Russ.: Sorgo; Yug.: Sirek.

Uses: Sorghum is the fourth most important cereal after Wheat, Rice and Maize, but its cultivation as a human food plant is restricted to Africa, India and China. Most Sorghums are grown for grain, but some are grown for sugar, like Sugar Cane, and Broom

Sorghums, first developed in Italy in the 17th century, are used for making brooms from the base of the 'brush' of green panicle, once the seeds and chaff have been removed. Most crops grown in Europe are used for forage or as fodder, the whole green plants being fed fresh or as silage, or the grains used for meals for cattle or poultry.

Origin, distribution and cultivation: The greatest concentration of both wild and cultivated forms of the genus *Sorghum* is to be found in Ethiopia and neighbouring countries. It is assumed that the earliest known immigrants to Ethiopia, Cushitic people who migrated from the Middle East several millenia BC brought with them Emmer Wheat and the techniques of cereal cultivation, which they applied to the native sorghums. Many wild forms had already evolved, and adapted to the different conditions prevailing in the great variety of environments and altitudes of Ethiopia, so these people were able to select and develop a range of cultivated forms at an early date. Sorghum reached India during the first millenium BC, and China, along the Silk Route, in the first centuries AD. They have been grown in Europe at least since Roman times; cultivation is restricted to the Mediterranean countries, the southern half of France, and central Europe eastwards to Russia.

Similar plants: The shape of the panicle is distinctive. Plants in the vegetative stage resemble Maize, but stems are more slender, not more than 3 cm in section. Bulrush Millet (below) has averagely narrower lvs, not more than 5 cm across, and is usually planted only in soils too arid and sandy even for Sorghum.

Other spp. of *Sorghum* such as Sudan Grass (*S. arundinarium*) are cultivated in the USA and parts of Africa as forage and fodder crops. These forms are more grass-like, tillering freely, and have very open panicles of smaller grains.

Pennisetum typhoides
BULRUSH MILLET
(p. 208)

Description: A tall annual, rarely less than 1 m, sometimes up to 4 m high, with a solid, slender or thick stem. Lvs in 2 opposite rows, with long clasping sheaths open at top, the blades long lanceolate, 30–100 x 0.5–5 cm, with a strong midrib. Inflorescence bulrush-like, 15–100 cm long, up to 4.2 cm in diameter, bearing densely packed spikelets each subtended by bristles, but these short, rarely projecting beyond mature grains; spikelets 2-flowered. Grains usually free of lemma and palea, globose to elliptic, 3–5 mm long, pearl-like, white, yellow, grey or bluish.

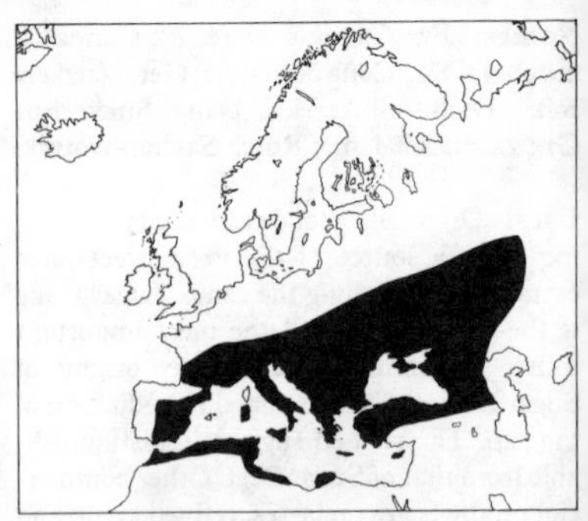
Distribution of Common Millet

Names: Syns.: *P. americanum*, *P. glaucum*, *P. tyhpoideum*, *P. spicatum.* Also known as Pearl Millet or Spiked Millet.
Fr.: Mil chandelle, Millet perle; It.: Miglio perlato; Sp.: Mijo perlado; Ger.: Perlehirse; Gr.: Kechri amerikis; Russ.: Pennizetum sizi.

Uses: Bulrush Millet is an important food crop in the driest parts of India, and even more in Sahelian Africa. The grain may be boiled or steamed like Rice, or ground for flour to make gruel or unleavened bread. In Africa, much of it is malted to produce 'beer', while in Europe the crops are used mainly to feed poultry and livestock.

Origin, distribution and cultivation: Bulrush Millet is not known in a truly wild state, but it is close to several wild spp. of West Africa, where it probably originated. Its particular value is that it is tolerant of very dry sandy soils, and for this reason was taken at an early date to other parts of Africa,

Arabia and India. Plants were first grown in Europe in the 16th century, but it has never been an important crop, being grown only to a small extent in the driest parts of Spain, Greece and the Soviet Union.

Similar plants: See Foxtail Millet, below.

Setaria italica
ITALIAN or FOXTAIL MILLET

(p. 208)

Description: An annual, 1–1.4 m tall, the stem, lvs and inflorescence often tinged with purple. Stems slender. Lf-sheaths long, open above; lf-blades 30–45 x 1.2–2.5 cm, tapering. Inflorescence a spike-like panicle 8–25 cm long, each short branch bearing 6–12 almost stalkless spikelets, each subtended by 1–3 bristles which project beyond the mature grains; grains tightly enclosed by pale yellow to dark reddish-brown lemma and palea, oval, 1.5–2 mm long, smooth, whitish when husked.

Names: Syns.: *Panicum italicum, Chaetochloa italica.*
Fr.: Millet des oiseaux, – d'Italie; It.: Panico; Ger.: Kohlbenhise, Hanepoot; Dan.: Kolbenhirse; Gr.: Italikó kekhrí; Russ.: Mogar; Yug.: Bar.

Uses: Although Foxtail Millet remains an important food crop in Japan, India and North Africa, and to a small extent in the Balkans, it is now grown principally as a commercial bird seed in the rest of Europe.

Origin, distribution and cultivation: This sp. is not known in a wild state; notwithstanding the epithet 'Italian', Foxtail Millet is thought to have been derived from *S. viridis* (see below: Similar plants) in China, perhaps as long as 5000 years ago. It probably reached Europe in the Paleolithic, and together with Common Millet was one of the most important grain crops of Europe until classical times. Today it is an unimportant crop, grown on a small field scale in central and southern Europe, somewhat more extensively in the Balkans.

Similar plants: See Bulrush Millet, above and key (p. 316). Foxtail Millet is closely related to Green Bristle Grass *S. viridis*, a wild weed of central and southern Europe and Asia which occurs in Britain, but is easily distinguished by the larger inflorescences and the spikelets from which the upper floret is shed at maturity.

Eleusine coracana
FINGER MILLET

Description: An annual tufted grass standing up to 1 m in height. Stems relatively thick. 4–12 mm across, the lvs with long overlapping sheaths: lf-blades 30–75 x 1–1.7 cm, often folded along midrib, hairless. Inflorescence a bunch of 4–6 dense erect spikes 5–15 cm long, compared to the fingers of a hand; grains globose, 1–2 mm in diameter, orange to dark reddish-brown.

Two major forms of this sp. are cultivated: The African Highland type with longer, laxer and straighter spikes and grains enclosed by long glumes, and the Afro-Asiatic types with shorter, denser, more curved spikes and mature grains exposed between short glumes.

Names: This is the grain known as Ragi in India and as Wimi or Bulo in East Africa.
Fr.: Eleusine; It.: Coracano; Sp.: Coracan; Ger.: Korakan; Gr.: Kekhrí daktylikó.

Uses: Finger Millet is the staple cereal of parts of Africa and India, used in the former for making gruels and for malting and brewing, and in India is often ground for flour after roasting. It is of little economic use in Europe, being grown only occasionally as a forage crop.

Origin, distribution and cultivation: It has long been supposed that Finger Millet originated in India, but more recent research suggests that the Indian form, which has been cultivated there since pre-Arian times arose through hybridisation of the native *E. indica* with African plants, which had also been cultivated in their homeland for several millenia. Finger Millet reached Egypt before the Christian era, but does not seem to have been adopted as a crop. The Romans introduced it to Europe, but with little subsequent success, though both forms are still grown to a very limited extent in the Mediterranean countries as fodder and forage crops.

Similar plants: The structure of the inflorescence is comparable only with *Digitaria* spp. (Finger grasses), which are not grown as crops in Europe. See also Japanese Barnyard Millet, p. 322.

Panicum miliaceum
COMMON MILLET
(p. 206)

Description: An annual, 30–100 cm high, hairy or hairless. Lvs 15–30 x 0.7–2 cm. Inflorescence a fairly dense panicle of many erect branches, up to 30 cm long, often drooping at maturity; spikelets 4–5 mm long, hairless, green or brownish, 2-flowered; grains enclosed by persistent lemma and palea, oval, 2 x 3 mm, smooth and whitish when husked.

Names: Also known as Russian-, Proso-, or Brown-corn Millet.
Fr.: Millet commun; It.: Miglio; Sp.: Mijo comun; Ger.: Echte Hirse; Dtch.: Pluigierst; Dan.: Alm. Hierse; Gr.: Koinó kekhrí; Russ.: Proso; Yug.: Proso.

Uses: The husked grain is eaten whole, usually boiled like Rice. The flour may be used for porridges of gruel, or mixed with wheat flour for making bread. Both green plants and grain are sometimes used as fodder.

Origin, distribution and cultivation: This is the true Millet, the *milium* of the Romans, whose name has been transferred to other fast-growing grain crops belonging to different genera. It was probably first taken into cultivation in central Asia, but it has been grown in Europe since early prehistoric times, before the introduction of wheat. Today Millet is principally a crop of central Asia, India and the Middle East. In Europe it has steadily lost ground to Wheat, but because it matures fast and is tolerant of drought it is still grown in many parts of the South and East, where excessively hot summers, short rainy seasons and poor soils prevent the cultivation of other cereals.

Similar plants: See *Echinochloa* spp., below, and Rice, p. 323. In India, a very similar but smaller plant, Little Millet *P. miliare*, is grown for the same purposes.

Echinochloa spp.
BARNYARD and JAPANESE MILLETS
(p. 208)

Description: Japanese Millet *E. frumentacea* is an annual, 50–100 cm in height, with smooth hairless branching stems. Lvs up to 37 x 2.5 cm, tapering, with finely toothed margins. Inflorescence a panicle of up to 15 closely-set branches, each resembling a small spike; spikelets 2-flowered, awnless, often tinged with dark red or purple; mature grains like those of Common Millet, but smaller and narrower. Common Barnyard Millet *E. crus-galli* also known as Cockspur Grass, is similar in structure but usually taller, 1 m or more in height, with smaller, more widely spaced branches of inflorescence and awned spikelets, and smaller grains.

Names: Syns.: *Panicum crus-galli*, *Panicum frumentaceum*.
(Barnyard Millet): Fr.: Panic d'eau; It.: Giavone; Sp.: Zacote de agua; Ger.: Hühnehirse; Dan.: Hanespore; Gr.: Agriokekhri; Russ.: Ezhovik; Yug.: Zitna kostreba.

Uses: Neither of these two spp. is a grain crop in Europe. *E. frumentacea* is a very fast-growing plant which is cultivated for human food in Asia, especially in poor areas or when rice crops fail. It has been grown in southern Europe as a forage crop. *E. crus-galli* is widespread in hot countries in marshy places, and one of the worst weeds of rice fields in Asia. It is used in parts of the Mediterranean for reclaiming brackish marshes because it is at the same time useful as a forage plant.

Origin, distribution and cultivation: Barnyard Millet occurs in the wild throughout the tropics and sub-tropics. Japanese Millet, considered by some botanists a cultivated ssp. of the former, is a native of tropical Asia and North America. Both have been introduced to central and southern Europe, and occur occasionally elsewhere, including Britain, on cultivated and waste land.

Similar plants: These spp. differ at first sight from other millets by their branching stems. The spike-like branches of the panicle do not arise from a single point, as they do in Finger Millet.

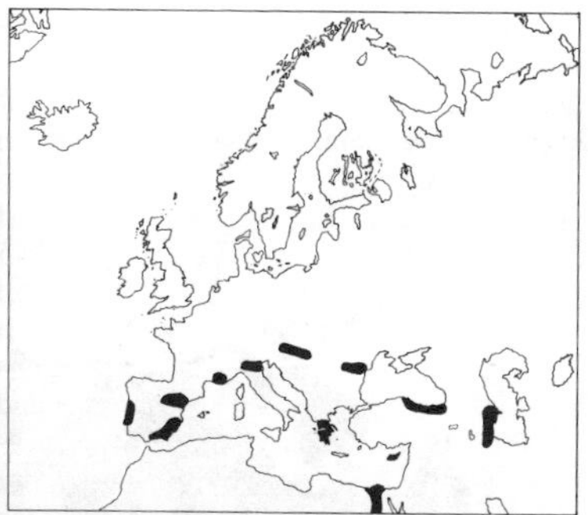

Distribution of Rice

Oryza sativa
RICE
(pp. 206, 216)

Description: The many thousands of recognised cvs of Rice fall into one of 3 subspecies: *japonica*, *indica* and *javanica*. The great majority of crops grown in Europe are short-grained varieties belonging to ssp. *japonica*, but some varieties of the less hardy long-grained *indica* are also grown to a small extent. Ssp. *javanica* is confined to S.E. Asia.

Japonica Rices stand 50–100 cm in height, and have rather dark green stem and lvs. Lvs alternate in 2 rows with single lf at each node; lf-blade long, narrow, 30–40 x 1.2–2 cm, hairless; uppermost lf shorter and broader than others, erect after flowering; ligule triangular; auricles long, sickle-like, or absent. Inflorescence a panicle 14–25 cm long, rachis drooping at maturity with 1 or more branches at each node; spikelets usually borne singly, each containing a single fl/grain standing upright; each spikelet consisting of 2 short glumes, a hard boat-shaped 5-veined lemma and narrower 3-veined palea enclosing grain; spikelets awned or unawned; grain white with brownish pericarp, short and broad.

Ssp. *indica* varieties, which are mostly long-grained, are more variable in form, but always a lighter green, usually taller, the lvs are densely hairy, and the uppermost lf-blade is long and narrow, drooping after flowering; panicles are usually longer and laxer, the grains mostly long and narrow.

Other forms of Rice are grown in the tropics. The most extreme are **Upland** or **Mountain Rice**, which is grown on 'dry' land (but always in areas of high rainfall) by the hill peoples of Assam and S.E. Asia, but which is now largely being abandoned in favour of Maize and other crops, and **Floating Rice**, which grows in deltas and places heavily flooded by monsoons, particularly in Bangladesh. This form grows very rapidly to keep afloat of the rising water, and may reach a length of 5 m.

Names: Fr.: Riz; It.: Riso; Sp.: Arroz; Ger.: Reis; Dtch.: Rijs; Dan.: Ris; Gr.: Rysi; Russ.: Ris; Yug.: Riž.

Uses: Rice is the staple food of more than half the world's population, and is second only to Wheat in importance on a world scale. In Europe it is less important than the indigenous cereals, but a more valuable crop to the farmer as it competes with imported Rice.

Rice is invariably eaten boiled or steamed, or fried before or after boiling. It contains almost no gluten, so cannot be used for bread. In China and Japan wines and spirits such as *sake* are made from it. Rice paper is not made from rice straw, but from the pith of *Tetrapanax papyrifera*, a tree of the family Araliaceae native to Taiwan, and sometimes from that of the Breadfruit Tree *Artocarpus communis*.

Long-grained rices are suitable to 'Oriental', ie. Arab, Turkish and Indian dishes such as *pilaus*, while the short-grained varieties which release more starch during cooking are appropriate for traditional W. European 'wet' rice dishes such as *paella*, *risotto*, *poule au riz*, etc. and for rice puddings.

The lemma and palea adhere strongly to the grain, and unlike Wheat or Rye are not removed during threshing. Therefore the frts must be pounded or milled to remove them. A further milling removes the brown pericarp to produce white pearled or polished rice. Unfortunately in this process most of the nutritional value is lost (the residue is a valuable cattle feed), resulting in cases of the disease beriberi, a thiamine deficiency, when the diet is not adequately supplemented. The peoples for whom Rice is a staple have nevertheless persisted in pearling rice for a good reason: the pericarp is unpalatable, and it appears perverse, from a gastronomic point of view, that 'brown' or unhusked rice should have recently become fashionable in the prosperous West, where a rich and varied diet makes this consideration unnecessary.

Origin, distribution and cultivation: The genus *Oryza* includes about 25 spp. of pan-tropical distribution. *O. sativa* for it has been in cultivation in India and China for at least 4 millenia. Indians introduced the practice of wet rice cultivation to S.E. Asia, where formerly only dry rice was grown, in the first centuries AD. Rice cultivation was brought to Spain by the Arabs in the 8th or 9th centuries, was first planted in the Camargue in France in the 19th century, but only became an important industry after the last war. Today the main centres of Rice cultivation in Europe are the Po Valley in Italy, the Camargue, parts of Spain, Hungary and the Danube Valley, and the Soviet Union.

Traditionally rice is sown densely in nurseries and transplanted in equally spaced bunches of 2–6 plants when the seedlings are about 20 cm tall. This system increases the yield, facilitates weed control, uses fewer seeds and has other advantages, but is highly labour intensive, so in many places in Europe the seed is simply drilled or broadcast. Rising labour costs in the 1950s and 60s threatened the rice industry in the wealthier European countries such as France, but the problems have been overcome. Rice in the Camargue is now transplanted by seasonal labour from Spain. The formerly difficult task of levelling fields to a perfect horizontal plane is now achieved by means of a scanning laser beam, installed in one corner of the field, which shows up any soil rising above the level of the beam on a screen on the tractor or bulldozer. A single operator can thus level the field without making any other measurements. The fields are drained before the grain is fully ripe, and the crop is later harvested with the same equipment used for Wheat and other cereals.

Similar plants: 'Wild Rice' imported from America is the grain of a quite different grass, *Zizania aquatica*, native of the North-Eastern States and East Canada. It was formerly an important food to the Indians, who harvested it from canoes, and is now cultivated on a large scale in Canada. The *Zizania* of China is a different sp., *Z. latifolia*; the young shoots, 3–5 cm in diameter, called *gau sun* and used as a green vegetable, are sometimes available from Chinese grocers in Europe.

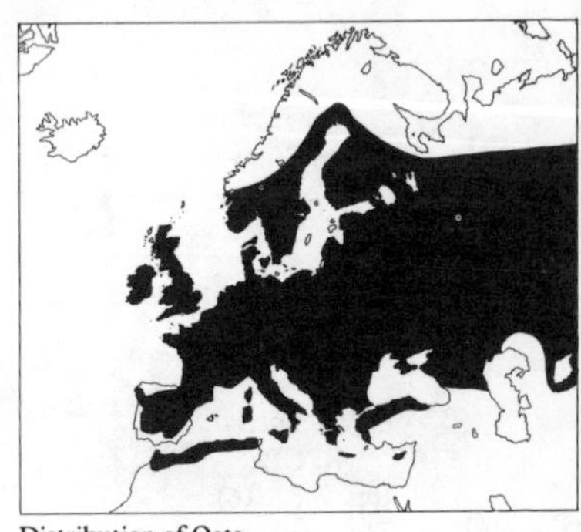

Distribution of Oats

Avena spp.

OATS

(p. 206)

Description: Three species of this genus which includes a number of Wild European ones are cultivated:

Common Oat *A. sativa*, is similar in appearance and stature to Wheat, etc. but is immediately recognisable by the inflorescence. Height ca. 1 m; lvs green or glaucous, flat, rough, with 12 veins; ligules long and pointed; auricles absent; inflorescence a panicle. Several forms of this sp. are grown. The most distinctive is Tartarian Oats, in which the branches of the panicle are more erect and all on one side of the rachis; in the other forms the branches spread more or less horizontally in all directions. Grey Winter Oats (sown in autumn) are less erect as young plants, with lvs fringed with hairs; their panicles are large and open, with numerous small spikelets. Spring Oats (sometimes called 'Black Oats', though this term may lead to confusion with 'Black Tartarian' or with Bristle Oat (below)) are more erect when young, the lvs are usually hairless, and the panicles are tighter, with fewer, larger spikelets. The spikelets of all these forms consist of 2 very large glumes (longer than fls/frts), and usually 3 fls, the upper one sterile, the lower one producing a large grain, the middle one a shorter grain. The lemmas of *A. sativa* are awnless in some cvs, or furnished with a long dorsal awn slightly angled in the middle, though rarely as long as in Wild Oats or Bristle Oat. The frt of Oats is elongate, white, yellowish, greyish or almost black. The grain remains enveloped in the palea after threshing, but can be separated by milling.

Red Oat *A. bizantina* is difficult to distinguish from Common Oat, differing essentially in the way in which the grains are shed: In *A. sativa* both grains separate from the rachilla at their base, whereas in *A. bizantina* the upper grain is left with a short 'stalk'.

Bristle-pointed Oat *A. strigosa* is distinguished by the pair of short bristles at the tip of each lemma (not to be confused with the long awn which arises from the dorsal surface of the lemma). The awn in this species is longer than in the awned forms of *A. sativa*, comparable with those of Wild Oat *A. fatua*.

Names: Fr.: Avoine; It.: Avena; Sp.: Avena; Ger.: Hafer; Dtch.: Haver; Dan.: Havre; Gr.: Vromi; Russ.: Ovets; Yug.: Oves.

Uses: Oats are grown as a food for livestock. The plants are either cut while still green and processed or fed whole, or harvested and threshed like other cereals, and the grains fed, usually crushed. Oats are a high energy cereal particularly useful for working horses. In northern or hill areas of acid or other poor soils, where wheat cultivation is or was not possible, Oats were and to a small extent still are used as human food, in the form of oat cakes and porridge. The latter is one of the few remaining cereal gruels which were the staple peasant diets in medieval Europe.

Origin, distribution and cultivation: Oat species occur throughout Eurpe and the Middle East. They probably first came to man's attention as weeds of other cereal crops; they have been cultivated in Europe since the Iron Age. Oats were a very important crop in the days when horses were vital for transport and agricultural work, and in Britain and northern Europe more land was given over to the crop than to Wheat or Barley. Today Common Oat is still cultivated on a fairly large scale in most of central and northern Eurpe. Tartarian Oats are hardier, and therefore grown locally in northern or hill countries - in Britain particularly in Wales. Red Oat replaces *A. sativa* in the hotter countries of southern Europe. Bristle Oat, often called 'Black' and therefore confused with Tartarian and other 'Black' forms of *A. sativa*, originated in the western Mediterranean, where it is still grown to a small extent. It was formerly cultivated in the poorest soil of Wales and Scotland, but now occurs mainly as a weed.

Oats are harvested when not fully ripe, or else the spikelets shatter, and much of the grain is lost.

Similar plants: Several spp. of wild oats are common and serious weeds of cereal crops, because until the panicles appear they are inconspicuous among Wheat, and indistinguishable from cultivated Oats. The commonest sp. in northern Europe is Common or Spring Wild Oat *A. fatua*, a usually much taller plant which towers above the other cereals, Wheat, Oats, etc. in infested fields. Its awns are long, and the base of lemma is covered in stiff brown hairs; the grains are shed very early, and singly. Winter Wild Oat *A. ludoviciana* is another weed sp., resembling *A. fatua*, but the 2 or 3 grains fall together. *A. sterilis* is a similar sp. with larger spikelets and grains, common in the Mediterranean, but absent from Britain and northern Europe.

Hordeum spp.
BARLEY

(pp. 206, 215)

Description: Although all the cultivated varieties of Barley are inter-fertile, the two principal forms are now usually treated as distinct species: **Two-rowed Barley** *H. distichum*, and **Six-rowed Barley** *H. polystichum*.

Barleys stand 50–150 cm high and tiller

freely. Lvs pale green, 20–30 x 1–1.5 cm, with ca. 20 veins; ligule medium-sized; auricles long, slender, hairless; lf-sheath usually hairless. Inflorescence a cylindrical spike 7.5–10 cm long, usually with a very long 'beard' or awns; the rachis is tough and does not break up at maturity; spikes are more or less dense in different cvs, bearing 3 single-flowered spikelets at each node alternately on either side of rachis.

In Two-rowed Barley only the central spikelet of each triplet is fertile and produces a grain; the two outer florets are sterile. Thus two vertical lines of grains are formed, one on either side of rachis.

In Six-rowed Barley all three florets are fertile and produce grains. Thus six vertical rows of grains are borne around the rachis. Another type of *H. polystichum*, Four-rowed Barley, is a laxer form of Six-rowed, with longer internodes. The lateral florets of each triplet lie in the same vertical plane as those of the ones below, so that four vertical rows of grains are seen, those of the lateral florets with twice as many grains as those of the central florets. These dispositions are perhaps most easily understood by means of the schematic diagram below.

The grains of all cvs grown in Britain and most of Europe are enveloped in the palea which adheres strongly to the pericarp, but 'Naked Barleys' are cultivated in Asia and parts of Russia. These forms usually have mre than 3 fertile florets per spikelet, and the threshed grain is free of the husk.

Distribution of Barley

Names: Syns.: *H. vulgare*, *H. sativum* (include both forms); *H. hexastichum* (Six-rowed).

Fr.: Orge, Escourgeon (Two-rowed); It.: Orzo; Sp.: Cebada; Ger.: Gerste; Dtch.: Gerst; Dan.; Byg; Gr.: Krithi; Russ.: Yachmen.

Uses: Barley was formerly used mainly as a human food, especially in areas unsuited to Wheat, for Barley is much hardier. Because it has a low gluten content Barley cannot be used for leavened bread; in areas such as Tibet, where it remains the staple human food, the grains are roasted and crushed to a paste with water or butter. 'Pearled' Barley, used to a small extent in Britain and northern European countries in soups, etc., consists of grains that have been milled to remove the pericarp, in the same manner as Rice. Most European crops today are grown for fodder, the whole green plants being used fresh or as silage, or the threshed grains fed crushed or rolled, but the most valuable crops are those (nearly all of them Two-rowed varieties) suitable for malting for the production of beer and whisky.

These varieties are ones in which germination is rapid and uniform. The process involves soaking the grain so that it germinates, during which the starch is converted to a sugar, maltose, which normally feeds the young seedling plant. In order to preserve the maltose the grains are killed by heating in a kiln. The resulting malt is then sold to the brewers who soak it in hot water to produce a solution called 'wort'; this is later filtered and boiled with hops, re-filtered and fermented by brewers' yeast to produce beer, or distilled to make whisky.

Origin, distribution and cultivation: Barley, together with Emmer Wheat, is the first cereal to have been cultivated in the Middle East, where it was domesticated nine or ten thousand years ago. It is derived from a wild sp. close to *H. spontaneum*, which occurs widely in Turkey and Syria. The essential morphological change in the wild form, which made harvesting possible, was the evolution of a tough rachis which does not shatter and scatter the grains prematurely.

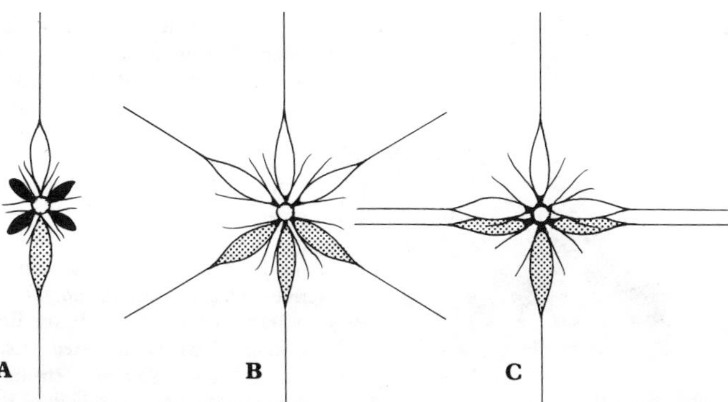

Schematic diagram of Barley types: Horizontal section including the spikelets of two nodes. Spikelet of the lower node shaded.
A: Two-rowed Barley, with sterile florets in black.
B: Six-rowed Barley.
C: Four-rowed Barley. The lateral florets/grains superimposed, almost in the same vertical plane.

Barley is very widely cultivated in Europe, especially in the northern half, with the Soviet Union and Germany leading production. The acreage devoted to Barley in Britain exceeds that of any other arable crop. Crops may be winter (sown in autumn) or spring varieties. Six-rowed Barley is hardier, and mostly confined to more northerly areas or to those with poorer soils.

Similar plants: Bearded Wheats are sometimes mistaken for Six-rowed Barley, but have a tough, crisp appearance which contrasts with the soft drooping ears of Barley, and a quite different arrangement of the spikelets. Einkorn Wheat, below, and wild spp. of *Hordeum* are the plants most similar in appearance to Two-rowed Barley. The latter include Meadow Barley *H. secalinum* and the very common Wall Barley *H. murinum* which occurs on waste land. These spp. are smaller than *H. distichum*, with small grains and slender fragile ears. They are unpalatable to cattle, and are not cultivated as forage meadow grasses.

Triticum spp.
WHEATS

(p. 206)

Description: Wheats are freely tillering, usually robust grasses 60–120 cm tall. Lf-sheaths usually softly hairy, with two prominent hairy auricles; lf-blades narrow, with ca. 12 veins. Inflorescence a spike with a single spikelet at each node; spikelets consist of a pair of stiff glumes and from 2 to nine florets; lemmas thinner than glumes, awned or awnless; grains large, more or less plump, in most spp. 'naked', ie. shedding out of lemma and palea when threshed. Thousands of cvs are recognised, which belong to one or other of several distinct spp. of *Triticum.* The species are classed into groups according to whether they have 2, 3 or 6 pairs of chromosomes. The main cultivated spp. are:
Bread Wheat *T. aestivum* is by far the most important sp., and includes the overwhelming number of cvs. Varieties may be awned or unawned; in most unawned cvs the internodes of the rachis are short, giving very compact heads; in many bearded varieties the head is laxer. Rachis tough; spikelets 5–9 flowered, with up to 5 grains; glumes red or white, hairy or hairless; grain large, plump, red or white, less hard and flinty than Durum Wheat but harder than Rivet, free-threshing.
Durum Wheat *T. durum*, also known as Macaroni Wheat, is the next most important sp. in terms of production. Ears large, always bearded, the rachis tough; spikelets 5–7 flowered, with 3–5 grains; grains large, somewhat triangular in section, hard and flinty, free-threshing.

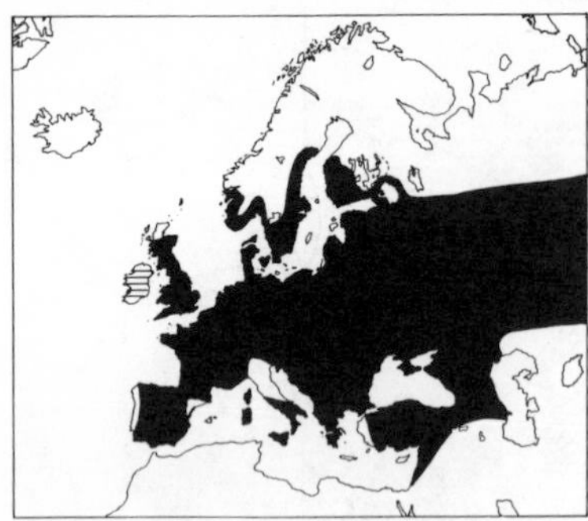

Distribution of Wheat

Polish Wheat *T. polonicum* is closely related to Durum Wheat and has similar flinty grains, but is easily recognisable by the very large, leaf-like glumes.

Rivet Wheat *T. turgidum.* This is a bearded wheat with very large ears and short broad glumes. It is most easily identified by the short broad grains which have a pronounced hump on the dorsal side; their endosperm is soft, floury, and the grains are free-threshing.

Spelt *T. spelta*, sometimes called Large Spelt to distinguish it from *T. monococcum* (below), is an odd-looking sp. with awned or unawned medium to long ears of very widely-spaced spikelets with square-tipped glumes. Spikelets 3–4 flowered, producing 2 grains; grains long and narrow, flinty, and do not thresh out of the palea and lemma.

Einkorn *T. monococcum*, also known as Small Spelt, has small bearded ears resembling those of Two-rowed Barley with a fragile rachis which breaks up on threshing. Spikelets 2–3 flowered, producing one or two long narrow grains which do not thresh out of lemma and palea.

Emmer *T. dicoccum* is similar to Einkorn, but the ear is larger and stouter, less flattened, the rachis fragile, and has the same number of fls and grains.

Names: Fr.: Froment, Blé; It.: Frumento, Grano; Sp.: Trigo; Ger.: Weizen; Dtch.: Tarwe; Dan.: Huede; Gr.: Sitari; Russ.: Pshenitsa; Yug.: Pšenica.

Uses: Wheat is the world's single most important cereal. It is grown almost exclusively as a human food crop, although the grain of poor quality crops may be used, mixed with other cereals, as fodder. So is the bran (the grain testa, removed before milling white flour; when it is not removed, 'wholemeal' flour is produced).

Bread Wheat is the sp. used for making bread. Suitable grains are those with a high gluten content, the softer grain, often resulting from insufficient sun and heat during ripening, being suitable only for biscuits and other unbaked articles. In the EEC much of baking wheat is imported from America, where hot dry summers ensure a uniform high quality. Other products of Bread Wheat are semolina, grains coarsely ground to large particles (which may be made from other cereals), kitchen flour and breakfast cereals.

Durum Wheat has a very hard endosperm not suitable for bread making, and a very high gluten content. The flour makes a stiff dough, generally known in English by the Italian word *pasta*, which can be boiled fresh without dissolving, or allowed to dry and harden, in which form it will keep almost indefinitely.

The little Polish Wheat that is still cultivated is used for the same purpose.

The soft endosperm of Rivet is used for biscuits, or mixed with Bread Wheat flour for bread. Spelt, which is not free-threshing, has to be milled like Rice or Pearl Barley, and is mostly used in the same way as the latter.

Origin, distribution and cultivation: The Wheats known today evolved in the Middle East through repeated hybridisations of *Triticum* spp. with members of a closely related grass genus, *Aegilops*. The process which began some ten thousand years ago involved the following major steps. Wild Einkorn *T. boeoticum* crossed spontaneously with *Aegilops speltoides* to produce Wild Emmer *T. dicoccoides*; further hybridisations with another *Aegilops*, *A. squarrosa*, gave rise to Spelt, Emmer *T. dicoccum* and early forms of Durum Wheat; Bread Wheat finally evolved when cultivated Emmer re-crossed with *A. squarrosa* in the southern Caspian plains. This evolution was accelerated by an expanding geographical range of cultivation and by human selection, and had produced Bread Wheats as early as the sixth millenium BC.

Bread Wheats have almost entirely replaced all the other spp. except Durum Wheat in cultivation. They are grown wherever the climate allows, with the main areas of production in N. America, Europe, North Africa, and the Middle East to India and northern China. In Europe the range is only limited by insufficiently hot dry summers in the North. So, in the rainy climate of Britain, cultivation is largely confined to southern and eastern England.

Durum Wheat is more tolerant of very hot dry conditions. It was cultivated by the ancient Egyptians, Greeks and Romans, and in classical times reached Ethiopia, where the greatest variety of cvs is now to be found. It is widely grown in the Mediterranean countries and in parts of eastern Europe.

Polish Wheat does not originate in Poland; it is only grown to a small extent in the Mediterranean. Rivet Wheat was widely grown in England until the 1950s; it is now also confined to the Mediterranean, although it is fast disappearing there in favour of new Bread Wheat cvs. Spelt is hardier than other wheats, especially as a young plant, and so has traditionally been grown in mountain areas. It is now rarely seen, but survives in cultivation in Spain and in a few parts of central Europe. Einkorn has been abandoned in all but a few remote localities in Turkey and the Balkans, while Emmer is now of purely historical interest as a crop plant.

Similar plants: Rye, below.

Triticale, sometimes called Triticosecale, are fertile hybrids of Bread Wheat and Rye which may be difficult to identify, as they have characteristics of both parents; but generally resemble wheats more than they do Rye. Although such hybrids have been experimented with for a long time, it is only since the 1970s that satisfactory ones have been developed and cultivated as field crops. Cultivation is spreading rapidly in areas that are too hot or cold, or arid, or where the soils are too poor, or in areas that suffer from combinations of these factors, for Wheat-growing. Large quantities are now produced in the Soviet Union, in Poland and in other parts of eastern and northern Europe, and in the Mediterranean, and the crop will probably be adopted elsewhere, including Britain. Triticale is grown exclusively as a fodder plant except in Brazil and Madagascar, where it is used as a human food.

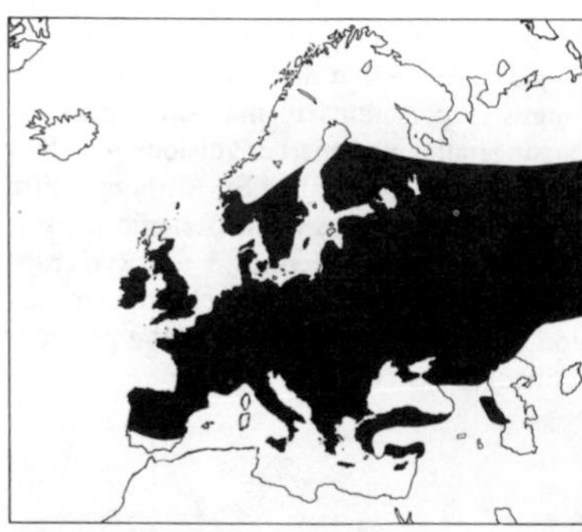

Distribution of Rye

Secale cereale

RYE

(p. 206)

Description: Rye resembles rather lax-headed forms of bearded Wheat, but is generally taller, 1–2 m high, with ears 7.5–15 cm long. The green plant tends to be a duller, more greyish-green. The ears have a more bristly appearance, because the lemma and palea of each fl are more open, exposing the tip of the grain. Rye is most clearly distinguished by the narrow, acute glumes which are one-veined and shorter than the lemmas. Spikelets single at each node, 3-flowered but apparently 2-flowered because the third is nearly always undeveloped, minute; two grains are produced in each spikelet. The free-threshing grains are similar in structure to Wheat but longer, more slender, and typically with darker, brown testa.

Ergot (see below) appears as single cylindrical purple-black structures, up to twice as long as the grains, protruding from infested fls.

Names: Fr.: Seigle; It.: Segale; Sp.: Centeno; Ger.: Roggen; Dtch.: Rogge; Dan.: Rug; Gr.: Sikalis; Russ.: Rozh; Yug.: Rz.

Uses: Rye is grown both as a cereal for human food and as a spring forage crop. The dark flour is used for making the black unleavened bread of Germany and central Europe and for crispbreads. The grains are used to make beer in the Soviet Union, gin in Holland, and Rye whisky in America.

Rye may have lost favour in western Europe due to Ergot *Claviceps purpurea*, a fungal parasite that attacks the grains. The fungus is poisonous to man and to cattle, causing hallucinations, convulsions and often death, a syndrome called St. Anthony's Fire in the Middle Ages, when periodic infestations caused many victims. A few Rye crops are grown annually in Europe for the production of Ergot, which is used in the pharmaceutical industry.

Origin, distribution and cultivation: Rye is derived from one of four wild *Secale* spp. which occur in S.E. Europe and W. Asia. Ancestral Rye was not cultivated in those areas, but occurred as a weed of Wheat crops. As Wheat cultivation moved northwards into areas increasingly unsuitable to it, the proportion of the much hardier Rye plants increased in crops, and by some time in the first millenium BC it had become established as a crop in its own right. Rye is mainly cultivated in the Soviet Union, Poland, Germany and Scandinavia. A few crops are grown in Britain, either under contract to crispbread manufacturers, or for fodder.

CYPERACEAE

Sedge Family

The sedges bear a superficial resemblance to grasses, but their stems are more or less triangular in section, and solid, and do not have the conspicuous nodes of grasses. The lvs are arranged in 3 rows, and fls are borne in the axil of a single bract.

The best known member of this family is the Papyrus plant of Egypt, is a giant member of the genus *Cyperus*; this and several other spp. are sometimes grown for ornament. Only one member of the family qualities for inclusion as a European crop plant.

Cyperus esculentus
CHUFA

Description: A typical *Cyperus* sedge standing 30–60 cm tall, with perennial slender rhizomes bearing tubers. Stems not striate; lvs many, as long as stems, 8–9 mm wide; sheath brownish; involucral bracts 2 to 6. Inflorescence a single or compound umbel of 5–10 rays, with spikelets distant on 12–60 cm long spikes, spreading, linear, pale brown.

Var. *sativus* which produces the edible tubers, rarely flowers. Tubers brown, 1–2 cm

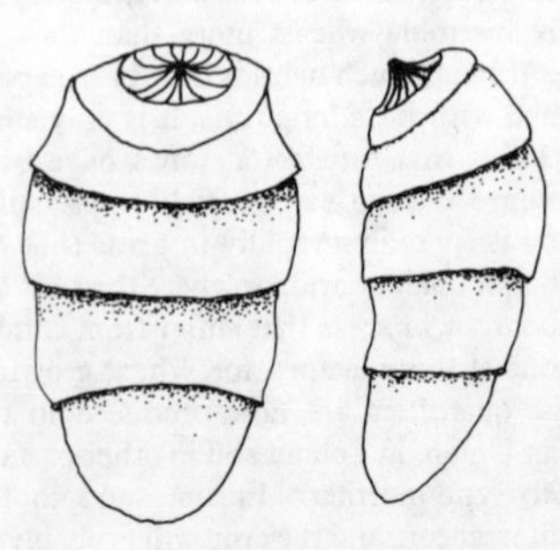

Chufa corms

Chufa plant

long, roughly top-shaped, the top flattened with radiating lines, below with 2–4 thin raised transverse ridges.

Names: Also known and marketed as Earth Almond, Tiger Nut or Sedge Nut.
Fr.: Souchet comestible; It.: Dolcichino; Sp.: Chufa; Ger.: Erdmandel; Gr.: Amygdalo edáfous; Russ.: Sit sedobni, Chufa.

Uses: The small edible corms are usually roasted but may be cooked in other ways, peeled, as a vegetable, or even eaten raw, as they are sweet and digestible. They have been used in the past, heavily roasted, as a coffee substitute, and as a source of starch for flour and of edible oil. They are commonly offered as *tapas* in Spain.

Origin, distribution and cultivation: This plant is native to central and southern Europe and North Africa. It has been cultivated in the Mediterranean for a very long time (corms have been found in Egyptian tombs of ca. 2000 BC), and has been taken to India, tropical Africa and the Far East. In Europe Chufa has decreased steadily in importance throughout the 20th century, but is still harvested in marshy areas of Spain, Italy, etc. and exported on a small scale to northern Europe.

Similar plants: Chufa is not obvious as a cultivated crop, and may be taken for natural growth of one of the many wild European sedges.

Chufa should not be confused with Water Chestnut *Eleocharis dulcis*, another sedge very widely cultivated in the Far East and available, especially from Chinese food markets, in Europe, nor with Pig Nut *Conopodium majus*, a wild European umbellifer which is also known as Earth Nut. The roots of this plant are sometimes gathered and eaten raw or boiled in western Europe; it is an irregular whitish tuber-like root bearing no resemblance to Chufa, and is of no economic importance.

PINACEAE

Pine Family

A family of ten genera and about 200 spp. with linear, flat or needle-like lvs and woody cones composed of scales bearing 2 seeds each. It includes many of the conifers such as cedars, larches, spruces and pines (80 spp.). The seeds of one European sp. are a locally important commercial food.

Pinus pinea
STONE PINE

Description: Sometimes known as Umbrella Pine owing to its broad dark crown with radiating branches, up to 25 m high. Bark is reddish brown weathering to grey, fissured to form large vertical plates. Lvs ('needles') in pairs, dark dull green, 12–15 cm long. Cone large (ca. 10 x 10 cm), globose with flattened base, pale brown, the ends of scales with darker centres. Seeds wingless.

Names: (Pine nut): Fr.: Pignon; It.: Pignolo, Pinolo; Sp.: Piñones; Ger.: Piniennuss; Dtch.: Pijnnoot; Dan.: Fyrrenød; Gr.: Koukoutsia Peýkou; Russ.: Sosna italianskaya.

Uses: Pine nuts or kernels have been used as food since classical times. The slight taste of turpentine is dissipated when they are heated, the remaining delicate nutty flavour making them an invaluable addition to many meat or poultry dishes of the Mediterranean. It is also one of the ingredients of *pesto genovese* (see under Basil).

Origin, distribution and cultivation: Stone pine is a native of the northern Mediterranean shores, from Turkey to the Atlantic coasts of Spain and Portugal. It is cultivated or preserved in large stands, particularly in Italy and Spain. The cones are gathered in winter and stored until the summer, when they are laid out in the sun to open, and the seeds removed and cracked to yield the kernels. It is these that are sold commercially.

Stone Pine: outline of tree

Similar species: The characteristic umbrella-shaped crown and wingless seeds make this species almost unmistakeable. However the seeds of other pines are eaten in the same way in other parts of the world. In eastern Switzerland to the Carpathians the Arolla Pine *P. cembra* is used, but this species is quite different in appearance, the crown columnar, with short branches turning up at the ends, and short (8–9 cm) lvs in clusters of 5, with shiny dark green outer faces, pale green on inner surfaces; the cone is ovoid, ca. 8 x 6 cms, blue during summer, ripening to chestnut brown.

Other species of pine are cultivated in Europe for products other than timber, namely resin. In the Landes of S.W. France as in many other areas Maritime Pines *P. pinaster* in extensive plantations are tapped by cutting shallow diagonal grooves in the bark from which the sap oozes, to be collected in a tin. The resin yields turpentine, used as a solvent for paints and varnishes and for coating paper to take printer's ink, while other products include soap and linoleum (see also linseed). The more widespread Aleppo Pine *P. halepensis* is tapped in the same way, and in Greece is used for flavouring wine (Retsina).

Maritime Pine is a native of the S. Atlantic and W. Mediterranean coasts of Europe. It is most easily identified by the lvs, borne in pairs, which are the longest (12–25 cm) and stoutest of any European pine, and the cones, which are also longer (up to 25 cm) than in other species.

Aleppo Pine is common all over the Mediterranean region; its lvs are also borne in pairs but are much shorter (6–15 cm) and less than 1 mm wide. Its most distinctive characteristic is the pale grey, almost white colour of first-year twigs and branches.

CUPRESSACEAE

Cypress Family

A family of some 130 species, almost half of which are junipers. Other genera are the true cypresses, 'false cypresses' such as Lawson's cypress, and Thujas. It is distinguished from other conifers by the appearance of the cone, in which the scales are arranged in opposite pairs at right angles to each other. In the genus *Juniperus* this is not obvious, as the cone scales are fused, forming a 'berry'.

Juniperus communis
COMMON JUNIPER

Description: A shrub up to 6 m, usually conical or columnar. Foliage consisting only of dense very prickly needle-like lvs, their inner sides concave with a single broad white band, the outer edge grey-green, 1 cm or less long; dried or bruised lvs emit a distinct scent of apple. Male fls very small, yellow, usually borne on separate plants. Frt a 'berry' containing ca. 3 seeds, green ripening in 2–3 years to blue-black with a bloom, 6–10 mm in diameter.

Names: Fr.: Genièvre; It.: Ginepro; Sp.: Enebro; Ger.: Wacholder; Dtch.: Jeneverbes; Dan.: Ene; Gr.: Moúra agriokyparissou; Russ.: Mozhevelnik obikhonenni; Yug.: Borovica.

Uses: The ripe berries are used for flavouring spirits such as gin and *steinhäger* (the words 'gin' and 'genever' (Hollands gin) come from the Italian ginepro, old French Genièvre and other derivatives of *Juniperus*, and not from the town of Geneva), and food. Distilled oil of Juniper is used nowadays for flavouring spirits, but (preferably fresh) partly crushed berries are used to flavour foods. Although it is an increasingly neglected flavouring, especially in England, Juniper enters the recipes of many traditional meat dishes in all the countries of Europe, from Lapland to Sicily, in which the plant occurs. It is used in marinades for game, in pâtés, stuffings, stews, and for curing hams. In Germany it is made into a preserve (Latwerge) to accompany cold meats, and is a common flavouring for sauerkraut.

The aromatic value of the berries depends

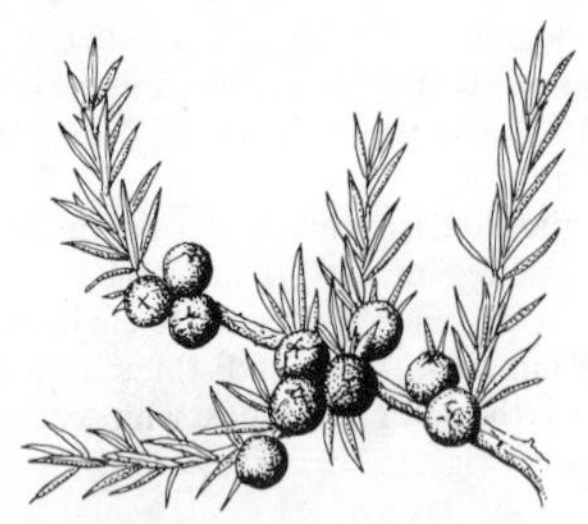

Common Juniper

largely on climate, those picked in autumn in the Mediterranean countries being the best, but also on freshness. The dried berries of commerce, if too old, are useless.

Origin, distribution and cultivation: Common Juniper occurs wild in the whole of the northern hemisphere, on dry limestone or chalklands in the south, and acid peat soils in northern Europe. It is not, or scarcely, cultivated on any scale; rather, productive stands of wild bushes are maintained (often on otherwise uncultivable land) for commercial exploitation.

Similar plants: Of the eight species of native European junipers only two others, Prickly Juniper (*J. oxycedrus*) and Syrian Juniper (*J. drupacea*) have exclusively needle-like leaves; the others' foliage is composed mostly of scale-like leaves. Both these species have two pale bands on the inner sides of the leaves (single in Common Juniper), and Prickly Juniper can further be distinguished by its red (not blue-black) fruit. Syrian Juniper is restricted in Europe to southern Greece, but Prickly Juniper is common in all the Mediterranean countries, especially near the sea. The berries of both these species are useless (although often picked mistakenly), but *J. oxycedrus* yields another commercial product, Oil of Cade, obtained by distillation from the roots, and used in medicine and as a veterinary vermifuge.

FUNGI

Mushrooms and Toadstools

The fungi are a huge class of plants differing from virtually all 'conventional' plants in their lack of chlorophyll. This is the green colouring matter that enables green plants to manufacture basic foodstuffs from the raw materials of carbon dioxide and water. Fungi clearly must obtain their nutrition from elsewhere: they extract it from other organisms, whether as parasites or as saprophytes (feeding on decaying organic material), or, in many cases, as symbiotes, where the fungus lives in association with the roots of a particular sp. or genus of tree, supplying the tree with certain useful substances while at the same time deriving its own nourishment from the host. The vegetative parts of fungi are minute or microscopic, consisting mostly of a cluster of thread-like filaments called the mycelium. In many fungi, called micromycetes, the spores or reproductive bodies are produced on the filaments of the mycelium, and the whole organism remains microscopic. These include many spp. of considerable economic importance, either as harmful parasites of man, animals or plants, or as useful organisms, yeasts, the sources of antibiotics, etc. Other fungi, called macromycetes, periodically produce large fruiting bodies, the carpophores, the mushrooms and toadstools described here, many of which are edible.

The few traditional cultivated spp. are saprophytes which can be grown on suitable organic substrates such as composts. A few others, which live as parasites or saprophytes on the trunks and branches of trees can be cultivated on stocks of cut wood, but the great majority of edible spp. including all the finest, have had to be gathered in the wild, because they are symbiotes of tree roots. Favourable conditions for these fungi can be encouraged, by planting or preserving the right spp. of trees in suitable conditions, and recent advances in the knowledge of symbiotic processes have enabled many of these spp. to be cultivated on a large scale.

In this book it is only possible to include a few of the hundreds of European edible spp. The selection is of those, cultivated or wild, which are the most commercially viable, and are often seen in supermarkets, grocers, or on market stalls. Because many European fungi are poisonous, some of them deadly, this book should not be used as a guide to edible spp. found in the wild. Those who wish to gather wild spp. could consult the *Collins New Generation Guide to the Fungi of Britain and Europe* or similar comprehensive works appropriate to each particular region of Europe.

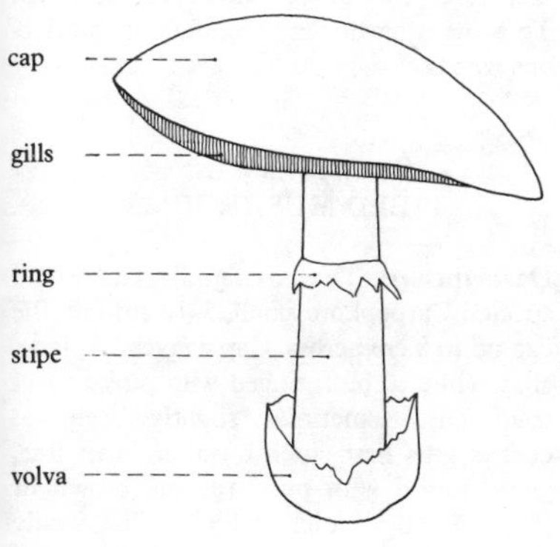

Development of an *Amanita* carpophore

A: Primordium enclosed in outer veil.
BC: Breaking up of outer veil leaving shreds on cap (the warts on some spp. such as Fly Agaric). Bottom part of veil remains around foot as the volva.
DE: Breaking up of inner veil, leaving the ring, and sometimes a fringe on margin of cap.

Amanita caesarea
CAESAR'S MUSHROOM

Description: A large stout carpophore up to 20 cm in height with a globular orange cap up to 10 cm in diameter, later with striate margins, underneath with yellow, deep gills. Stipe thick, tubular, yellow, easily broken off from cap; foot swollen, with membranous volva; spores yellowish white.

Names: Fr.: Oronge; It.: Orolo; Sp.: Amanita caesarea; Ger.: Kaiserschwamm, Orongenwulstling; Dtch.: Keizer amaniet; Dan.: Kejservamp; gr.: Kaisariko manitari.

Uses: This is one of the most highly esteemed fungi in Italy and in the South of France, and is always expensive. It may be eaten raw after marinating in lemon juice, or cooked.

Origin, distribution and cultivation: Caesar's Mushroom occurs in the Mediterranean, the Balkans and parts of south central Europe from July until October under oaks, beeches, etc. It is only found in the wild.

Similar plants: In shape this sp. resembles *Boletus* spp., which have tubular, not gilled hymenia. The genus *Amanita* contains the most deadly of all European fungi, but the only one of comparable colour is Fly Agaric *A. muscaria* which has a usually brighter red cap covered in white warts (which may wash off in rain), and has white, not yellow gills. This sp. is poisonous, but is commonly eaten in eastern Europe, after certain precautionary preparations.

Lepiota procera
PARASOL MUSHROOM
(p. 210)

Description: A tall sp. growing to nearly 30 cm in height, with fully developed cap almost as broad as the length of stipe. Cap globular, then expanded, flat with a raised bump in the centre, brownish, with scales that break off to reveal the whitish subcuticle, the margin fringed; gills white, turning yellowish; stipe white with brown mottling, slender, easily broken off from cap; ringed in several layers, large, persistent; flesh soft, white, darker and fibrous in stipe, with a faint but pleasant scent; spores white.

Names: Fr.: Lepiote élevée; It.: Fungo parasole; Sp.: Galamperno; Ger.: Grosser Schirmling; Dtch.: Grote parasolzwam; Dan.: Stor parasolhat; Gr.: Parasolikó manitári.

Uses: This sp. is thought to be slightly poisonous when raw, but is highly esteemed when cooked. The caps may be dried and stored.

Origin, distribution and cultivation: A fairly common fungus which grows in a wide variety of habitats, under trees or shrubs, in hedgerows and meadows in most of Europe. It is not often available from grocers, but is gathered in the wild for home consumption and is commonly offered for sale on country markets on the continent.

Similar plants: *L. rhacodes* is one of several closely related spp. which are also eaten. This one is particularly common in coniferous woods.

Psalliota campestris
FIELD MUSHROOMS

Description: The most familiar edible wild species. Carpophore small, 5–10 cm tall, the cap up to 8 cm across. Cap convex to plane, silky white to buff, tinged with pink in wet conditions, sometimes slightly scaly at centre; gills first stuck together, then free, white tinged with pink, turning brown or blackish; stipe thick, white, solid, easily detached from cap, no volva; flesh tender, white or slightly pink, with characteristic hazelnut scent; spores chocolate brown.

Names: Syn.: *Agaricus campestris.*
Fr.: Champignon des près; It.: Prataiolo; Sp.: Hongo silvestre; Ger.: Essbarer Pilz, Wiesenchampignon; Dtch.: Weide champignon; Dan.: Mark champignon; Gr.: Agrou manitári; Russ.: Shampinyon.

Uses: This is, together with the closely related cultivated mushroom (below), the most widely consumed sp. in Europe, and the only wild fungus commonly gathered in Britain, despite the presence of so many other good edible spp.

Origin, distribution and cultivation: *P. campestris* is a common sp. throughout Europe. It is not a symbiote of trees, but a saprophyte which thrives on organically rich ground such as pastures, particularly where horses are present. Large quantities are gathered between June and October for home use or for sale in markets and grocer's shops. The flavour of young carpophores is superior to that of the cultivated mushroom.

Similar plants: *P. bisporus*, below; *P. arvensis* and other *Psalliota* spp., many of which are eaten, while others are mildly poisonous. The highly toxic spp. of *Amanita* (*A. phalloides*, *A. verna*) are distinguished from *Psalliota* by the presence of an ample volva.

Psalliota bisporus
CULTIVATED MUSHROOM

(p. 210)

Description: Very similar to *P. campestris*, but wild carpophores typically have a darker, light-brown cap; the membranous ring is usually persistent and leaves a ragged fringe on the down-curved margin of cap. The only way to distinguish the two spp. with absolute certainty is by microscopic examination of the spores which are produced in pairs on the basidia of *P. bisporus* and in fours in *P. campestris* and other related spp.

The cultivated form is white, the cap only tinged with pale buff in some cases. The carpophores are usually picked immature, before the cap expands ('button mushrooms', champignon de Paris).

Names: Syn.: *Agaricus bisporus.*
Fr.: Champignon de couches, – de Paris; It.: 'Champignon de Paris', Funghi di coltura; Sp.: Hongo plantado; Ger.: Kulturpilz, Champignon; Dtch.: Champignon; Dan.: Hvid champignon; Gr.: Kalliergiméno manitári; Russ.: Shampinyon kyltivatni.

Uses: The most widely used fungus in European cooking. Large quantities are canned.

Origin, distribution and cultivation: The wild form occurs in most of Europe on or near dung, in country lanes, meadows, pastures, etc. The cultivated form is grown in the dark, in cellars or in special buildings, in trays of processed horse manure, occasionally on other composts.

Similar plants: Other *Psalliota* spp. Because the carpophores are white they closely resemble *P. arvensis*, below.

Psalliota arvensis
HORSE MUSHROOM

Description: Very much like *P. campestris* and *P. bisporus* but paler and larger. Carpophore up to 20 cm high, the cap white, yellowish when bruised, first globular then flattening, sometimes concave, easily detached from stipe; gills white, darkening with age through pink to dark brown or blackish; stipe thick, white, the foot not or scarcely swollen; no volva; ring white, broad, soft, with ragged edges; flesh firm, white or yellowish, with a faint hint of aniseed; spores reddish-brown.

Names: Syn.: *Agaricus arvensis.* In some books this is wrongly given as a synonym of *P. campestris.*
Fr.: Boule de neige; It.: Prataiolo maggiore; Sp.: Hongo commun, Seta; Ger.: Acker-champignon, Schaf-Egerling; Dtch.: Bos weide champignon; Dan.: Ager mandel champignon; Ger.: Alogoú manitári; Russ.: Shampinyon polevoi.

Uses: As Field Mushroom.

Origin, distribution and cultivation: A common sp. of hedgerows, the borders of meadows, and gardens, but not cultivated.

Similar plants: Field and Cultivated Mushrooms, above. *P. arvensis* is naturally white even when mature, resembling large cultivated specimens of *P. bisporus*. It is perhaps best characterised by the faint aniseed scent, which it shares with another closely related sp., *P. silvicola*; this sp. is also often gathered for food.

Pleurotus ostreatus
OYSTER MUSHROOM
(p. 210)

Description: A readily recognisable sp. which grows in clusters of overlapping caps on the trunks of deciduous trees or on fallen wood. Cap semi-circular, 3–10 cm across, flat, slightly concave, smooth and slightly downy, bluish-grey or brownish; gills widely spaced, white, becoming yellowish; stipe eccentric or lateral, very short; flesh firm in the cap, with a faint floury scent; spores greyish-pink.

Names: Fr.: Pleurote en forme d'huître; It.: Gelone, Ostriato; Sp.: Orellana, Girbola de pollancre; Ger.: Austernseitling; Dtch.: Oesterzwam; Dan.: Almindelig østerhat; Gr.: Streidioú manitári; Russ.: Veshenka obiknovennaya.

Uses: Although it is not one of the finer edible spp., the young carpophores are good when cooked, and have the advantage of being available throughout the winter.

Origin, distribution and cultivation: A common European fungus which can be found growing on the dead or living wood of deciduous, rarely coniferous trees, from September until March. Large quantities are gathered in the wild on the continent, and more recently in Britain, to supply home consumers, grocers and supermarkets.

Similar plants: Among commercial fungi: none.

Lentinus edodes
SHIITAKE MUSHROOM
(p. 210)

Description: This sp., which is rarely seen fresh in Europe, is readily recognisable by the broad umbonate cap 2–10 cm in diameter with downward curving margins, light to medium brown with a reticulate pattern of cracks showing the whitish sub-cuticle; stipe slender, rough, usually curved almost to 90°. Dried carpophores are shrivelled and darker, but still recognisable.

Names: Also known as Japanese Tree Mushroom; to the Chinese as *leong goo* or *dong* (winter) *goo.*

Uses: The carpophores of commerce are dried and must be soaked in water before use in various cooked dishes. Small (2–5 cm in diameter) caps are the best.

Origin, distribution and cultivation: This sp. has been cultivated for many centuries in China and Japan, and recently in the Netherlands and perhaps elsewhere in Europe. It grows on logs of *shiitake*, a sp. of oak belonging to the genus *Pasania.*

Similar plants: The dried carpophores of Matsutake, a similar sp. which is cultivated on pine logs in Japan, are also exported and available commercially in Europe.

Lactarius deliciosus
SAFFRON MILK CAP
(p. 210)

Description: A small carpophore, up to 8 x 8 cm, the cap soon depressed at centre after expansion, with downward curling margins, orange, sometimes with concentric rings of greenish-blue; gills creamy, turning orange, sometimes mottled with blue; stipe stout, swollen at base, orange, usually pock-marked; flesh soft, orange turning green when exposed, with a fruity scent, releasing an orange fluid when cut; spores off-white.

Names: Fr.: Lactaire délicieux, Rouzillon; It.: Fongo dal pin, Lopacendro buono; Sp.: Miscalo, Rebollon; Ger.: Blut Reizker, Röstling; Dtch.: Melkzwam; Dan.: Maelkehat; Gr.: Galaktokroeidís pílos; Russ.: Rizhik.

Uses: A fine flavoured fungus which deserves to be treated as a dish on its own, as well as a flavouring agent.

Origin, distribution and cultivation: This sp. is locally abundant throughout Europe, often in large colonies, in grassy situations at the margins of or amongst young conifer plantations.

Similar plants: The colour and structure of this sp. make it unmistakeable on market stalls. It could easily be confused with a poisonous sp., the Woolly Milk Cap *L. torminosus*, which is associated with broad-leaved trees, especially birch.

Boletus edulis
CEP
(p. 210)

Description: A large robust carpophore belonging to an easily recognisable genus in which the hymenium is composed of a dense spongy mass of parallel tubes instead of gills. *B. edulis* may stand up to 25 cm in height; the cap is hemispherical, whitish to buff-brown; tubes 1-5-3 cm long, white turning yellow then brownish, in mature specimens easily detached in chunks; stipe very thick, cylindrical or pear-shaped, paler than cap, with a fine network or raised white lines; flesh firm in young carpophores, soft later, white, with a faint scent and hazelnut flavour; spores olive-brown.

Names: Also known in Britain as 'Penny bun'. Fr.: Cèpe de Bordeaux, Bolet comestible; It.: Porcino; Sp.: Boleto, Cep; Ger.: Edelpiltz; Dtch.: Eerkhoorntjesbrood; Dan.: Spiselig rørhat, Carl Johan; Gr.: Piloforos; Russ.: Borovik.

Uses: *B. edulis* is one of the best, and the most commonly sold edible *Boletus* sp. It is used fresh, and large quantities are sliced and dried for storage, later to be used after soaking in water for flavouring a great variety of dishes. In commercial terms, Cep is one of the most important economic spp. gathered in the wild.

Origin, distribution and cultivation: *Boletus* spp. are symbiotes of tree roots and therefore cannot be cultivated. *B. edulis* is locally abundant throughout Europe on the ground in coniferous or broadleaf woodland; the carpophores may be gathered from August until the end of October.

Similar plants: *B. edulis* is one of many *Boletus* spp., most but not all of them edible. A few spp. are poisonous, though only mildly so, and some of those may be eaten after cooking. The flesh of certain spp., including some of the edible ones, turns an alarming blue-black when cut.

Cantharellus cibarius
CHANTERELLE or **GIROLE**
(p. 210)

Description: An unmistakeable species, small, 3-9 cm tall, the cap convex at first, then deeply concave, irregular, with lobed and wavy margin, smooth, dark yellow to orange; gills rough, widely spaced, joined in places, concolorous with cap; stipe tapering to foot, solid, concolorous with cap; flesh firm, white or yellowish, with a faint scent; spores yellow.

Names: Fr.: Chanterelle, Girole; It.: Cantarello cibario, Capo gallo, Galletto; Sp.: Canterello; Ger.: Pfefferling, Eierschwamm; Dtch.: Hanekam; Dan.: Kantarel; Gr.: Tsarterelli; Russ.: Lisichka.

Uses: An excellent, relatively inexpensive fungus which makes a good dish on its own. It can be dried for long storage. The firm flesh requires longer cooking than most mushrooms.

Origin, distribution and cultivation: This sp. is common in summer in forests in most of Europe; the larger, more fleshy and paler forms are usually to be found in deciduous woodland. Smaller, thinner and darker orange forms, which are frequently rather bitter, are found in coniferous woods.

Similar plants: This sp. is unlikely to be confused with any other European fungus. A related sp., *C. tubaeformis*, which is also edible and sometimes offered for sale, has a narrower, pale yellow stipe and a brownish cap.

Craterellus cornucopioides
HORN OF PLENTY
(p. 210)

Description: A distinctive sp., 2-7 cm in height, funnel-shaped, with a wavy and lobed margin, the upper/inner surface scaly, dull, pitchy-brown, the outer surface smooth or wrinkled, pale to medium brownish-grey, the whole carpophore turning black in wet conditions; flesh rubbery, pitch-brown, with a pleasant fungus scent and rather spicy flavour; spores white.

Names: Fr.: Trompette de la mort, Corne d'abondance; It.: Trombetta dei morti; Sp.: Trompeto de las muertos; Ger.: Herbsttrompete; Dtch.: Hoorn des overvoeds; Dan.: Død trompet, Horn af overflod; Gr.: Amaltheiakos.

Uses: A good edible fungus which can easily be dried for preservation. The slightly peppery quality of the flesh makes it particularly useful as a flavouring agent, but it is also a good dish on its own.

Origin, distribution and cultivation: This is a fairly common sp. throughout Europe in deciduous or coniferous woodland, often found in large dense colonies throughout the summer and autumn. Large quantities are gathered all over the continent, and it is also cultivated on a large scale. This fungus is commonly available from grocers and supermarkets even in Britain.

Similar plants: Cannot be confused with any other European fungus. A related European sp., *C. cinereus* is smaller, pale grey, much narrower, and of no culinary value.

Morchella esculenta
EDIBLE MOREL

(p. 210)

Description: *M. esculenta* is one of a number of European *Morchella* spp. which are very distinctive as a genus. Carpophore 5–15 cm tall; cap hollow, conical oval or almost spherical, the surface honeycombed, like a coarse sponge, yellowish, buff or brownish, with sharp-edged irregularly reticulate paler ribs separating the alveolae; stipe hollow, tubular, whitish; flesh fragile, fragrant, with a faint but pleasant flavour; spores buff.

Names: Fr.: Morille comestible; It.: Spugnola; Sp.: Cagarria, Murgula, Colmenilla; Ger.: Speisemorchel; Dtch.: Morielje; Dan.: Morkle; Gr.: Výssano; Russ.: Smorchok.

Uses: The edible Morel is one of the most savoury of all fungi, and commands a high price, especially when it is available fresh. Large quantities are dried, especially in eastern Europe.

Origin, distribution and cultivation: *M. esculenta* and other Morels are vernal spp., appearing from April to June in hedgerows and on organically rich soils, at the edges of pastures, all over Europe. The high price they command and the intensive scale on which they are gathered all over the continent has undoubtedly contributed to their rarity, and has led to cultivation of several spp.

Similar plants: *M. esculenta* is the most generally prized sp., but a number of others, difficult to distinguish even by experts, are used in the same way. *M. vulgaris* is much more common, smaller (3–7 cm), with a cap of a dull grey with shades of olive-brown, and is inferior in flavour. *M. deliciosa*, more difficult to distinguish from *M. esculenta*, is a continental sp. which appears to vary according to local soils and climate: in the Jura it is regarded as by far the best Morel, while in parts of Italy it is considered inferior to *M. esculenta*. This sp. is as large as *M. esculenta*, but usually has a more elongate cap, with thicker flesh, and the surface ribs are less isodiametrical, more longitudinal. Other less valuable spp. such as *M. conica* and *M. rimosipes* are easily distinguished by their proportionately smaller, sharply conical caps with shallow alveolae separated by parallel longitudinal ridges.

Tuber melanosporum
PERIGORD TRUFFLE

(p. 210)

Description: An underground carpophore, more or less irregularly globose, somewhat knobbly, 2–10 cm in diameter, with a cleft at base, the surface dull, coal-black, covered with small warts; flesh dark brown to black with a network of pale markings; scent characteristic, very strong.

Names: Fr.: Truffe noire, – vraie, – du Perigord, Rabasse (Provence); It.: Spoleto,

Tartufo di Norcia; Sp.: Trufa del Perigord, Turma de tierra; Ger.: Perigord-Trüfel; Dtch.: Perigord truffle; Dan.: Perigord trøffel; Gr.: Galliko Ydyo; Russ.: Fransuzskoe triufel.

Uses: The value of the Périgord Truffle, like that of the White Truffle (below) is as a flavouring: the flesh has only a very faint flavour, but a powerful aroma that will permeate foods in which it is used. The best-known use of the truffle is in pâtés, particularly *pâté de foie gras*, but it is called for in many other gastronomic recipes including fine stuffings for poultry. Truffles should never be soaked or washed in water, and preferably not peeled; should cleaning be necessary, it should be done with dry white wine. Along with White Truffle, the Périgord Truffle is one of the most expensive foods in the world. This has inevitably led to the use of other spp. (see below) as adulterants or substitutes. Large quantities are canned, but with the exception of a few reputable brands these are truffles of inferior quality or even those of other spp. It is these poor quality or even useless sorts which enter most commercial pâtés.

Origin, distribution and cultivation: The natural distribution of this sp. ranges over the southern half of France and extends to parts of Spain and northern Italy. Throughout this range it is local, being associated with the roots of various spp. of oak. Périgeux is the centre of production of the best truffles, with Provence (particularly the region of Apt) and the hills of the Rhône valley north to Burgundy also supplying large quantities. Truffles from other parts of France, Italy and Spain are of lesser quality. The carpophores are located with the aid of muzzled pigs or trained dogs between November and early spring.

Similar plants: The only other fungus that can vie with the Périgord Truffle is the Italian White Truffle. Opinions, almost invariably determined by patriotism, are divided as to which is the finest. The two are however quite different in scent and in appearance.

Of the black or dark spp. substituted for the Périgord Truffle, Winter Truffle *T. brumale* is probably the best. It is usually smaller, with much finer warts on the surface and paler, brown flesh. This sp. occurs in November and December in most of Europe including Britain; *T. mesentericum*, a continental sp., is similar in appearance but has a bitter taste and a scent reminiscent of creosote. Summer Truffle *T. aestivum* also occurs in Britain, where it used to be gathered for commerce in late summer and autumn. It differs from *T. melanosporum* in having much larger, pyramidal warts, paler, violet-grey flesh, and only a faint scent which is lost with cooking. See also under Italian White Truffle, below.

Tuber magnatum
ITALIAN WHITE TRUFFLE

(p. 210)

Description: The underground carpophores are very variable in size, usually between 2 and 5 cm in length, but gigantic specimens occur. They resemble a misshapen potato with a matt, slightly powdery looking yellowish or pale buff skin; the flesh is almost concolorous, with a dense network of pale marbling; scent very strong, reminiscent of cooked garlic, but richer and at the same time more delicate.

Names: Fr.: Truffe des magnats, – piemontaise; It.: Tartufo bianco; Sp.: Trufa blanca; Ger.: Piemontesiche Trüfel; Dtch.: Witte truffle; Dan.: Piemonteser trøffel; Gr.: Leuko Ydyo; Russ.: Italyanskoe triufel.

Uses: Like the Périgord Truffle, this is primarily a flavouring agent, the flesh having only a faint flavour, but a delicious penetrating aroma. It is nearly always used raw, cut into paper-thin slices which are added to dishes such as *risotto*, pâtés or hot meat dishes, salads, cheese fondue and *bagna cauda* immediately before serving.

Origin, distribution and cultivation: The Italian White Truffle is found associated with oak roots in suitable situations in northern Italy, in the hills bordering the Lombardy plain, in Piedmont and Emilia. The commercial centre is Alba, where a fair in October marks the beginning of the truffle season which lasts until the first snowfalls of winter. Dogs, and occasionally pigs, are used to locate the carpophores. This sp. also occurs, in inferior forms, in parts of south-east France and Yugoslavia, whence they are imported to Italy and dishonestly sold as local produce. Few truffles are exported, and these mostly to luxury Italian restaurants and grocers. Some are canned, but lose most of their flavour in the process.

Similar plants: Pig Truffle *Choiromyces meandraeformis*, also often called 'White Truffle', is a quite different fungus belonging to a separate group. It is similar in appearance, but occurs on the surface, under dead lvs in deciduous woods all over Europe, including Britain. It is edible but of no gastronomic interest.

In France 'truffe blanche' sometimes designates *T. aestivum* (above).

GLOSSARY

Achene
A little dry one-seeded fruit that does not split to release the seed. There are usually many achenes on a fruiting head .

Adpressed
Pressed flat to a surface, eg. adpressed hairs.

Aggregate species
A group of very closely related species, often including fertile hybrids of some of them. These are often in taxonomic confusion; treated in this book as one species.

Fig. 1

Alternate leaves
Leaves placed singly, first on one side, then on the other, of a stem (Fig. 1).

Alternate husbandry
The reversing, every few years, of arable and grassland cultivation on a farm.

Annual
A plant which completes its life-cycle, from germination to fruiting and dying, in one year.

Anther
The little sac at the top of a stamen which contains the pollen grains.

Arable
From the Latin *arabilis* 'that can be ploughed'. Land regularly cultivated, or crops grown on such land.

Auricle
An ear-like lobe or pair of lobes at the base of a leaf, of diagnostic importance in the identification of grasses.

Awn
A bristle-like projection at the end or back of a lemma or a glume in grasses.

Axil
The upper angle between a leaf and the stem on which it grows.

Axillary
Flowers or other structures borne in an axil.

Berry
A fleshy round fruit, containing two or more seeds or pips which do not have a stony inner casing around each seed (see Drupe).

Biennial
A plant completing its life-cycle in two years, usually germinating and forming the vegetative parts in the first year, and flowering and fruiting in the second.

Fig. 2

Bipinnate
Twice divided into leaflets; the leaflets of

the leaf being themselves divided into smaller leaflets (Fig. 2).

Blade
The flattened part of an organ such as a leaf or petal.

Bolt
(Verb) used to describe individual plants cultivated as biennials which flower and fruit prematurely in the first year.

Fig. 3

Bract
A little leaf or scale-like structure with a flower or part of a flower growing in its axil. In Umbellifers, used to describe the whorl of small leaves at the base of the main umbel (Fig. 3).

Break crop
Any crop grown for one season to give the land a rest from its usual crop(s).

Bulb
An underground swelling at the base of a plant which remains dormant until required for rapid growth.

Bulblet
A small bulb, usually one of several which are ancillary to the main bulb.

Bulbil
A small bulb, usually growing above ground on a leaf or axil, which may drop off and grow into a new plant.

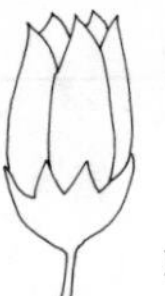
Fig. 4

Calyx
The whorl of sepals in a flower, sometimes fused in a tube, the calyx tube (Fig. 4).

Capsule
A dry fruit of two or more carpels which splits open to release the seeds when ripe.

Carpophore
The fruiting body of macromycete Fungi. See Fig. on p. 335.

Carpel
One of the units of the female part of a flower and fruit; they may be either separate or joined together in an ovary. Each carpel has a style at its apex.

Cash crop
A crop not grown for home consumption, but only for sale. In the modern economy this applies to nearly all crops except, obviously, green manure crops, forage or fodder crops etc., but on smallholdings food crops may still be grown primarily for the owner's use, with only the surplus sold for cash.

Catch crop
A fast-growing crop grown between an early harvest and a late sowing, usually of grain crops.

Clamp
A free-standing heap of roots or other produce covered in straw and earth, or with plastic sheeting, to protect it from the elements.

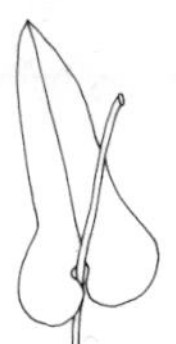
Fig. 5

Clasping leaf
A stalkless leaf with large basal lobes that appear to clasp the stem.

Cleaning crop
A crop which requires or allows thorough weed control, thus cleaning the land for subsequent crops of cereals, etc.

Compound leaf
A leaf divided into two or more quite separate leaflets, without any flange joining them together along their common stalk.

Composite
A member of the Daisy family, so called because their 'flowers' are composed of numerous small complete flowers.

Cone
A rounded or elongate structure composed of overlapping scales which bear pollen or seeds.

Convar.
Short for *convarietas*, a taxon larger than variety, but below subspecies.

Corm
Underground base of a stem swollen with food and surrounded by scales, but solid, not composed of overlapping leaf bases as in a bulb. Each corm is a one year's growth, replaced by another in the following year.

Corn
In Britain, any cereal crop grown for grain; in America, used only for Maize.

Corolla
The whorl of petals of a flower.

Corona
A crown of appendages between the petals (corolla) and the stamens.

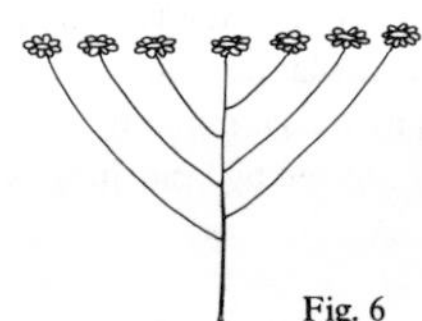
Fig. 6

Corymb
A raceme in which the outer flower-stalks are much longer than the inner ones, producing a flat-topped cluster, (but unlike an umbel, do not all arise from a single point at the apex of the stalk). (Fig. 6.)

Cotyledon
The first leaf produced by a seedling, single in *Monocotyledons*, paired in *Dicotyledons*.

Cover crop
A crop planted between main crops to prevent soil erosion or to provide green manure.

Crucifer
A member of the Mustard family, so called because their flowers have four petals disposed in the shape of a cross.

Cultivar
(abbreviated cv, cvs) An agricultural or horticultural variety which has originated and persisted under cultivation.

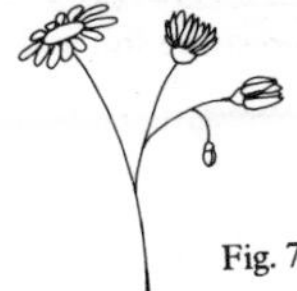
Fig. 7

Cyme
An inflorescence in which the terminal flower opens first, followed by lateral flowers borne in bract axils further down the stalk (Fig. 7).

Deciduous
A woody plant which sheds its leaves in autumn, and produces new leaves from buds the following spring.

Dicotyledon
A member of one of the two subdivisions of the flowering plants, with two first leaves produced by the germinating plant. Most can be recognised by branching veins of leaves.

Dioecious plants
Plants with male and female flowers each on separate individual plants.

Disc floret
One of the tubular florets in a flower head in the Daisy and some other families.

Drill, drilling
The mechanical sowing of seed on a field scale; machine used for that purpose.

Drupe
A fleshy fruit resembling a berry, but with the seed enclosed in a stony case (eg. Plum).

Entire leaf
A leaf without teeth, indentations, etc. on its margins.

Exotic
Introduced from abroad; alien to the area under discussion.

Fallow
Land ploughed and harrowed but left uncropped to rest the soil and destroy weeds.

Family
One of the ranks of classification, grouping a number of genera (sometimes only one genus) which have one or more characters in common. Similar families are grouped in one Order. Most plant family names end in *ceae*.

Female flower
Flowers with an ovary but without stamens.

Fertile
One capable of producing fruit.

Field crop
One grown on extensive surfaces, such as most agricultural crops, and some market-garden crops.

Floret
A small flower, either the individual tiny flower on grasses, rushes etc., or one of the flowers in the compound flower heads of members of the Daisy and related families.

Flower
A specialised shoot consisting of the reproductive organs of a flowering plant.

Fodder
Bulky crop produce harvested for feeding to animals, especially, but not always, preserved by drying, as hay.

Fold
Moveable enclosure, for instance electric wire, for cattle or sheep on a small area of growing food.

Forage
Growing food eaten by cattle or sheep in the field, also such food cut with a forage harvester. Forage crops are ones grown expressly for that purpose.

Fruit
Strictly, the dry or fleshy case formed from the ovary and surrounding a plant's seeds. Also applied to other plant produce consumed as fruit.

Genus
The second major rank in classification. A genus groups a number of related species; genera form a family. The generic name is the first part of the Latin binomial.

Glaucous
Green with a whitish bloom which gives the plant a blue-green colour, eg. Cabbage leaves.

Glume
The pair of chaff-like bracts at the base of the spikelets of grasses (single in Sedges).

Grain
Mature seed, especially of the Graminae Family, but also applied to the smaller pulses, buckwheat, etc., grown for their food value.

Hay
Long grass or mixed herbage cut and sun-dried for use as winter stock food.

Head
Of flowers or fruit crowded together at the end of a stalk.

Herbaceous
Non woody, soft and green.

Herb
Botanically, a plant which does not have a woody stem or trunk; in culinary terms, certain plants containing essential oils and used for flavouring, especially members of the Mint Family.

Herbicide
'Weed killer'. Modern agriculture is very dependent on these. They are of several distinct types: Selective, which affect only certain families, genera or species, for biological or chemical reasons, or for purely physical ones, eg. those that drain off the narrow vertical blades of cereals but settle and kill broad-leaved plants; Contact, which devastate most or all species on a short term, leaving ugly swathes of brown similar to burning; Translocated, which when sprayed on foliage, seep into every part of the plant; it is used to kill perennials.

Hermaphrodite
Of flowers in which both stamens (male) and ovaries (female) are present.

Hilum
The whitish scar left on a seed, such as beans, marking the point of attachment.

Home-garden
Small-scale cultivation principally for the gardener's use, although his produce may be offered for sale in local markets.

Hybrid
Strictly, the first generation of a cross between two species or two individuals differing in one or more genes. Loosely (as sometimes used in this book) the resulting strains of such original crossings.

Inflorescence
A group of flowers on a stem, leaf axil, etc.

Involucre
Whorls of bracts beneath a flower or flower cluster.

Keel
The edge of a leaf folded lengthwise, or the keel-like ridge along one side of a leaf; also, the two lower partly-fused petals in flowers of the Pea Family.

Fig. 8

Lanceolate leaf
One in the shape of a spear-head, ie. long, narrow, broader before middle, tapering to a point (Fig. 8).

Leaf-stalk
Otherwise called Petiole; the stalk of a leaf which bears the blade.

Leaflet
One of the separate blades of a compound (pinnate, trifoliate, palmate) leaf.

Legume
Any member of the Pea Family (Leguminosae).

Lemma
The bract which bears the flower (in members of the Grass Family), thus the lower of the two bracts of the flower.

Ley
Temporary grassland maintained from two to a dozen years before it is ploughed and turned back to arable crops.

Ligule
The small flap at the junction of the leaf blade and its sheathing base, in members of the Grass Family.

Linear
A long narrow parallel sided leaf, eg. grasses.

Male flower
One with stamens but no ovary.

Manure
Any organic fertiliser. *Green manure* crops are those which partly or solely have to be ploughed into the soil while the plants are still green.

Market-garden
A farm devoted to the production of crops for sale to greengrocers. Market-garden crops are grown on smaller surfaces than field crops, traditionally in alternate strips of different vegetables, like a larger version of the home-garden.

Meadow
A permanent hayfield, but sometimes applied to any long ley.

Monocotyledon
One of the two subdivisions of the flowering plants, with only one seed leaf (cotyledon). The members of this group can mostly be recognised by their parallel, not branching leaf veins (eg. grasses, palms, lilies, etc.).

Monoecious plant
One on which the male and female flowers are separate, but borne on the same plant.

Mucilage
A polysaccharide present in certain plant tissues; when these are cooked they gel, providing a useful thickening for soups, etc.

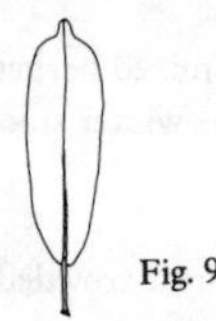
Fig. 9

Mucron, Mucronate
A small sharp point on an otherwise blunt or rounded leaf, fruit, etc. (Fig. 9).

Native
A plant occurring in an area which is within its natural geographic range; not introduced by man from elsewhere.

Naturalised
Wild plants originally introduced from abroad.

Node
A point (swollen on grasses) at which one or more leaves arise.

Nut
Strictly, a one-seeded indehiscent fruit with a hard woody pericarp or shell; often applied to other fruits, seeds, even tubers, with a hard shell.

Fig. 10

Oblong leaf
One about 2 or 3 times as long as broad, and parallel-sided at least in the central part of the blade (Fig. 10).

Fig. 11

Obovate leaf
One broadest above the middle, tapering gradually to base, and suddenly to its more or less blunt tip (Fig. 11).

Opposite leaves
Ones arising in pairs, one opposite the other on either side of a stem.

Fig. 12

Oval or **ovate leaf**
One which is egg-shaped in outline, scarcely twice as long as broad, with the broadest part below the middle (Fig. 12).

Ovary
The enlarged base of the pistil, or the carpels of a flower collectively. This is the female part of the flower, which after fertilisation develops into the fruit.

Ovoid
A solid object which is egg-shaped in section.

Ovules
The minute structures inside the ovary or carpels, which after fertilisation become seeds.

Palea
The upper and thinner, usually papery and translucid of the 2 scales which surround the stamens and ovary of a grass floret.

Fig. 13

Palmate leaf
A compound leaf with more than 3 leaflets arising together from the tip of the leaf-stalk. (Fig. 13).

Palmately-lobed leaf
A leaf with the main veins all radiating from the tip of a stalk, resembling a palmate leaf, but not compound.

Fig. 14

Panicle
A branched raceme (Fig. 14).

Parthenocarpic
The production of fruit without pollination.

Pasture
Grassland used for grazing stock, not cut for hay or silage.

Perennial
A plant that lives for at least two years.

Perianth
The collective name for the calyx and/or

the corolla segments, particularly when the two are indistinguishable, or when there is only one whorl.

Perianth segments
The sepals, sometimes including the petals, that constitute the perianth of a flower.

Petal
One of the inner whorl of segment leaves, usually white or coloured, rarely green, that surround the stamens and carpels of a flower.

Fig. 15

Pinnate leaf
A compound leaf with the leaflets arising from the leaf-stalks, usually in opposite pairs, with or without a terminal leaflet (Fig. 15).

Fig. 16

Pinnatifid leaf
A leaf more or less deeply divided into pinnately-arranged lobes, these remaining connected near the mid-rib, not completely separate (Fig. 16).

Pod
A rather vague term for a dry dehiscent fruit; in the context of this book particularly applicable to the Leguminosae.

Pollen
Minute dust-like granules containing the male cells that are produced within the anthers. Fertilisation of the eggs is produced when they fall on a stigma upon which they develop long microscopic pollen-tubes which convey the male nuclei to the egg.

Pome
From the old French for apple; fruits of that type in which the seeds are surrounded by a tough fleshy layer, the whole fused with the cup-shaped receptacle (see Rosaceae p. 27).

Prickle
A sharp, often flattened or angled spine born on a shoot or leaf.

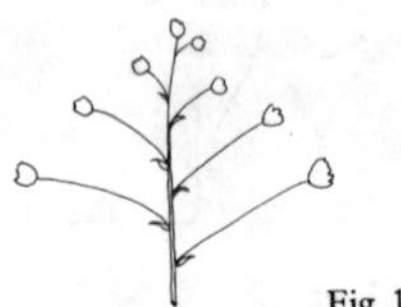

Fig. 17

Raceme
An unbranched elongate inflorescence in which the lowest flower opens first, and then the others in sequence towards the apex (Fig. 17).

Ray floret
The outer florets of an inflorescence of the Compositae, strap-shaped and different from the disc florets at the centre.

Receptacle
The flattened, concave or convex part of the stem from which the parts of a flower arise.

Rhizome
A creeping underground stem, often fleshy, distinguished from roots by the presence of nodes, buds, and scales or leaves.

Runner
A slender trailing shoot rooting at the end.

Seed
The reproductive unit formed by the fertilised egg, consisting of embryo and seed-coat.

Seed-pod
An ovary containing seeds.

Sepal
One of the outer set of flattened, usually green organs surrounding the flower bud, collectively forming the calyx. They may be more or less fused or free; in some plants they are brightly coloured and petal-like.

Shrub
A woody branched perennial plant, usually under 6 m tall, without a main trunk, as in a tree.

Silage
Green vegetation preserved from excessive decomposition by excluding air, used for feeding livestock.

Fig. 18

Siliqua
An elongate pod-like fruit of the Mustard Family. (Fig. 18).

Silo
A sealed container for silage or wet grain destined for feeding livestock. It may be a tall cylindrical metal container filled from the top and emptied through shutes at the bottom, or a simple clamp with floor and low walls made of concrete, metal sheeting, etc., and covered in plastic sheeting held down by old motor tyres or straw bales.

Simple leaf
A leaf that is not compound, ie. not divided into separate leaflets; it may however be deeply lobed, toothed, etc.

Spadix
A flower spike with a thick fleshy axis, as in Aroids and some Palms.

Spathe
A large bract enclosing a spadix, or two or more bracts enclosing a flower cluster.

Species
(abbreviated sp. (singular) and spp. (plural)). Any of the taxonomic groups into which a genus is divided, the members of which are able to interbreed. A species is designated in italics by the genus name followed by the specific name, eg. *Malus pumila*, the common Crab Apple.

Fig. 19

Spike
An elongate head of more or less stalkless flower (Fig. 19).

Spikelet
One of the elements of a compound spike. In grasses a group of one or more flowers above two glumes, or sterile bracts.

Stamen
One of the male reproductive organs of a flower which bears the pollen.

Staminode
A rudimentary or imperfectly developed stamen.

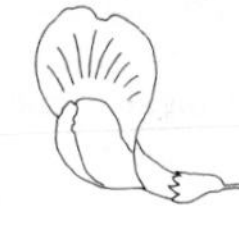
Fig. 20

Standard
The broad upper petal of a flower in the Pea family. In the Iris family, the erect inner petals. (Fig. 20).

Stem leaves
Those arising from a plant's stem (as opposed to root leaves or basal leaves).

Sterile
Lacking functional sex organs; incapable of sexual reproduction.

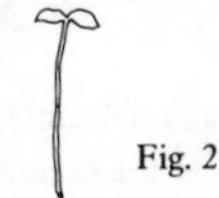
Fig. 21

Stigma
The part of the style, or female organ, which receives the pollen, and where the pollen grains are stimulated to germinate, usually covered in a sticky substance (Fig. 21).

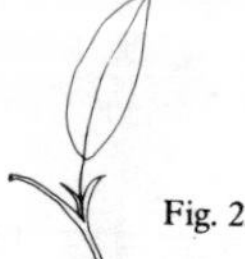
Fig. 22

Stipule
A scale-like or leaf-like appendage, usually paired, at the base of a leaf-stalk (Fig. 22).

Style
The stalk-like structure at the top of an ovary or a carpel, bearing the stigma.

Stolon
A runner not necessarily forming a new plant at its tip.

Straw
The dry stalks of mature grain crop plants, baled after threshing. Unlike hay it is of very little nutritional value unless chemically treated. Often used as litter.

Subspecies
(abbreviated *ssp.* (singular) and *sspp.* (plural)). A sub-division of some species, grouping individuals which share one or more distinctive characteristics, which are more marked than those separating varieties. Most natural subspecies arose in distinct geographical ranges.

Sucker
A shoot arising below ground, sometimes at a distance from the main stem.

Superior ovary
One which sits above and within the whorl of stamens, petals and sepals, and is free, as opposed to an inferior ovary, in which the other organs of the flower sit above it.

Taxon
Any one of the ranks of biological classification Species, Varieties, Family, Class are all taxa (plural).

Tap-root
The main vertical root.

Fig. 23

Tendril
A slender wiry twining or clasping organ, often a modified leaf or part of a leaf (Fig. 23).

Testa
The outer coat of a seed.

Fig. 24

Tiller
A shoot arising from the axils of lower leaves, as in wheat and some other grasses (Fig. 24).

Thorn
A sharply pointed woody spine, a modified branch or stem.

Thresh
To separate mature grain from chaff, husks or pods.

Trefoil
Not a botanical taxon, but the common

name for various plants of the Pea Family belonging to several genera (*Trifolium, Lotus, Medicago*) having trifoliate leaves. As an adjective, synonymous with trifoliate.

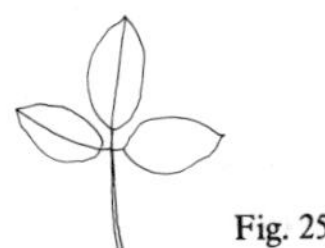
Fig. 25

Trifoliate
A leaf divided into three leaflets (Fig. 25).

Tuber
A swollen part of an underground stem or root, formed annually for food storage; also used for certain perennial swollen stems, as in Cyclamen.

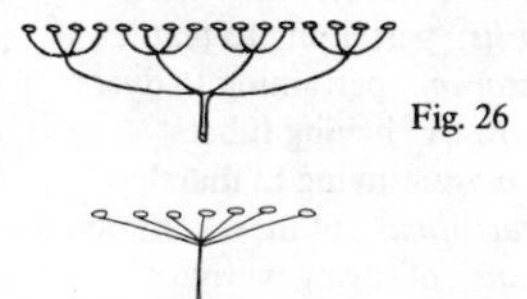
Fig. 26

Fig. 27

Umbel
A more or less flat-topped cluster of flowers whose spreading stalks all arise from a single point at the apex of a stem (Compound umbel Fig. 26; simple umbel Fig. 27).

Umbellifer
A member of the Celery Family (Apiaceae, or Umbelliferae), with flowers in umbels.

Variety
(Abbreviated *var.*) A subgroup of a species and/or a subspecies grouping individuals with one or more common distinctive characters eg. leaf form, size, marked colour variation, etc. See also cultivar.

Vein
A strand of conducting and strengthening tissues running through leaves and other organs.

Waste ground
Disturbed but uncultivated ground, eg. the verges of new roads, around buildings or industrial sites, quarries, etc.

Whorled leaves
Three or more leaves arising from the same level or point on a stem.

Wild crop
One which is harvested by man but not cultivated. Many of the herbs offered on Mediterranean markets, as well as certain fruits. Lime leaves, Blackberries picked for home consumption or for sale, etc. fit into this category.

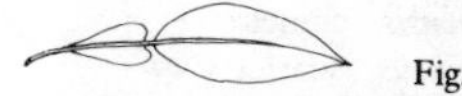
Fig. 28

Wing
One of the two side petals in members of the Pea family. Also the broad flanges along the stems, leaf-stalks or pods of certain plants, hence *winged stem*, etc. (Fig. 28).

MEANINGS OF SOME LATIN SPECIFIC EPITHETS COMMON IN CULTIVATED PLANTS

(Given in the masculine endings, eg. *albus* may be *album, alba*)

albus white
angustifolius narrow-leaved
annuus annual
aquaticus of water
arvensis growing in cultivated fields
avius 1. of birds; 2. out of the way
basilicus royal
bulbosus swollen like a bulb
coeruleus sky blue
campestris of the fields
cerasus cherry-bearing
chinensis chinese
coccineus scarlet
communis 1. gregarious, living in colonies 2. common
crispus curled
culinaris used in cooking
dulcis sweet
esculentus edible
falcatus sickle-shaped
fragrans sweet-scented
fragrantissimus most sweet-scented
frutescens becoming shrubby
fruticans shrubby
gallicus French
glabrus hairless
hispanicus Spanish
hispidus bristly, spiny
hortensis of gardens
hybridus intermediate, hybrid
hypogeus underground, buried
indicus Indian, from the Indies
laevigatus smooth
lanatus woolly
lunatus crescent-shaped
luteus yellow
maculatus spotted
maritimus of the sea
medicus medical, medicinal
mixtus confused
mutabilis changeable, variable
niger black
occidentalis western
odoratus odorous
officinalis used in pharmaceutics
orientalis eastern
oleiferum oil-producing
oleraceus used as a green garden vegetable
polymorphus with many different forms
repens creeping
ruber red
rusticus, rusticanus of the country
sativus cultivated
somniferus inducing sleep
subterraneus underground
spinosus spiny
sylvestris of forests, woods
textilis pertaining to textiles
tinctorum pertaining to dyers
tuberosus having tubers
uliginosus living in marshes
usitatissimus of most common use
vernus of spring, vernal
viciifolius with leaves like vetch
viniferus wine-producing
vulgaris common
vulnerarius healing

INDEX OF SCIENTIFIC NAMES

Main references are denoted by **bold** figures.
Illustrations appear on pages shown in *italic.*

Abelmoschus esculentus 88
Acacia 36, 42
Acinos arvensis 295
Acorus calamus 301
Actinidia
arguta 92
chinensis **92**
kolomikta 92
ACTINIDIACEAE **92**
Aegilops
speltoides 328
squarrosa 328
Aesculus hippocastanum 65
Agapanthus 304
Agaricus
arvensis 337
bisporus 337
campestris 336
AIZOACEAE **234**
Allium 304, **305**
altaicum 311
ampeloprasum *204*, **308**
var. *ampeloprasum* 308
var. *kurrat* 308
var. *porrum* *204*, 308
ascalonicum 309
cepa **309**
var. *aggregatum* *204*, **309**
var. *ascalonicum* *204*, **309**
var. *cepa* *204*, **309**
var. *proliferum* *204*, **309**
chinense **311**
fistulosum *204*, **311**
longicuspis 307
odorum 306
sativum *204*, **306**
schoenoprasum *204*, **310**
scorodoprasum **307**
tuberosum *204*, **306**
ursinum 307
Alocasia 302
Althaea 88
officinalis **90**
Amanita
caesarea **336**
muscaria 336
phalloides 337
verna 337
Amherstia 36
ANACARDIACEAE 111
Anacardium occidentale 111
Andropogon 319
sorghum 319
Anethum **255**
graveolens *184*, **255**
Angelica
archangelica *186*, **256**
sylvestris 257
Annona
cherimolia **15**, *168*
reticulata 15, 16
squamosa 15
ANNONACEAE **15**
Anthemis nobilis 266
Anthriscus
cerefolium *182*, **258**
sylvestris 257, 259
Anthyllis vulneraria **49**, *144*
Antirrhinum 117
APIACEAE **249**
Apium
graveolens *184*, **253**
var. *dulce* *184*, 253
var. *rapaceum* *184*, 254
nodiflorum 231
ARACEAE **301**
Arachis hypogea **50**
Arbutus **96**
andrachne 97
unedo **96**, *158*
Armoracia
lapathifolia 230
rusticana *174*, **230**
Artemisia
abrotanum *192*, **266**
absinthium *192*, **265**
dracunculoides 265
dracunculus *192*, **264**
stellerana 266
vulgaris 266
Artocarpus 72
communis 323
Arundo donax *318*, 319
Asparagus 312
acutifolius 313
officinalis *198*, **312**
plumosus 313
ASTERACEAE **264**
Astragalus glycyphyllos 50
Atriplex 234
hortensis *180*, **244**
Atropa bella-donna *194*, **277**
Aucuba 17
Avena *206*, **324**
bizantina **325**
fatua 325
ludoviciana 325
sativa *206*, **324**
sterilis 325
strigosa *206*, **325**

Barbarea
verna *172*, **232**
vulgaris 232
Bauhinia 36
Beta vulgaris *180*, **241**
var. *cicla* *180*, 242
var. *esculenta* *180*, 242
var. *maritima* 242
Blastophaga 72
psenes 72
Boehmeria nivea 69
Boletus 339
edulis *210*, **339**
Bombyx mori 74
BORAGINACEAE **288**
Borago officinalis 288
Brassica 122, 125
campestris 123, *170*, **227**
ssp. *nipposinica* 227
ssp. *oleifera* 227
var. *rapifera* 227
carinata 127
chinensis *174*, **225**
cretica 127
juncea *170*, *174*, 225, **228**
napobrassica 225
ssp. *oleifera* 226
napus 123, 127, *170*, **225**
var. *napobrassica* 225
nigra 122, 170, **227**
oleracea 122, **126**, *170*, 233
convar. *acephala* 126, *224*
convar. *botrytis* 127, *224*
var. *botrytis* 127, *224*
var. *bullata* 126, *224*
var. *capitata* 127, *224*

subvar. *gemmifera* 126
var. *gongylodes* 126, *224*
var. *italica* 127, *224*
subvar. *laciniata* 126
var. *subauda* 127, *224*
pekinensis *174*, **225**
perviridis 227
rapa *170*, **226**
var. *campestris* 227
BRASSICACEAE **122**
Broussonetia 72

CACTACEAE **85**
CAESALPINIACEAE 36
Cajanus cajan 53, 55
Calamintha 291
Calluna 93
CANNABACEAE **70**
Cannabis sativa **71**, *150*
Cantharellus cibarius *210*, **339**
tubaeformis 339
CAPPARACEAE **75**
Capparis
inermis 75
rupestris 75
spinosa **75**, *150*
var. *inermis* 75
CAPRIFOLIACEAE **63**
Capsicum **278**
annuum *194*, **278**, 280
frutescens *194*, 278, **279**
Carpinus 65
Carthamus 272
tinctorius *192*, **272**
Carum
carvi *186*, **260**
petroselinum 258
Carya 68, 69
illinoensis **69**
Castanea sativa **65**, *148*
Centaurium erythraea *247*
Ceratonia siliqua **42**, 144
Chaemomeles 25
japonica 25
speciosa 25
Chaerophyllum
bulbosum **259**
temulentum 259
Chaetochloa italica 321
Chamaemelum nobile *192*, **266**
Chamomilla recucita 267
CHENOPODIACEAE **241**
Chenopodium 234, 241, **245**
album *180*, **245**
bonus-henricus *180*, **245**
Choiromyces meandraeformis 342
Chrysanthemum 264
balsamita **268**
cinerarifolium *192*, **267**
coronarium 268, *269*
Cicer arietinum **51**, *140*
Cichorium 274
endivia **275**
var. *crispa* *223*, 275
var. *latifolia* *223*, 275
intybus *188*, *223*, **274**
Cinchona 115
Cissus 101
Citrullus
colocynthis 79
lanatus **83**, *154*
Citrus **105**
aurantifolia 109, 111
aurantium **107**, 108, *164*
bergamia **107**, *164*
decumana 109, 110
grandis **109**, 110, *166*
limetta 109
limon **108**, *168*
maxima 109, 110
medica **109**, *166*
mitis 108
paradisi **110**, *166*
reticulata **107**, *164*
sinensis **106**, *164*
Claviceps purpurea 330
Claytonia perfoliata *235*
Cnicus benedictus **272**
Cochlearia armoracia 230
Coffea 115
Colchicum autumnale 304
Coleus parviflorus 289
Colocasia esculenta **301**, *302*
var. *antiquorum* 301
var. *esculenta* 301, *302*
COMPOSITAE **264**
Conopodium majus 249, 331
CONVULVULACEAE **286**
Corchorus
capsularis 86
olitorius ***84***
Coriandrum sativum *186*, **259**
CORNACEAE 17, **62**
Cornus mas **62**, *146*
CORYLACEAE **66**
Corylus
americana 67
avellana **66**, *148*
colurna **67**, *148*
maxima **67**, *148*
Crambe maritima *172*, **233**
Crataegus 25
azarolus *19*, **24**
laciniata 24
Cratarellus
cinereus 340
cornucopioides *210*, **339**
Crescentia cujete 77
Crithmum maritimum ***262***
Crocus
cancellatus 304
nudiflorus 304
pallasi 303
sativus *198*, **303**
Crotalaria juncea 37
CRUCIFERAE **122**
Cucumis
anguria 83
melo **81**, *152*
sativus 77, **82**, *152*
Cucurbita 77
maxima 77, **80**, *154*
mixta 77
moschata 77, **81**
pepo 77, **79**, 80, *154*
CUCURBITACEAE **77**
Cuminum cyminum *186*, **260**
CUPRESSACEAE **333**
Curcuma longa 304
Cydonia oblonga **25**, *128*
Cymbopogon nardus 119, 266
Cynara
cardunculus *190*, **271**
var. *altilis* *190*, 271
scolymus *190*, **271**
CYPERACEAE **330**
Cyperus 330
esculentus ***330***, *331*
var. *sativus* *330*, *331*
Cyphomandra betacea **283**

Datura stramontium 277
Daucus carota *182*, **252**
ssp. *gummifer* 252
Derris 37
Digitalis
grandiflora 118
lanata *117*, 118
purpurea **117**
Digitaria 322
Diospyros **103**
kaki **103**, *160*
lotus **104**, *160*
virginiana 104

EBENACEAE **103**
Echinochloa *208*, **322**
crus-galli 322

frumentacea *208*, 322
ELAEAGNACEAE **100**
Eleagnus angustifolia **100**
Eleocharis dulcis 248, 331
Eleusine coracana **321**
Ensete 300
Epilobium 248
Erica 93
arborea 93
ERICACEAE **93**
Eriobotrya japonica **26**
Eruca sativa *172*, **232**
vesicaria var. *sativa* 232
Eucalyptus 97
Eugenia caryophylla 97
Euphorbia 85

FAGACEAE **64**
Fagopyrum
esculentum *178*, **236**
tataricum 237
Fagus
orientalis 65
sylvatica **64**, *148*
Feijoa
sellowiana **97**, *160*
Ferula 249
Ficus 72
bengalensis 72
carica **74**, *150*
ssp. *sylvestris* 74
elastica 72
Foeniculum
vulgare *184*, **254**
var. *dulce* *184*, 254
var. *piperatum* 255
Fortunella
japonica 111
margarita **110**, *160*
Fragaria *19*, **22**
× *ananassa* **24**, *136*
chiloensis 24
moschata **23**
vesca **22**, *136*
var. *semperflorens* 22
virginiana 24
viridis 23
Fraxinus
exelsior 113
ornus 113
FUNGI **334**

Gardenia 115
Gentiana lutea *247*
GENTIANACEAE **247**
Gladiolus 303
Glaucium 121
Gleditsia 42
Glycine
hispida 52
max **52**, *140*
soja 52
Glycyrrhiza glabra **49**, *144*
Gossypium **89**
arboreum 89
barbadense 89
herbaceum 89, *156*
hirsutum 89
GRAMINAE **313**, *315*
GROSSULARIACEAE **60**

Helianthus
annuus *190*, **269**
var. *macrocarpus* *190*, 270
rigidus 270
tuberosus *190*, **270**
Hevea brasiliensis 72
Hibiscus
cannabinus 88
esculentus **88**
sabdariffa 88, 89
Hippophae rhamnoides 100
Hordeum *206*, **325**, *327*
distichum *206*, *215*, 325, *327*
hexastichum 325, 326
murinum 327
polystichum *206*, 326, *327*
sativum 326
secalinum 327
spontaneum 326
vulgare 326
Humulus lupulus **70**, *150*
HYDROPHYLLACEAE **287**
Hypecoum 121
Hyssopus officinalis **293**

Illicium verum *261*, 262
Inula helenium **268**, *269*
Ipomeoa
aquatica 287
batatas *196*, *214*, **286**
IRIDACEAE **303**
Iris florentina 303
Isatis tinctoria *172*, **233**
Ixora 115

Jasminum
grandiflorum 115
odoratissimum 115.
officinale **115**, *176*
JUGLANDACEAE **68**
Juglans
cinerea 69
nigra 69, *148*
regia **68**, *148*
Juniperus 333
communis **333**, *334*
drupacea 334
oxycedrus 334

LABIATAE **289**
Lablab niger 55
Lactarius
deliciosus 210, **338**
torminosus 339
Lactuca
saligna 274
sativa *188*, **273**
var. *angustana* *223*, 273
var. *capitata* *223*, 273
var. *crispa* 273
var. *romana* *223*, 273
serriola 274
Lagenaria siceraria 77
LAMIACEAE **289**
Lathyrus 58
sativus 58
LAURACEAE **16**
Laurus
azorica 17
nobilis **16**, *168*
Lavatera 88
Lavandula
angustifolia 291
dentata 292
intermedia 292
latifolia *200*, *217*, **292**
officinalis *200*, **291**
spica 292
stoechas 292
LEGUMINOSAE 36
Lens culinaris **51**, *140*
Lentinus edodes *210*, **338**
Leopoldia comosa 312
Lepidium sativum *172*, **231**
Lepiota
procera *210*, **336**
rhacodes 336
Leucanthemum vulgare 268
Levisticum officinale *186*, **256**
Ligusticum
officinale 256
scoticum 256
LILIACEAE **304**
LINACEAE **91**
Linum 91
angustifolia 91
perenne 91

usitatissimum **91**, *156*, *215*
Lippia citriodora **119**
Lotus
angustissimus 48
corniculatus **47**
hispidus 48
major 48
tenuis 48
tetragonolobus **48**, *140*
uliginosus **48**
Luffa cylindrica 77
Lupinus
albus **41**
angustifolius **41**, *142*
arboreus 41
luteus **41**, *142*
micranthus 41
mutabilis **41**
nootkatensis 41
polyphyllus 41
Lycopersicon esculentum *194*, *218*, **282**
var. *cerasiforme* 282, 283
var. *commune* 282
var. *grandifolium* 282
var. *pyriforme* 282
var. *validum* 283

Maclura pomifera 72
Malus *19*, 29
baccata 27
communis 27
domestica 27
florentina 28
floribunda 27
orientalis 27
prunifolia 27
pumila **27**, *130*
sieversii 27
sylvestris 27, **28**
ssp. *domestica* 27
trilobata 28
Malva 88
MALVACEAE **88**
Mandragora officinalis 277
Mangifera indica 111
Marjorana
heracleotum 290
hortensis *202*, **290**
onites *202*, **291**
paniflorum 290
smyrnaicum 290
vulgare 290
Matricaria
chamomilla 267
matricarioides 267
recucita *192*, **267**
Medicago
arabica **46**
coerulea 44
falcata 44, 45
hispida 46
lupulina **45**, *142*
minima 46
polymorpha **46**
sativa **44**, *142*
Melanorrhea usitata 111
Melilotus
alba **46**, *142*
altissima 47
arvensis 47
indica 47
officinalis **47**
Melissa officinalis 266, **291**
Mentha **297**, **299**
aquatica 298
citrata 298
longifolia 297
× *niliaca* 298
× *piperata* *202*, **298**
pulegium **298**
rotundifolia **298**
spicata *202*, **297**, 298
suaveolens 298
Mespilus germanica **25**
MIMOSACEAE 36
Monarda 289
Monstera 301
MORACEAE **72**
Morchella 340
conica 340
deliciosa 340
esculenta *210*, **340**
rimosipes 340
vulgaris 340
Morus 20
alba **73**, *150*
var. *heterophylla* 73
nigra **73**, *150*
rubra 73
Musa **300**
MUSACEAE **300**
Muscari
atlanticum 312
comosum **312**
Mussaenda 115
Myrrhis
odorata *186*, **257**
MYRTACEAE **97**
Myrtus communis 97

Nasturtium
microphyllum 231
officinale *172*, **231**
Nicotiana 280
rustica **280**
tabacum *196*, **280**
Nigella 261
damascena 120
sativa **120**, *176*

Ocimum
americanum 294
basilicum *200*, **294**
canum 295
minimum *200*, **295**
Oenanthera 248
Olea europaea **114**, *176*, *213*
var. *oleaster* 114
OLEACEAE **113**
ONAGRACEAE **248**
Onobrychis
sativa **45**, *142*
viciifolia 45
Ononis spinosa 45
Opuntia 85
coccinellifera 86
ficus-indica **85**, *156*
maxima 86
monocantha 86
Origanum
marjorana 290
vulgare **290**
Ornithopus
perpusillus 45
sativus **45**, *142*
Oryza
sativa *206*, **323**
ssp. *indica* 323
ssp. *japonica* *206*, 323
ssp. *javanica* 323
Ostrya 66
Oxalis acetosella 238

Pachyrrhizus erosus 36
Paliurus spina-christi 100
Panicum
crus-galli 322
frumentaceum 322
italicum 321
miliaceum *206*, **322**
miliare 322
Papaver
rhoeas 122
setigerum 121
somniferum **121**, *176*
ssp. *hortense* 121
ssp. *somniferum* 121

PAPAVERACEAE **121**
PAPILIONACEAE 36
Passiflora 76
coerulea 77
edulis **76**, *152*
PASSIFLORACEAE **76**
Pastinaca sativa *182*, **253**
ssp. *sylvestris* 253
PEDALIACEAE **116**
Pennisetum
americanum 320
glaucum 320
spicatum 320
typhoides 208, **320**
typhoideum 320
Persea americana **17**, *168*
Petroselinum
crispum *182*, **257**
var. *tuberosum* 258
hortense 258
sativum 258
Phacelia 287
tanacetifolia *198*, **287**
Phaseolus
angularis 55
aureus 55
coccineus **56**, *138*
inamoenus 56
limensis 56
lunatus 54, **56**, *138*
multiflorus 56
mungo 55
vulgaris **54**, *138*
Philodendron 301
Phylloxera vastatrix 102
Physalis **284**, **285**, 286
alkekengi *196*, 284, **285**
edulis 284
ixocarpa *196*, 285
peruviana **284**
var. *edulis* 284
pruinosa **284**
Pimenta dioica 97
Pimpinella anisum *186*, **261**
PINACEAE **332**
Pinus
cembra 332
halepensis 333
pinaster 332, 333
pinea **332**
Piper nigrum 279
Pistacia
atlantica 113
lentiscus **112**, *168*
var. *chia* 113
var. *latifolia* 113
terebinthus 113, *168*
vera **112**, *168*
Pisum
arvense 57
hortense 57
sativum **57**, *140*
ssp. *arvense* 57, *140*
ssp. *sativum* 57, *140*
PLANTAGINACEAE **240**
Plantago
coronopus 240
indica *178*, **240**
lanceolata 240
major 240
psyllum 240
ramosa 240
Plectanthrus esculentus 289
Pleurotus ostreatus *210*, **338**
POACEAE **313**
Pogostemon cablin 289
POLYGONACEAE **236**
PORTULACACEAE **235**
Portulacca oleracea *178*, **235**
Potentilla 23
Prunus *19*, **30**
amygdalus 32
armeniaca **31**, *132*
avium **33**, *132*
brigantina 35
cerasifera **34**, *134*
cerasus 33, **34**, *132*
cocomilla 35
communis **32**, *132*
var. *amara* 32
var. *dulcis* 32
damascena 35, *134*
domestica 34, **35**
ssp. *domestica* 35, 36, *134*
ssp. *italica* 36, *134*
ssp. *insititia* 35, 36, *134*
dulcis 32
fruticosa 33
laurocerasus 34
lusitanicus 34
mahaleb 34
padus 34
persica **31**, *132*, *221*
var. *nectarina* 31, *132*
serotina 34
serrulata 34
speciosa 34
spinosa **35**, *134*
× *syriaca* 34
tomentosus 32
Psalliota
arvensis **337**
bisporus *210*, **337**
campestris **336**
sylvicola 337
Psidium guajava 97
Psophocarpus tetragonolobus 49
Pterocarya 68
Punica granatum **98**, *160*
PUNICACEAE **98**
Pyrethrum cinerarifolium 267
Pyrus
amygdaliformis 29
communis **28**, *130*
cordata 29
eleagrifolia 29
malus 27
nivalis 29
pyraster 29
salvifolia 29
syriaca 29

Quercus
coccifera 66
ilex 66
lanuginosa 66
macrolepis 66
suber **65**, *148*, *219*

Radicula armoracia 230
RANUNCULACEAE **120**
Ranunculus 120
Raphanobrassica 230
Raphanus
raphanistrum 230
sativus *174*, **229**
var. *oleifera* 229
RHAMNACEAE **99**
Rhamnus 99
Rheum 237
alpinum 237
officinalis 237
palmatum 237
rhabarbarum *178*, **237**
rhaponticum 237
undulatum 237
Rhus 111, *112*
coriaria 111
verniciflua 111
Ribes **60**
alpinum 62
divaricatum **61**, *146*
grossularia 60
hirtellus 61
nigrum **61**, *146*
petraeum 62
rubrum 62
sativum 61, **62**, *146*

sylvestre 62
uva-crispa **60**, *146*
vulgare 62
Rorippa nasturtium-aquaticum 231
Rosa **18**, *19*
canina **18**
centifolia **18**
damascena **18**
gallica medicinalis **18**, *128*
rubiginosa 93
ROSACEAE **18**
Rosmarinus officinalis 200, **292**
Rubia tinctorum 115, *116*
RUBIACEAE **115**
Rubus 19
alleghanensis 20
caesius **20**, *136*
chamaemorus **22**, *136*
fruticosus **19**
idaeus *19*, **20**, *136*
laciniatus 20, *136*
loganobaccus **21**, *136*
occidentalis 21
phoenicolasius **21**, *136*
ulmifolius 20, *136*
vitifolius 21
Rumex
acetosa *178*, **238**
acetosella 238
hydrolopathum 239
montanus 239
patientia **239**
rugosus 239
scutatus *178*, **239**
Ruscus aculeatus 313
Ruta
chalepensis 105
graveolens 104
RUTACEAE **104**

Saccharum officinarum ***318***
Salicornia 246, 262
europaea **245**, *246*
Salsola kali 246
Salvia
officinalis *200*, **295**
sclarea *200*, **296**
triloba 295
verbanacea 296
Sambucus
nigra **63**, *146*
racemosa 64
Satureja
hortensis *200*, **294**
montana *200*, **293**
Schinus mollis 111
Scolymus 272
Scorzonera hispanica *188*, **276**
SCROPHULARIACEAE **117**
Secale cereale 206, **329**
Sechium edule ***84***
Sesamum indicum **116**, *176*
Setaria
italica *208*, **321**
viridis 321
Sinapis 125
alba 122, *170*, **228**
arvensis *170*, **229**
hirta 228
Smyrnium olusatrum 256
Soja max 52
SOLANACEAE **277**
Solanum
intrusum *194*, **282**
lycopersicon 283
melongena *196*, **281**
nigrum 282
ssp. *guineense* 282
tuberosum *196*, **281**
Sorbus
aucuparia 27
var. *edulis* 27
cashmiriana 26
commixta 26
domestica **26**, *128*
sargentiana 26
torminalis 27
Sorghum 318, 319, 320
arundinarium 320
bicolor *208*, **319**
cernuum 319
dochna 319
durra 319
guineense 319
nervosum 319
subglabrescens 319
vulgare 319
Spinacea oleracea *180*, **244**
Stachys
affinis *202*, **299**
sieboldii 300
Symphytum
asperum *198*, 289
officinale 289
× *uplandicum* *198*, **288**

Tanacetum balsamita 268
Taraxacum
officinale *188*, **273**
kok-saghyz 273
Terminalia catalpa 33
Tetragonia expansa *178*, **234**
Tetrapanax papyrifera 323
Thymus 294
citriodorus 119, *202*, 296
drucei 297
herba-barona *202*, 297
pulegioides 297
serpyllum 296, **297**
var. *lanuginosa* 297
vulgaris *202*, **296**
Tilia **87**
cordata 87
× *europaea* 87, *156*
platyphyllos 87
TILIACEAE **86**
Tragopogon porrifolius *188*, **276**
Trapa
bicornis 248
bispinosa 248
natans ***248***
quadrispinosa 248
Trifolium 46
alexandrinum 44
aureum 46
campestre 46
hybridum **43**, *144*
incarnatum **43**
medium 43
pratense **42**, *144*
var. *sativa* 42
repens **44**, *144*
Trigonella **53**
foenum-graecum **53**, *144*
ornithopodiodes 54
Triticale 329
Triticosecale 329
Triticum **327**
aestivum *206*, 327
boeticum 328
dicoccoides 328
dicoccum *206*, 328
durum *206*, 327
monococcum 328
polonicum 328
spelta 328
turgidum *206*, 328
Tuber
aestivum 341, 342
brumale 341
magnatum *210*, **341**
melanosporum *210*, **340**
mesentericum 341

UMBELLIFERAE 249
Urena lobata 88
Urtica 300

dioica **69**
pillulifera 70
urens 70
URTICACEAE **69**

Vaccinium **93**
angustifolium 96
corymbosum **96**, *158*
macrocarpon **94**, *158*
microcarpum 94
myrtillus **95**, *158*
oxycoccus **94**, *158*
uliginosum 96
vitis-idaea **95**, *158*
Valeriana officinalis 263
VALERIANACEAE **263**
Valerianella
carinata 263
dentata 263
eriocarpa 263, 264
locusta 188, **263**
olitoria 264
rimosa 263
Verbascum 117
Verbena officinalis **118**, *119*, *176*
VERBENACEAE **118**
Vicia 51
bithynica 59
cracca 59
faba **58**, *138*
sativa **59**, *142*
ssp. *angustifolia* 59, *142*
villosa 59
Vigna
sesquipedalis 55
sinensis 55
unguiculata 54, 55
VITACEAE **101**
Vitis 101
labrusca 103
vinifera **101**, *162*, *216*
Voandzia subterranea 51

Xanthosoma 302

Zanthoxylum alatum 111, 112
Zea mays 208, **317**
Zizania
aquatica 324
latifolia 324
Zizyphus
jujuba **99**
lotus 99, 100
mauritania 100
sativa 100
vulgaris 100

INDEX OF VERNACULAR NAMES

Main references are denoted by **bold** figures.
Illustrations appear on pages shown in *italic.*

Absinthe 265
Alecost ***268***
Alfalfa **44**, *142*
Allspice 97
Almond **32**, *132*
  Earth 51, 331
Angelica *186*, **256**
  Wild 257
Anise *186*, **261**
  Star *261*, 262
Aniseed 261
Apple *19*, **27**, 28, *130*
  Custard 15, 16
  European Crab **28**
  Sugar 15
Apricot **31**, *132*
Aramina 88
Artichoke
  Chinese *202*, **299**
  Globe *190*, **271**
  Jerusalem *190*, **270**
Asafoetida 249
Ash
  Common 113
  Flowering 113
  Mountain 27
  Prickly 111
Asparagus *198*, **312**
  Wild 313
Asparagus Pea **48**, *140*
Atemoya 15
Aubergine *196*, 277, **281**
Avocado **17**, *168*
Azarole *19*, **24**, *128*

Badam 33
Balm 266, **291**
Balsam Herb 268
Banana ***300***
Barbary Fig **85**, *156*
Barbe de Capucin 274
Barley *206*, *215*, **325**
Basil *200*, **294**
  Bush *200*, **295**
  Hoary 295
  Holy 295
  Sweet 295
Bean
  Adzuki 55
  Arpajon 54
  Berlotti 54
  Black-eye 55
  Broad 55, **58**, *138*
  Burma 56
  Butter **56**, *138*
  Canellini 54
  Carob **42**, *144*
  Chili 54
  Common **54**, 56, *138*
  Fazolia *54*
  Field *54*, **58**, 138
  Flageolet 54
  French 54, *138*
  Frijoles 54
  Goa 48
  Haricot 54
  Kidney 54
  Lima 55, **56**, *138*
  Locust 42
  Madagascar 56
  Mangetout 54
  Mexican Black 54
  Michelet 54
  Mojhettes 54
  Pea 54, *138*
  Pinto 54
  Runner 55, **56**
  Salad 54
  Scarlet Runner 55, **56**, *138*
  Sieva 56
  Snap 54
  Soya **52**, *140*
  String 54
  Winter 58
  Yam 36
Beech **64**, *148*
  Oriental 65
Beet
  Fodder **241**
  Sugar *180*, **241**, 319
  Seakale *180*, **241**
  Spinach *180*, **241**
  Wild Sea 241
Beetroot *180*, **241**
Bergamot 289
Bergamot Orange **107**
Berseem 44
Bilberry **95**, *158*
Bindweed **286**
Blackberry **19**, *136*
  Cut-leaf 20, *136*
Blackthorn **35**, *134*
Blaeberry 95
Blueberry 93
  Highbush **96**, *158*
  Lowbush 96
Bo Tree 72
Borage **288**
Borecole 126
Bramble **19**
Breadfruit 72
Briar 93
Broccoli 127, *224*
  Sprouting 127, *224*
Brussels Sprout 126, *224*
Buckthorn 99
  Sea 100
Buckwheat *178*, **236**
  Tartarian 237
Bullace **35**, *134*
Butcher's Broom 313
Buttercup **120**
Butternut 69

Cabbage **122**, **126**, *170*, *224*
  Abyssinian 127
  Black 127
  Cattle 127
  Celeri 225
  Chinese *174*, 225
  Head 127, *224*
  Round 127, *224*
  Savoy 127, *224*
  Sea 126, 127, 233
  Wild 126, 127, 225
Cactus **85**
Calabash 77
Calabrese 127
Caltrops ***248***
Cane
  European *318*, 319
  Sugar ***318***
Cantaloupe 82
Cape Gooseberry **284**
Caper **75**, *150*
Caprifig 74
Capuchin's Beard 240

INDEX OF VERNACULAR NAMES

Caraway *186*, **260**
Cardoon *190*, **271**
Carob Bean **42**, *144*
Carosella 255
Carrot *182*, **249**, **252**
Cashew **111**
Cassia 36
Cauliflower 127, *224*
Celeriac *184*, **253**, 254
Celery *184*, **253**
Celtuce *223*, 273
Centaury *247*
Cep *210*, **339**
Chamomile *192*, **266**
German *192*, **267**
Roman *192*, 266
Wild *192*, **267**
Chanterelle *210*, **339**
Charlock *170*, **229**
Chayote ***84***
Cherimoya **15**, *168*
Cherry
Bigarreau 33
Bird 34
Black 34
Bladder 286
Cornelian **62**, *146*
Ground 33, **284**
Morello 33, **34**, *132*
St Lucie's 34
Sweet **33**, *132*
Wild 33
Cherry Laurel 17, 34
Cherry Plum **34**, 36
Chervil *182*, 232, **258**, 259
Rough 259
Turnip-rooted **259**
Wild 259
Chestnut **65**, *148*
Horse 65
Water 248, 331
Chick Pea **51**, *140*
Chicory *188*, *223*, 240, **274**, 276
Catalonia *223*, 274
Magdeburg 274
Treviso *223*, 274
Witloof *223*, 274
Wild 274
Chilli *194*, **278**, 279
Bird *194*, **279**
Chinese Lantern Plant 286
Chives *204*, **310**
Chinese *204*, **306**
Christophene *84*
Christ's Thorn 100
Chrysanthemum
Garland 268, *269*
Chufa 248, 249, ***330***, *331*
Citron **108**, *166*
Citronella 266
Citrus **105**
Clary *200*, **296**
Wild 296
Cloudberry **22**, *136*
Clover
Alsike **43**, *144*
Bokhara **47**, *142*
Burr 46
Crimson **43**
Dutch **44**, *144*
Egyptian 44
Hubam 47
Red **42**, *144*
Sweet 47
White **44**, *144*
Zigzag 43
Cloves 97
Cocoyam 302
Coffee 115
Colocynth 79
Colza 227
Comfrey
Common 289
Prickly *198*, 289
Russian *198*, **288**
Coriander *186*, **259**
Cork Oak **65**, *148*, *219*
Cornsalad *188*, **263**
Italian 263
Costmary 268
Cotton 88, **89**, *156*
Courgette 79, *154*
Cowberry **95**, *158*
Cranberry 93, **94**, *158*
American **94**, *158*
Cress 231
American 232
Belle Isle 232
Garden *172*, **231**
Land *172*, **232**, 268
Spring- 232
Water *172*, **231**
Winter 232
Crook-neck 79, 81, *154*
Cuckoo Pint 301
Cucumber 77, **82**, *152*
Cumin *186*, **260**
Black **120**, *176*, 261
Currant **60**
Black **61**, *146*
Red **62**, *146*
White **62**, *146*
Currant-Gooseberry 61
Cypress **333**

Daisy **264**
Ox-eye 268
Damson **35**, *134*
Dandelion *188*, 240, **273**
Dasheen 302
Date-Plum 103, **104**, *160*
Deadly Nightshade *194*, **277**
Dewberry **20**, *136*
Dill *184*, **255**
Dock 236
Dogwood **62**
Durra 319
White 319

Earth-Almond 51, 331
Ebony **103**
Eggplant *196*, **281**
Einkorn 328
Elder **63**, *146*
Red-berried 64
Elecampane **268**, *269*
Endive **275**
Ergot 329, 330
Etrog 109
Eucalyptus 97
Euphorbia 85

Fat Hen *180*, **245**
Feijoa **97**, *160*
Fennel *184*, **254**, 256
Florence *184*, *255*
Sweet 254
Wild 254
Fenugreek **53**, 54, *144*
Fig **74**, *150*
Barbary ***85***, *156*
Figwort 117
Filbert **67**, *148*
Flax **91**, *156*, *215*
Fleawort *178*, **240**
Fordhook 79
Foxglove
Common **117**
Large Yellow 118
Woolly *117*, 118

Gage **35**
Gai Tsoi *174*, 225
Gaoliang 319
Garlic *204*, **306**
Great-Headed **308**
Gean **33**
Gentian **247**

Yellow *247*
Gherkin 77, **82**, *152*
West Indian 83
Girole *210*, **339**
Good King Henry *180*, **245**
Gooseberry **60**, *146*
Cape **284**
Chinese 92
Goosefoot **241**
Gourd
Bottle 77
Gram
Black 53
Green 53
Grapefruit **110**, *166*
Grape Hyacinth ***312***
Grapevine **101**, *162*, *216*
Grass **313**
Cockspur 322
Finger 322
Sudan 320
Greengage 36, *134*
Groundnut **50**
Bambara 51
Guava 97
Guinea Corn 319
Gumbo 88

Hawthorn
Common 24
Midland 24
Hazel **66**, *148*
Turkish **67**, *148*
Heath
Tree 93
Heather **93**
Hemp **70**, **71**, *150*
Sunn 36
Herb Patience **239**
Hickory 68
Honeysuckle **63**
Hop **70**, *150*, *222*
Hornbeam 65, 66
Hop 66
Horn of Plenty *210*, **339**
Hubbard 80
Huckleberry 96, *194*, **282**
Hyssop **293**

Ice Plant 234

Jackfruit 72
Jamberry 285
Jasmine
White **115**, *176*
Jerusalem Thorn 100
Jew's Thorn 100
Jujube
Common ***99***
Indian 100
Juniper
Common **333**, *334*
Prickly 334
Syrian 334
Jute 86

Kaki 103, *160*
Kale
Asparagus 226
Curly 126, *224*
Hungry Gap 226
Marrow-stem 126, *224*
Rape 226
Sea 126, *172*, 233
Sheep 226
Kaller 15
Kenaf 88
Kiwi **92**, *156*
Kohlrabi 126, *224*
Kumquat
Oval **110**, *160*
Round 111
Kurrat **308**

Lablab 55
Laurel **16**, *168*
Cherry 17
Portugal 34
Lavandin 292
Lavender
Broad-leaved *200*, *217*, **292**
True *200*, **291**
Leek *204*, **308**
Sand **307**
Lemon **108**, *166*, *212*
Lentil **51**, *140*
Lentisc **112**, *168*
Lettuce *188*, **273**
Cabbage *223*, 273
Cos *223*, 273
Leaf 273
Lime **86**, **87**, 109
Common 87, *156*
Large-leaved 87
Small-leaved 87
Sweet 109
Limequat 111
Linen 89, 91
Ling Kok 248
Linseed **91**
Liquorice **49**, *144*
Wild 50
Loganberry **21**, *136*
Loquat **26**, *128*
Lords and Ladies 301
Lovage *186*, **256**
Scot's 256
Lubia 55
Lucerne **44**, *142*
Lupin
Annual **41**, *142*
Bitter Blue 41
Blue **41**, *142*
Garden 41
Pearl **41**
Tree 41
White **41**
Yellow **41**, *142*

Madder **115**, *116*
Maize *208*, **317**
Mallow **88**
Jew's 86
Mandarin **107**
Mandrake 277
Mangel *180*, **241**
Mangetout 57
Mango 111
Manna 113
Marjoram
Knotted 202, **290**
Pot *202*, **291**
Sweet *202*, **290**
Wild **290**
Marrow **77**, 79, *154*
Boston 80
Custard 79, *154*
Vegetable 79
Marshmallow ***90***
Mastic
Peruvian 111
Mastic Tree **112**, *168*
Medick
Black **46**, *142*
Burr 46
Hairy **46**
Sickle 45
Spotted **46**
Toothed **46**
Medlar **25**, *128*
Melilot
Common **47**
Ribbed **47**
Small 47
Small-flowered 47
Tall 47
White **46**, *142*
Yellow **47**

INDEX OF VERNACULAR NAMES

Melokhia ***86***
Melon **81**, 85, *152*
  Honeydew 82, *152*
  Musk 82, *152*
  Ogen 82
  Water **83**, *154*
  Winter 82, *152*
Mercury *180*, **245**
Millet
  Barnyard **322**
  Brown-corn 322
  Bulrush *208*, **320**
  Common *206*, 321, **322**
  Finger **321**, 323
  Foxtail *208*, **321**
  Italian *208*, **321**
  Japanese *208*, 322
  Little 322
  Pearl 320
  Proso 322
  Russian 322
  Spiked 320
Milo 319
Mimosa 36
Mint **297**
  Bergamot 298
  Eau de Cologne 298
  Horse 297
  Lavender 298
  Orange 298
  Pepper 202, **298**
  Round-leaved **298**
  Spear *202*, 297
  Water 298
Mirabelle **34**, 36
Morel *210*, **340**
Mugwort 266
  Hoary 266
Mulberry 20, **72**
  American 73
  Black **73**, *150*
  Downing 73
  English 73
  Paper 72
  Persian 73
  Red 73
  White **73**, *150*
Mung 55
Mushroom **334**
  Caesar's **336**
  Cultivated *210*, **337**
  Field **336**
  Horse **337**
  Matsutake 338
  Oyster *210*, **338**
  Parasol *210*, **336**
  Shiitake *210*, **338**
Mustard 122
  Black 122, *170*, **227**, 228
  Brown 122, *170*, **228**
  Chinese 228
  Field *170*, **227**
  Indian 228
  White 122, *170*, **228**
Mustard Greens 232
Myrobalan **34**
Myrtle **97**

Nectarine **31**, *132*
Nettle **69**
  Common 70
  Dead 70
  Roman 70
  Small 70
  Stinging 69
New Zealand Spinach *178*, **234**
Niger 264
Nightshade **277**
  Black 282
  Deadly *194*, **277**
Nonsuch **46**, 142
Nut
  Cob 67
  Earth 249, 331
  Ground 50
  Hazel **66**, *148*
  Jesuit's 248
  Monkey 50
  Pecan 69
  Pig 51, 249, 331
  Pine 332
  Sedge 331
  Singhara 248
  Tiger 331

Oak
  Cork **65**, *148*, *219*
  Hairy 66
  Holm 66
  Kermes 66
  Valonia 66
Oats *206*, **324**
Okra **88**, *156*
Oleaster **100**, 114
Olive 101, **113**, **114**, *176*
  Wild 101
Onion *204*, **309**
  Catawissa 309
  Common *204*, 309
  Tree *204*, 309
  Welsh *204*, **311**
Orache *180*, **244**
Orange
  Bergamot 107, *164*
  Seville 107, *164*
  Sour 107, *164*
  Sweet 106, *164*
Orangequat 111
Oregano ***290***
Oyster Plant 276

Pak Choi *174*, **225**
Paprika 278
Para Rubber Tree 72
Parsley *182*, 232, **257**
  Cow 258
  Continental 258
  Curled *182*, 258
  Hamburg *182*, 258
  Naples 258
  Sheep's *182*, 258
  Turnip-rooted 258
Parsnip *182*, **253**
  Wild 253
Passionflower/-fruit **76**
  Purple **76**, *152*
  Blue 77
Patchouli 289
Pea **36**
  Asparagus **48**, *140*
  Chick **51**, *140*
  Dun 57
  Field 57, *140*
  Garden 57, *140*
  Grey 57
  Mangetout 57, *140*
  Maple 57
  Partridge 57
  Pigeon 53, 55
  Sugar 57
Peach **31**, *132*, *221*
Peanut ***50***
Pear **28**, *130*
  Almond-leaved 29
  Common 29
  Wild 29
Peepul 72
Pepper **194**
  Chilli *194*, **278**
  Sweet *194*, **278**
  True 279
Peppermint *202*, **298**
Pepper Tree 111
Persimmon 104
  Chinese **103**, *160*
  Japanese 103
  Oriental 103
Pe Tsai 225

INDEX OF VERNACULAR NAMES

Pignut 51, 249, 331
Pine **332**
 Stone ***332***
Pineappleweed 267
Pistachio **112**, *168*
Plantain **240**, 300
 Branched 240
 Buck's-horn 240
 Crow's-foot 240
 Giant 240
Plum *19*, **35**, *134*, *221*
 Alpine 35
Poison Ivy 111
Pomegranate **98**, *160*
Pomelo **109**, *166*
Poppy
 Opium 121, *176*
Potato *196*, 277, **281**
 Sweet *196*, 277, **286**
Prickly Pear ***85***
Proso 322
Pummelo 109
Pumpkin 77, **79**, **80**, **81**, *154*
 Cushaw 81
Purslane *178*, **235**
 Winter *235*
Pyrethrum *192*, **268**

Quince **25**
 Flowering 25
Quinine 115

Radicchio *223*, 275
Radish *174*, **229**
 Horse *174*, **230**
Rakkyo **311**
Ramsons 307
Rape
 Forage **225**, 227
 Oil, Oilseed *170*, **225**, 227
Rape-kale 226
Raspberry *19*, **20**, *136*
 Black 21
 Yellow *136*
Reine Claude 36
Rhubarb *178*, 236, **237**
Rice *206*, **323**
 Wild 324
Rocambole **307**
Rocket *172*, **232**, 268
Rose **18**, *19*, *128*
 Dog **18**
Rosemary *200*, **292**
Rowan 27
Rye *206*, **329**

Safflower *192*, **272**, 304
Saffron Crocus *198*, **303**
Saffron Milk Cap *210*, **338**
Sage *200*, **295**
 Three-lobed 295
Sainfoin **45**, *142*
Salsify *188*, **276**
Saltwort 246
Samphire 246, ***262***
 Marsh **245**, *246*
 Rock *262*
 Golden 246
Savory
 Summer *200*, **294**
 Winter *200*, **293**
Scarole 275
Scorzonera *188*, **276**
Seakale 126, *172*, **233**
Seakale Beet *180*, **241**, 243
Sedge Nut 331
Sesame 116, *176*
Serradella **45**, *142*
Service Tree **26**, *128*
Shaddock 109
Shallot *204*, 309
Sloe **35**, *134*
Sorghum *208*, **319**
Sorrel 236, 268
 French 239
 Garden *178*, **238**
 Round-leaved *178*, **239**
Sorrel Dock **239**
Southernwood *192*, **266**
Soya **52**, *140*
Spearmint *202*, **297**
Spinach *180*, **244**
 New Zealand *178*, **234**, 244
Spinach Beet *180*, **241**
Spiny Rest-harrow 45
Squash
 Banana 80
 Mammoth 80
 Show 80
 Summer 77, **79**
 Table Queen 79
 Turban 80, *154*
 Winter 77, **80**, **81**, *154*
Star Anise *261*, 262
Strawberry *19*, **22**
 Alpine **22**, *136*
 Garden **24**, *136*
 Haubois **23**
 Wild **22**
Strawberry Tree **96**, *158*
Sugar Apple 15
Sugar Beet *180*, 241

Sugar Cane **318**
Sumach ***112***
Sunflower *190*, **269**
Swede *170*, **225**
Sweet Bay **16**, *168*
Sweet Cicely *186*, **257**, 259
Sweet Corn 317
Sweet Flag 301
Sweet Potato *196*, 277, **286**
Sweetsop 15

Tamarind 36
Tangerine **107**, *164*
Tare **59**, 142
Taro **301**, *302*
Tarragon *192*, **264**
 Russian 265
Terebinth 113, *168*
Thell 258
Thistle
 Blessed **272**
Thyme
 Basil 295
 Breckland **297**
 Caraway *202*, 297
 Common 296
 Continental Wild 297
 French 296
 Garden *202*, **296**
 Lemon 119, *202*, 296
 Mountain 297
 Spanish 119, 297
 Wild 297
Toadstool **334**
Tobacco *196*, **280**
Tomatillo *196*, 284, **285**
Tomato *194*, *218*, **282**
 Cherry 282
 Husk 284
 Pear 282
 Plum *194*, 282
 Potato-leaved 283
 Strawberry 284
 Tree ***283***
 Upright 283
Trefoil
 Common Bird's-foot **47**
 Greater Bird's-foot **48**
 Hairy Bird's-foot 48
 Narrow-leaved Bird's-foot 48
 Slender Bird's-foot 48
 Yellow **46**, *142*
Truffle
 Italian White *210*, **341**
 Perigord *210*, **340**
 Pig 342

Summer 341
Winter 341
Turnip *170*, **226**
Wild 227
Turnip Oil Rape *170*, 227
Turnip Rape 227
Turpentine Tree 113

Valerian ***263***
Verbena 118, 266
Lemon-scented ***119***
Vervain **118**, *119*, *176*
Vetch
Common **59**, *142*
Kidney **49**, *144*
Tufted 59
Viburnum 63

Walnut **68**, *148*
Black 69, *148*
Watercress *172*, **231**
Brown 231
Fool's 231
Green 231
Winter 231
Water Melon **83**, *154*
Wheat 314, **327**, 330
Bread *206*, 314, 327
Durum *206*, 314, 327
Einkorn 327, 328
Emmer *206*, 328
Macaroni 327
Polish 328
Rivet *206*, 327, 328
Spelt 328
Willowherb **248**
Wineberry **21**, *136*
Wingnut 68
Woad *172*, **233**
Worcesterberry **61**, *146*
Wormwood *192*, **265**

Yang Tao **92**, 156

Zucchini 79